First edition published in Germany 2002
by
IKAN - Unterwasserarchiv
Waldschulstrasse 166
65933 Frankfurt, Germany
e-mail: ikanuw@aol.com

Distribution: ConchBooks   Mainzer Str. 25, D-55546 Hackenheim, Germany.
e-mail: conchbooks@conchbooks.de
home-page: http://www.conchbooks.de
ISBN 3-925919-58-9

Layout & compilation/processing of picture stories: **Helmut Debelius**
Original German text revision & type-setting: **Ralf Michael Hennemann**
Editing and translation of original German edition: **Dr. Bernd Peyer**
Print & production: **Grupo M&G Difusión, S.L.**

Unless specifically credited to other sources, all images contained in this book were provided by IKAN UW-Archives, Frankfurt, Germany. Zoogeographical maps: Luís Carlos Mendes da Costa.

Photo credits cover, left to right:
Physeter catodon – Howard Hall
Tursiops aduncus – Helmut Debelius
Orcinus orca – Francois Gohier

Megaptera novaeangliae – Ralf Kiefner
Phocoena phocoena – Florian Graner
Delphinus delphis – Ralf Kiefner

Backcover: Tursiops truncatus – Donald Tipton

Inside covers: Boris Paulmann

Ralf Kiefner

WHALES & DOLPHINS
CETACEAN
WORLD GUIDE

**Pacific Ocean • Indian Ocean • Red Sea
Atlantic Ocean • Caribbean • Arctic • Antarctic**

Over 500 photographs
of cetaceans taken in
their natural habitat

CONTENTS

PICTURE STORIES

INTRODUCTION and GLOSSARY

"To the dolphin alone, beyond all others, Nature has granted what the best philosophers seek: friendship for no advantage."   Plutarch, 46-119 AD

All of us are familiar with whales and dolphins in one way or another. These in part very large and intelligent marine mammals have long been known to us through countless feature films and documentaries, as well as works of literature, history and art. The Greek naturalist and philosopher Aristotle (384-322 BC) already made them the object of his scientific investigations. He recognised early on that whales and dolphins are mammals. He writes in his *Historia Animalum* (History of Animals): "All animals have breasts that are internally and externally viviparous, as for instance all animals that have hair, as man and the horse; and the cetaceans, as the dolphin, the porpoise, and the whale - for these animals have breasts and are supplied with milk."

For thousands of years whales and dolphins have played an important role in the myths, sagas and stories of the ancient Greeks and Romans, the Indians of the Americas and the Aborigines of Australia. For an equally long period of time, whales have also been an important source of food for coastal peoples. A single stranded Sperm Whale, for instance, once sustained an entire village for several weeks. Even the industrial revolution would not have developed as it did if it were not for the advent of commercial whaling.

At present our knowledge about whales and dolphins remains full of gaps and is even contradictory in part. What we know is not nearly as up to date as the information available to us about terrestrial mammals. As unbelievable as it may sound in the age of space travel and computers, there are still species of whale roaming around our planet that no one has ever seen. Today we continue to admire dolphins and are fascinated by their intelligence and their elegance and speed in the water. Whales and dolphins are emblematic for the beauty and variety of life in the oceans. But the tragic fate of these animals also reflects our disrespect for nature.

As we all know, life began in the sea. In the course of millenniums, some of these sea-dwellers evolved into terrestrial beings. A few of these animals eventually chose to return to the sea in order to take advantage of the sheer unlimited sources of nourishment found there. The archetype of all contemporary species of whale is found in the group of Mesonychidae, which existed more than 70 million years ago. Biochemical and genetic examinations conducted during the 1950s have vindicated Flower, an American scientist who postulated in 1883 that the marine mammals of our day are related to the cloven-hoofed animals.

In the course of their evolution, whales and dolphins (cetaceans) have successfully carved numerous ecological niches for themselves throughout the world's seas and oceans, and their distribution now ranges from the tropics to the polar regions. They have adapted to the most diverse and inhospitable areas, and they have visited depths that are inaccessible to many other original denizens of the seas. Whales and dolphins are the most intelligent of the aquatic beings. They make the most effective use of the available food sources and are the swiftest swimmers. They have the most complex social relations, and have developed effective strategies to cope with the conditions of the various regions they inhabit. In order to survive in the marine environment, the primeval whales had to undergo a continuous process of metamorphic transformation. The most acute physiological adjustment they had to make was the adaptation of their eyes and kidneys to the salt content in the water. Body hair became

Graceful and playful: Humpback Whales.

redundant and was replaced by a much more effective means of isolation, namely a thick layer of blubber that also serves as a nutritional reserve in times of need.

On land most whales would be crushed by their own weight and invariably asphyxiate. Since they are practically weightless in the water, however, their growth process has hardly been impeded. Indeed, the Blue Whale is the largest being that ever lived on our planet. Such rapid growth has slowed down some species of whale to the point that they have had to develop special hunting techniques and alter their feeding habits. **Baleen whales**, for instance, have specialised in hunting slow-swimming zooplankton and small shoaling fish that occur in unimaginable quantities in polar waters. In order to feed on masses of krill they developed huge mouths with fibrous baleen plates in parallel rows on either side of the upper jaw. These baleen plates, a unique biological development among mammals, function as a filtering device. Baleen whales still have rudimentary teeth in the embryonic stage, but these are soon eliminated. **Toothed whales,** on the other hand, still have teeth instead of baleen plates and prey primarily on fish and cephalopods (squid), which they will swallow whole.

To survive underwater, cetaceans have had to reduce water drag to a minimum and develop as streamlined a body as possible. Their anterior extremities (arms) were transformed into flippers, which serve as steering and stabilizing devices rather than a means of propulsion. As an additional stabiliser, most (fast-swimming) whales and dolphins have also developed a boneless dorsal fin. The posterior extremities (legs) also became superfluous. Rudimentary hip and thigh bones are still present in the skeleton of a whale, but they no longer fulfill a function and are not connected to the rest of the skeleton. All other parts of the body that might hinder the streamline flow, such as the male genitals and female mammary glands, have been neatly tucked away into the skin folds of the hindquarters. The horizontal tail fin, or fluke, is the primary source of propulsion for whales and dolphins. A whale's fluke has no skeletal appendages or muscle tissues. It is a regenerated connective tissue made up primarily of fine, interwoven, collagenous fibres. The horizontal position of a cetacean's fluke is a definite advantage when the it surfaces to breathe: If it were positioned vertically it would project out of the water and thus be practically useless for forward propulsion. In the course of their evolution the head of these animals gradually merged with the trunk to form a single motoric unit. The cervical vertebrae have shrunk considerably and are now bonded to each other in the case of most species of cetacean. The stiffened vertebrae insure that the head always remains pointed in the direction of minimal water resistance without muscular exertion.

Like most terrestrial mammals, the nares of the land-dwelling ancestors of the whales were originally located on the front of their skulls. In time, these nasal cavities travelled back along the bridge of the nose until they reached the apex of the head. By virtue of this modification of the skull, which was one of the most crucial adaptations to aquatic life, the animals attained a perfectly streamlined swimming position. The apex of the head with the nares is now the first part of the body to come out of the water whenever a whale surfaces.

This process of transformation can still be observed today in the embryonic development of the skull. During the early embryonic stage, the nares of a whale are still situated on the tip of the snout. As the embryo develops further, the nares move towards the apex of the skull.

The three most important senses for terrestrial mammals - **smell, touch, taste** - have degenerated among cetaceans. So has **sight** in the case of some species of dolphin. **Hearing**, on the other hand, has become increasingly vital to them. In addition, cetaceans have honed the skill of **echolocation** and further developed their **sense of magnetism**.

The degeneration of the **sense of smell** is of no grave consequences for marine animals as smell does not carry nearly as well in water as it does in air.

The **sense of touch** is fairly well developed among whales and dolphins. Some species of whale even have very sensitive bristles on the tips of their snouts. Receptors in their skin optimise the dolphins' ability to swim swiftly and efficiently by compensating surface water turbulence with an elastic wave-like motion of the skin itself. The sense of touch also plays an important role in the daily social life of cetaceans. The close physical contact between a mother and its young is a frequently observed phenomenon in the wild. Furthermore, the skin of a cetacean is extremely sensitive to environmental stimuli, as it is vital for any marine mammal to know just when its nose is out of the water and free to breathe again.

The **sense of taste** has presumably been preserved, even though it is relatively insignificant under water. Just what effect the taste buds may have on the choice of nourishment among cetaceans has not been fully determined so far. Captive dolphins certainly do show a marked preference for certain foods.

Sight plays a minor role among marine animals. It only serves a practical purpose relatively close to surface, or no deeper than 300 m at the most. The sense of sight among cetaceans distinguishes itself from that of terrestrial mammals in that many species of the former can see equally well under and above water. Since water is much denser and has a higher refractive index than air, humans are only able to see clearly under water with the aid of a diving mask. In the human eye, an unsharp image is projected behind (rather than on) the retina. In contrast to humans, whales and dolphins have soft and extremely elastic lenses that can be adapted to various environmental conditions.

Dolphins are among the most advanced mammals and for many people a symbol for a better world: Striped Dolphins at the Azores.

Hearing is especially important for orientation under water. Contrary to light, which is absorbed by water, sound is transmitted much faster and for far greater distances in water than in air. Consequently, the ears of cetaceans have had to undergo a major transformation. Humans are unable to determine the direction of sound under water. Air transmits sound at a speed of 330 m/sec. We perceive sound by way of the eardrum and the inner ear. Because there is a delay of about 1/5,000 sec before a sound reaches both ears, we are able to determine the direction an acoustic signal is coming from on the surface. Submerged our bodies and outer ears are completely surrounded by water. When we are struck by sound waves under water our bodies, which consist primarily of water, react in unison with the surroundings. Sound is then no longer reflected, as it would be in air, but absorbed and transmitted directly to the inner ear by way of the tissues and cranial bone. Since the human inner ear is surrounded by, rather than isolated from the cranial bone, the sound delay between both ears is less than 1/10,000 sec under water. This is why humans are unable to determine the direction of sound under water.

Echolocation is undoubtedly the most important sense for (toothed) whales. Dolphins have the most sophisticated system of echolocation in the entire animal kingdom. They are capable of transmitting high-frequency sound waves and registering their reflections. This skill, which defies the human imagination, is also referred to as "**so**und **na**vigation and **r**anging" **(sonar)**. With the aid of emitted clicking sounds and their reflections from objects, dolphins are able to obtain a precise "acoustic image" of their surroundings. These acoustic signals are transmitted from the melon and when they strike some object or animal, their reflection will be received by it again and then transformed into a perceptible "acoustic image."

The **magnetic sense** is used for navigation and in the case of whales and dolphins it functions on the basis of the magnetic field, much like it does among bats, birds , fish, sea turtles and some subterranean rodents. Whales and dolphins can recognise and interpret fluctuations in the magnetic field by way of the iron-oxide crystals (magnetite) found in their heads. Just how this organ functions and its precise location have not yet been clearly determined. It is assumed that whales and dolphins use the iron-oxide crystals in their heads for magnetic orientation in much the same way as the Loggerhead Turtle does, which has an inborn magnetic field map that serves them as a guide on their long migrations across the world's seas. In 2001 Kenneth Lohmann, a biologist at Carolina University (USA), and his colleagues managed to prove that Loggerhead Turtles not only recognise the cardinal points, but that they appear to be born with an "imaginary" map of the earth's regional magnetic fields. These "imaginary" maps are typical for certain regions of the world.

Acknowledgements

This book is dedicated to my parents, without whom it would not never have materialised. I am also indebted to those who were directly involved in its production. Without their invaluable assistance this project would never have gotten off the ground. Representative for all other scientific institutions, I wish to express my gratitude to the Smithsonian Institution (Washington, D.C.), Dalhousie University (Nova Scotia, Canada), Nigel Robinson of Biosis and the University of California at Santa Cruz. A hearty thanks goes out to the numerous whale-watching tour organisers and their skippers, who accompanied me on countless expeditions and never tired in sharing their expertise and enthusiasm. I am also grateful to the many authors and photographers whose work and experiences have gone into this book. Finally, a very special thanks to biologist Andrea Ramalho, who always took the time to assist me in my research and to answer all of my technical questions.

GLOSSARY

adult - Mature animal capable of reproduction.

ambergris - A waxy, dark substance formed in the intestines of a Sperm Whale from the undigested beaks of squid.

amphibian - Lives in water and on land.

agonistic - Aggressive behaviour, usually between members of the same species.

baleen - Fibrous plates hanging from the upper jaws of baleen whales, which serve as a filtering device for nutrients in the water.

benthic - Bottom-dweller. Antonym for pelagic.

blow - A cloud of exhaled air and condensed water. Many whales have a characteristic blow.

blowholes - respiratory openings (nares) on the apex of the skull. Single among baleen whales, paired among toothed whales.

blubber - Thick subcutaneous layer of fat, serves as nutritional reserve and provides isolation from the cold.

breaching - When whales leap upward through the water surface.

bubble netting - hunting technique used by some cetaceans whereby shoaling prey is herded together on the surface by vocalizing, bubble blowing and swimming manoeuvres.

cetaceans - Scientific designation for all whales and dolphins.

cephalopods - Invertebrates with tentacles on the head and capable of ejecting an inky substance as a defence mechanism (e.g. squid, sepia, octopus).

continental shelf - a shallow submarine plain forming a border to a continent, extending from the shore to about a depth of 200 m.

copepods - Minute crustaceans in plankton.

crustaceans - Aquatic mandibulate arthropods such as lobsters, shrimps, crabs, krill and water fleas.

Cyamidae - A family of water fleas that live parasitically on the skin of whales, popularly known as whale lice.

dorsal - Relating to the back or upper side of the body.

ear plug - Hardened obstruction in the outer ear of whales. Growth layers on it are used to determine the age of baleen whales.

echolocation - A physiological process for locating objects by means of high-frequency sound waves that are reflected back to the emitter.

endemic - Restricted or peculiar to a certain locality.

Euphausiacea - Small usually luminescent crustaceans that resemble shrimps and are generally known as krill.

diatom - Minute planktonic unicellular or colonial algae.

dorsal fin - Cartilaginous fin along the midline of the back that serves as stabiliser.

falcate - Curved, sickle-shaped.

flippers - Forelimbs (with bone structure) that have been morphologically modified for swimming.

fluke - Horizontally positioned cartilaginous tail fin that is moved up and down for forward propulsion.

gulping - Typical feeding technique of most rorquals, whereby the animals swallow a large quantity of water and nutrients at once and then close their mouths again and press the water through the baleen plates with the aid of the tongue.

hybrid - Offspring of two animals of different species.

juvenile - Young, sexually immature animal.

krill - Tiny crustaceans, such as the genus Euphausiacea, which form part of the zooplankton.

lobtailing - When whales slap the surface of the water with their flukes.

logging - When whales rest motionless on the surface.

matriarchal group - Group led by a female.

mandibula - Lower jawbone.

maxillaries - Upper jawbone.

median - Situated in or near the middle.

melon - Bulge on the forehead of many toothed whales, consisting of fatty tissue and air sacks (extension of upper nasal passages). Soundwaves are transmitted from it for purposes of orientation and communication. In case of Sperm Whales it also serves as a buoyancy compensating device.

migration - Seasonal wanderings from one region to another.

monophydont - With only one generation of teeth.

morphological - Pertaining to the form and structure of an organism.

myoglobin - A red iron containing protein pigment in muscles, similar to haemoglobin and can also bind oxygen.

patriarchal group - Group led by a male animal.

pelagic - Living on the open seas, antonym for benthic.

plankton - Passively floating minute animal and plant life of a body of water, such as one-celled algae, animal larvae and krill.

phytoplankton - Passively floating one-celled plant life (bacteria, algae). Forms the first link in the marine food chain and has the capability of transforming sunlight into energy which is stored as an organic substance (e.g. sugars).

pod - A group of whales.

polygamy - Mating behaviour among whales whereby a male copulates with several females in a "harem" and fights off all potential rivals.

polygyny - Mating behaviour among whales whereby a male competes with rivals to copulate with a certain female only once. Both partners will then seek new mates.

population - One or more isolated groups of one species of animal.

porpoising - When cetaceans (primarily dolphins) skim over the surface while swimming at a fast pace.

promiscuity - Several males fertilise several females. The continuity of the species has priority over the urge to pass on individual genes.

rete mirabile (pl. retia mirabilia) - So-called "miracle net," which is composed of a bundle of fine, interwoven blood vessels. It allows whales to compensate pressure in the circulatory system by pumping it full of blood.

rostrum - Snout, beak. Actually refers to the extended upper jaw of a cetacean, but is usually applied to the anterior beak-like projection of the skull.

sexual dimorphism - Gender-based differences in body size, colouration or extremities.

skimming - Typical feeding technique used by some baleen whales (e.g. Right Whales), whereby they swim through water with their mouths partially open to filter out the nutrients.

sonar - "**So**und **na**vigation and **r**anging," abbreviation for echolocation.

spermaceti - A waxy substance found in the spermaceti organ, a hollow space in the skull of a cetacean (particularly large among Sperm Whales). Used in cosmetics. Early whalers erroneously thought it to be whale sperm.

splash guard - Protective bulge of tissue before a blow hole.

spy-hopping - When cetaceans poke their heads out of the water to have a look around.

terrestrial - Living on land.

teutophagous - Feeding on cephalopods.

tubercles - Latin *tuberculum*. Small humps or knobs on a whale's skin (e.g. Humpback Whales).

ventral - On the underside or belly of a whale.

vibrissae - Stiff hairs located in the region of the mouth or nose of a whale with a sensory function like a cat's whiskers.

whalebone - Articles made from the horny substance of baleen plates.

whale lice - See Cyamidae.

zooplankton - Free-floating microorganisms in water. Zooplankton feeds on phytoplankton and consequently forms the second link in the food chain.

Facing page: Two Northern Bottlenose Whales. Atlantic, Canada. Photo: Boris Paulmann

A Gray Whale surfaces at the Californian coast. Its baleen plates are clearly visible.   Francois Gohier

GRAY WHALES   ESCHRICHTIIDAE

Distinguishing Characteristics of this Family
Their bodies are stocky but streamlined. Instead of a dorsal fin, they have a small dorsal hump and a series of knuckles (crenulations) along the dorsal ridge. Their rostrums are dimpled and their jawlines arched in profile. Two to five longitudinal grooves run down their ventral throats. Their skin is mottled grey in colour. A single species: Gray Whale, *Eschrichtius robustus*.

Gray Whale, *Eschrichtius robustus*

Distinguishing Characteristics
Mottled grey colour, rounded rostrum, and lack of a dorsal fin are the earmarks of this species.

Description
Gray Whales are stocky but streamlined. They grow to about 12-14 m in length and weigh between 15-35 t. Instead of dorsal fins, they have a small dorsal humps and a series of knuckles along the dorsal ridges. Their rostrums are slightly rounded. Like the angle of the jawlines, their heads curve downward from the blowholes.

Other than 2-5 throat grooves, their undersides are smooth. The throat grooves can diverge or run parallel to each other. Their fairly small flippers are paddle-shaped and pointed. Their flukes, which can span up to 3 m, are relatively large in proportion to their bodies. The tips of the flukes are somewhat frayed and convex, with a conspicuous median notch.

The Gray Whale has 130 baleen plates on each side of its jaws, the fewest of all baleen whales. Their baleen plates are relatively short (0.5 m), but course and strong. The size and num-

Gray Whales also feed on the seafloor. California.   Howard Hall

ber of a Gray Whale's baleen plates vary according to its feeding habits and favourite prey. Like all baleen whales, Gray Whales have paired blowholes. Their blows rise to about 3-4 m and are bush-, heart- or V-shaped.

Gray whales are infested more than most other whales with epidermal parasites, like whale lice and barnacles . Their skin colour is mottled grey, sometimes also blue-grey or marbled white.

Easily Mistaken For
At first glance the Gray Whale bears a certain similarity to right whales and rorqual whales. Basically, this species is fairly easy to identify because of their unique appearance (head shape and colour), behaviour and, above all, geographical range.

Other Names
Devilsfish, Musseldigger, Scrag Whale, Californian Grey Whale (English); Grauwal, Kalifornischer Grauwal (German); Baleine Grise (French.); Balena Grigia (Italian); Ballena Gris (Spanish); Baleia Cinzenta, Baleia Cinzenta do Pacífico (Portuguese); Grijze Walvis (Dutch); Gråhval (Norwegian.); Harmaavalas (Finnish); Gråval (Swedish); Gråhval (Danish).

Meaning of the Scientific Nomenclature
Eschrichtius robustus (Lilljeborg 1861) - The Latin generic name *Eschrichtius* commemorates Danish zoologist Eschricht. The Latin species name *robustus* means "strong" and refers to the toughness of the baleen plates.

Behaviour
Because of their playfulness and marked interest in boats, Gray Whales are especially popular among whale watchers. The greatest concentration of Gray Whales occurs in their habitual mating, calving and nursing grounds in the shallow bays of Baja California (Mexico) between December and April.

Gray Whales are currently one of the most active species of whale. One can frequently observe them breaching, lob-tailing or spy-hopping. They will often swim close to a boat and sometimes even allow humans to stroke them. According to some reports, they apparently also enjoy surfing in the surge.

Gray Whales migrate over 20,000 km each year, farther than any other mammal. Between April and November they congregate in their feeding and grazing grounds in the Bering Sea, Chukchi Sea and Beaufort Sea. In the course of their approximate 10,000 km migration to their southern mating grounds in Baja California, Mexico, they come very close to the Northamerican westcoast between October and February. Gray Whales separate themselves according to gender, age and reproductive stage when they migrate.

Gray Whale cows that are about to deliver will be the first to go. Each one will migrate independently. Then the fertile cows will set off, followed by the mature bulls and the younger bulls respectively. The latter usually migrate in groups of 2-3.

Almost all of the animals will migrate past the coast of Monterrey, coming within 1.5 km of the shoreline. During their migration the whales average about 8 km/h, which means that they can cover a daily distance of nearly 200 km.

Between December and April they remain in their mating grounds in Mexico. Most of the calves are born between January and the middle of February. At calving time the whale mothers seek out the shallow and well protected bays of the region. The remaining

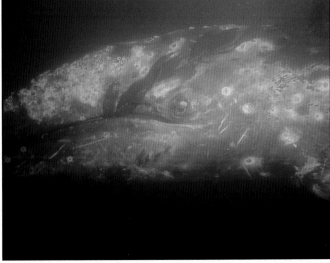

Gray Whales eat Californian kelp, a large brown alga.   Howard Hall

population will usually spend the winter somewhere farther out to sea.

On their slower paced migration north between March and July the whale cows and their young will also come close to the shoreline. Once again, they migrate in a specific order. The recently impregnated whale cows will be the first to make their way to the northern feeding grounds, followed by the nonpregnant cows, the mature bulls and the younger animals respectively. The last whales to undertake the strenuous journey, about a month later, are the cows with their recently born calves.

Spy-hopping Gray Whale. Baja California, Mexico.   Howard Hall

Diving

The diving sequences of Gray Whales while in their mating grounds are very irregular. They will frequently change course and usually not remain under water for longer than 18 minutes. In their search for nourishment they can dive to a depth of 100 m, but they generally prefer shallower waters.

During migration they tend to breathe 3 to 6 times in short intervals before diving for about 3 to 5 minutes. Their average speed rarely surpasses 2-5 knots, whereby the offspring will slow down the cows considerably on their way north.

When they surface to breathe their heads will seldom come out of the water. Their dorsal ridges only become visible when the blowholes are under the surface again. Just before they raise their flukes and sound, their dorsal ridges and the tail stocks are almost bent double.

Facts & Figures Gray Whale	Quick ID-Check Gray Whale
Size: 12-14 m	Mottled grey colour
Weight: 15-33 t	
Longevity: up to 40 years	Stocky, but streamlined body
Sexual maturity: at 6-9 years	
Mating season: November-December	No dorsal fin, small hump instead
Gestation period: 12-13 months	
Size at birth: 4-5 m	Long, narrow, slightly-domed head
Weight at birth: 0.5 t	
Nursing period: 6-9 months	Slightly-arched jawlines
Dive depth: max 120 m	
Dive time: max 18 min	Thick growth of barnacles, especially on the
Maximum speed: 15 km/h	head
Baleen plates: 130 tough, short baleen plates	
(0.5 m) on each side of the jaw	Low V- or heart-shaped blow
Blow: bush-, heart- or V-shaped, 3-4 m high	
Group (Pod) size: 1-3 individuals, occasionally	Frequently raises fluke when sounding
larger numbers	
Population: 20,000-25,000 in the Eastern Pacific	Very friendly and active on the surface

The elastic baleen plates of all baleen whales filter food organisms from the water.   Francois Gohier

Feeding Habits

Gray Whales subsist on more than 100 species of benthic and pelagic organisms, along with some vegetal substances. Algae, which is often found in their digestive tracts, makes up about 35% of their stomach content. A few scientists believe that the algae is ingested accidentally along with the prey, while others feel that the whales purposely feed on it.

Their main food source in the Arctic feeding grounds are countless small benthic organism like isopods, mysids, polychaet bristle worms and amphipods (e.g. *Gammarus*), as well as various other invertebrates.

During the summer months they consume at least 61,000 kg of these tiny crustaceans. At this time their blubber will increase by 16-30%, which corresponds to an additional weight of 5 t.

Earlier theories contended that the whales refrain from feeding while in their mating grounds. Now it is known that they do feed on various pelagic species found in the lagoons of Baja California, such as certain species of shrimp, krill (Euphausiacea), calamari and sardines. Occasionally they also eat certain organisms that live on kelp.

Gray Whales are the only bottom-feeders among the baleen whales. They usually roll over on their right sides and plow through the seabed in search of small shrimps, worms and other benthic organisms.

When they bottom-feed like this the sediment they turn over often gathers into thick clouds. The water and sediment are ingested along with the food and then filtered out through the baleen plates with the aid of the tongue. For this reason the baleen on the right side of their jaws are usually shorter and more worn down than those on the left side, and the right side of the heads also bear more pock marks than the left. Unless, of course, the whale in question is one of the few "lefties" that prefers to

Gray Whale seen from the air. US West coast.   Marty Snyderman turn over on its left side while bottom-feeding. Short and tough baleen plates are advantageous for this kind of feeding technique. Because they are bottom-feeders, Gray Whales will often ingest sand, rocks and other materials strewn along the seabed.

When Gray Whales plow through the seabed in search of nourishment they fulfill an important ecological function. It is estimated that they churn up some 160 million tonnes of sediment from the seabed each feeding season, thereby bringing important nutrients back into solution. This in turn promotes the growth of phytoplankton.

General Information

Gray Whales were the first species of whale to come under intensive observation and study. In 1861 W. Lilljeborg first identified them as a distinct species. Basing his investigation on subfossil remains discovered in Sweden, he named the species *Balaenoptera robusta*. In 1864 Gray introduced the name *Eschrichtius*. Eventually this species came to be known under the current scientific name of *Eschrichtius robustus*.

Early Yankee whalers designated Gray Whales as "Devilsfish" because the whale cows often attacked the whaling boats and fiercely defended their young. Many a whaling boat suffered the dire consequences. Contemporary whale watchers have gotten to know Gray Whales as particularly docile and friendly creatures.

Gray Whales still populated the North Atlantic up until the 17th century. With the advent of commercial whaling, however, the whale population there was soon exterminated. Today the species can only be encountered in the Northern and Northeastern Pacific.

Gray Whales were the first species of whale to be reduced to a few hundred specimens by the beginning of the 20th century. They were also the first species of whale to be placed under full legal protection in 1946. The population in the Northeastern Pacific has since recovered remarkably well and now numbers about 20,000-25,000 animals. Due to the destruction of the environment along the Asian coastline and a severe food shortage, the fewer than 100 remaining Gray Whales of the Western Pacific have little chance of survival.

The sound repertoire of a Gray Whale includes moans, clicks, whistles and rumbles. The sounds are relatively low-key and generally lie in the range of 15 Hz to 2000 Hz. Their frequency range is 15 Hz to 20 kHz.

Where & When

Gray Whales live exclusively in the Northern Hemisphere, preferably in the shallow coastal waters of the northern Eastern Pacific and the Arctic. Depending on the season, they congregate in various regions. Gray Whales are known for their long migrations close to the shoreline.

From April-November they live in their Arctic feeding grounds in the Bering Sea, Chukchi Sea and Beaufort Sea. From October-February they migrate 8,000-9,500 km to their southern mating and nursing grounds in Baja California (Mexico). On their way they come close to Oregon's shoreline. They will remain in their Baja California mating grounds between December and April. Their preferred sites there are San Ignacio, Magdalena and Scammon's bays. Between March and July one can sight the Gray Whale cows from the shore as they migrate back north at a slower pace with their young.

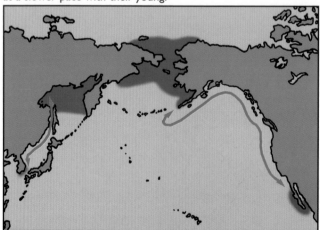

A subpopulation, numbering just few animals, lives in the Sea of Okhotsk to the north of Japan.

Distribution and migration paths: Shallow coastal waters in the Northern Pacific (during the summer also in the Arctic Pacific).

WHACKED BY A GRAY WHALE

There is a feeling among many wildlife enthusiasts that whales and dolphins are universally benevolent creatures; that their massive brains are less subject to the violence and stupidity that often tarnishes human behaviour. Some believe that these animals may recognise humans as other creatures of intellect and that, in some way, we share a cognizance of life beyond the laws of survival that govern less complicated life forms. Well, perhaps. The famous uw-filmer Howard Hall narrates a very personal experience.

It may be that in our loneliness and our hunger to reconcile individual human potential with a deluge of social stupidity, that some have found false comfort in the dream that whales are something more than wild creatures struggling to survive in a hostile environment. There are many levels of these whale ideologies born from speculation about cetacean intelligence. My good friend, Hardy Jones, is a film maker who specialises in films about marine mammals. He dreams of one day finding a bridge between the minds of these animals and our own. Hardy recognises that if lucid communication were made possible between our species, the revelations for mankind might be incalculable. He has travelled to many parts of the world observing whales and searching for that spark of recognition in their eyes. I recently met a woman at the other end of the spectrum. She told me she believes that cetaceans have an extraterrestrial origin and that these "beings" came to Earth to passively oversee the development of the human race. Variations of this sort of theory are surprisingly, if not frighteningly, common.

Faith in a philosophy holding that cetaceans are intelligent and, therefore, benevolent is certainly harmless enough. In fact, the growth of these ideologies at all levels has contributed toward saving many species of whale from possible extinction. However, when a diver finds himself swimming underwater toward a group of animals several hundred times his size, such beliefs can be just plain dangerous. The memory of one such encounter, undoubtedly influenced by optimistic attitudes toward cetaceans, still raises the hairs on the back of my neck and produces a deep and distant pain in my left arm and shoulder. The "event" occurred as result of circumstances somewhat more complicated than that of a simple gullible fool swimming up to pet a forty ton leviathan. Marty Snyderman and I had been asked by a German film production company to film gray whales in San Ignacio Lagoon on the Pacific coast of Baja California.

Over breakfast, on the day Marty and I first met with the producers of the film, our employers explained that they were under contract to deliver a variety of underwater scenes depicting several whale behaviours. Mr. Lazi explained that these necessary scenes included: Whales feeding, whales mating, a female whale giving birth, and finally a whale breaching. Again, all of these from an underwater perspective. Marty almost choked to death on his scrambled eggs and I blew my last sip of coffee up into my sinuses. After recovering from near shock, I explained that there were a few flaws in the plan. First, gray whales are extremely difficult to approach underwater, and second, visibility in the Lagoon ranges from zero

PHOTOS: HOWARD HALL & MARTY SNYDERMAN

A Gray Whale peeks above the water surface in San Ignacio Lagoon, Baja California, Mexico.

to a murky fifteen feet on a really nice day. An underwater cameraman, I explained, would have to be within six feet of a whale, in the best of conditions, to capture clear images on film.

Filming gray whales feeding would be an almost miraculous achievement in such conditions. The diver would have to be in exactly the right place as a whale approached from out of nowhere and scooped up the muddy lagoon

To capture clear images on film, visibility in the murky lagoon is simply not good enough.

floor within a few feet of the camera (gray whales generally feed on bottom dwelling crustaceans by turning on their sides and swimming across the bottom using their mouths like a scoop). Capturing a whale birth would be equally unlikely. Not only must one be fortunate enough to find a whale in the process of giving birth (an event observed very rarely in the lagoon), but the whale must permit the cameraman to wait around in the very murky water only feet away as the birth occurred. No chance. Filming mating whales, I said, would also be a bit more than difficult since the courtship process is rather aggressive and involves three whales (one female and two males) thrashing around violently. I admitted that the thought of being caught between the massive bodies of blissfully cuddling whales made me more than a bit nervous. Marty agreed without any further comments.

But it was the final objective - filming a breach from underwater, that qualified as the craziest idea I'd ever heard. Capturing a whale's breach underwater in 200 foot visibility must be considered a long shot. But in the murky conditions of San Ignacio Lagoon, the idea is laughably ridiculous. Even assuming that it were possible to film a gray whale leaping clear of the water from beneath the surface in ten foot visibility, I suggested that the chances of recovering the shattered remains of the movie camera (and less useful though no less damaged cameraman) after the forty ton beast came crashing back down, were poor in the murky conditions of the lagoon.

The only thing that an underwater photographer is likely to accomplish in San Ignacio Lagoon is to film the faces of "friendly" whales as they approach to investigate the skiff. This is best done by a diver leaning over the side of the boat with just his head and camera in the water. Very graceful and glamorous work.

Several weeks later, despite my negative comments concerning the underwater objectives, Marty and I found ourselves adrift in a small inflatable boat under the intense San Ignacio sun waiting for a "friendly whale". The producers conceded that the mating, feeding, birthing, and breaching objectives were somewhat unrealistic and decided that any image of a whale underwater would be useful to their project.

Unfortunately, two days had passed and we hadn't had an opportunity to get our cameras wet. Mr Lazi and his assistant watched in growing frustration as whales swam back and forth all around us, often engaging in courtship or breaching only a few hundred yards away. After two days under the relentless sun, our producers began to wonder at the inactivity of their heroic underwater team. Occasionally they would suggest that we attempt filming a whale that slowly passed by the boat (at only three or four times the speed a diver can swim) or one that breached less than a half mile away. Again I would explain that in ten foot visibility, attempting to film anything at ranges in excess of six or seven feet was a waste of time, and getting an image underwater at several hundred yards was strictly impossible. "But you can just try," Mr Lazi pleaded. "We have plenty of film. Just put the camera over and just try." I just shook my head as the whale he was watching passed a mere thirty yards from our boat.

A tourist pets a "friendly" Gray Whale.

"Friendly" behaviour was first noticed in San Ignacio in the late 1970's when whales began approaching the small whale watching boats and allowed passengers to actually touch them. Since then the behaviour has become common and has begun to spread to areas outside the Lagoon. No one is certain why the whales seek this contact. Most passengers believe that the whales are curious about people. That perhaps they like the affection that passengers shower on them. But the truth is that the whales don't care a hoot for the people in the boat. It's the boat itself that draws their affection. Specifically, it's sound produced by the outboard motor. Gray whales, it seems, find ecstasy in the music played by a Johnson twenty horse power motor (!). Whatever the reason, a "friendly" encounter can be one of the most thrilling and beautiful experiences of a lifetime. Breathing through a snorkel while holding on to the side of the inflatable, I have watched as many as three whales at a time rolling over and over on their sides as if dancing to the tunes produced by the outboard motor. One eye of a whale would roll up to within touching distance then it would roll down and a few seconds later I would be looking into the other eye. With each roll the pectoral fin would miss the boat by mere inches. Sometimes the whales would keep this up for more than an hour only pausing every few minutes to breathe. But if the motor was turned off, they quickly lost interest and swam away.

While adult whales roll under the boat, the calves sometimes spin vertically. They seem to pivot on their tail and will spin very rapidly making nearly sixty revolutions per minute, often with their heads out of the water right alongside the boat. It was this kind of encounter that Marty and I needed with growing desperation. Despite the certain knowledge that we were doing the very best that we could (which unfortunately happened to be doing nothing at all) Marty and I began to feel

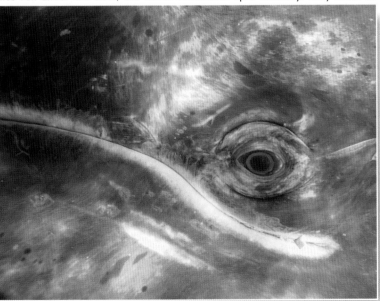

"For a fraction of a second our eyes made contact. What I saw in that animal's eye was fear."

17

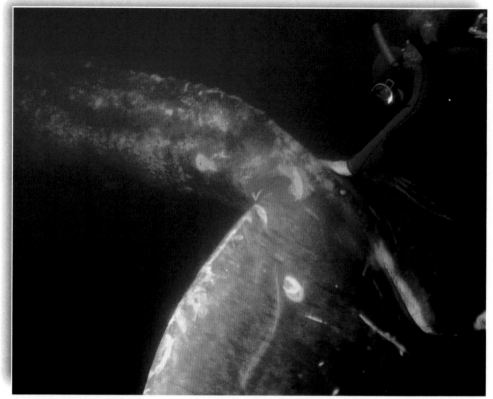

"At my left side I caught the fleeting image of a great fluke just before it smashed into my body."

guilty at our own lack of productivity. So when three courting whales began circling fifty yards away, we decided to swim over and see how close we could get. We knew this was a useless waste of time if not a dangerous waste of time. But anything was better than hearing Mr Lazi plead with us to "just try". To the great grinning glee of our producers, Marty and I donned our masks, fins, and snorkels and slipped over the side with our cameras. I noticed after lowering myself feet first into the water that I could see my ankles but the tips of my fins disappeared into the murk. Yuck! For a moment I considered swimming down to the bottom and filming the muddy floor from about seven feet away and then telling our producers it was the side of a sleeping whale. I doubt anyone would have known the difference.

As we swam (extremely slowly, each of us hoping the other would take the lead) towards the three whales, we could occasionally see the enormous splashes produced by huge tail flukes. The whales were moving in a slow circle. Slow for whales, however, is still much faster than a diver can swim. I didn't seriously think that we would get close to the animals. We had tried this sort of thing many times before without success. The whales would either move slowly away, faster than we could swim, or they would detect us acoustically with some form of active or passive echolocation that is not yet clearly understood and leave the area. But this time things went differently. As I looked up to see where the group was, I realised they were moving rapidly our way. Where earlier I hadn't thought we had any chance of getting close enough to film these animals, I now felt a close encounter may be unavoidable. Thirty yards away a large whale surfaced, blew, and dived, heading right for me. I flicked the safety catch off the trigger of the camera, took three quick deep breaths and dived. Hell, this was what I was hired for, I guessed.

At a depth of about thirty feet, I stopped and hung motionless - waiting. The darkness of the murky green water was intensely oppressive. I hung suspended between the surface ten yards above and the muddy bottom an unknown distance below wishing my eyes would more quickly adjust to the darkness. The senses that one depends upon so much aided me little here. I could hear nothing and could see only a few feet into the dark turbid water. Had I been there to film sharks or some other form of large, potentially dangerous marine animal, I probably would have swam back to the boat as quickly as possible. But I was there to film whales and, despite my instincts, my mind told me that whales are gentle and don't hurt people. Suddenly there were shadows; great ominous shadows swirling all around and I knew that huge rapidly moving creatures

While rolling at the surface this male Gray Whale exposes its pink penis.

were only a few feet away. But there was no shape to the shadows. I squinted my eyes into the darkness for some hint of form, some idea of what to do, where to point the camera, where to go. I switched on the camera and pointed it in front of me (quite randomly) almost hoping that I would run out of film before anything happened and I could go back to the boat.

A moment later a shadow darkened and transformed itself into a huge mountain of grey flesh. The face of a whale suddenly materialised and I found myself looking directly into the eye of a leviathan only six feet away. For a fraction of a second our eyes made contact. What I saw in that animal's eye sent a rush of adrenalin through my system like no sight I had seen before. I saw fear. A short moment after our eyes made contact I saw a discernible tremor in the whale's body as it turned and suddenly accelerated away. For perhaps two seconds I was alone but instinctively I was certain that I was in great danger. I felt like the mouse that had frightened the elephant causing it to jump into the air only to be crushed as the beast came crashing down. I was curled up in a ball holding the camera close to my chest when the impact came.

Four things happened nearly simultaneously. I saw what looked like a shining semicircular white arch of light extending from the distance in front of me to my left side. At my left side I caught the fleeting image of the great fluke as it smashed into my body edge on. In my head I heard the sound of an explosion as if a shotgun had been fired in my ear. Then the lights went out.

In a semiconscious state I managed to struggle to the surface. Marty swam up to me quickly and asked "Are you ok?" "Yeah," I said. "No you're not", Marty said as he grabbed my arm and guided me back to the boat. I had lost my mask and one glove and had acquired two broken ribs and a fracture in my left arm. Fortunately, I still had my camera, but only because it had been attached to my wrist with a lanyard. Within a few hours I was aboard a sport fishing boat bound for San Diego and lying in a warm comfortable bunk quietly contemplating the effects of a slightly excessive dose of codeine.

Looking back on the event during the following months, some things seemed to become more clear. And I had every reason to dwell on the attack since the producers of the film informed Marty and I that we must return to the Lagoon the following year to complete the project. "Attack" is the proper word for the incident. Gray whales are relatively slow moving animals and are easy targets for killer whales and sharks. In the lagoon you can't help but notice that the flukes are often scalloped with angry red semicircular bites. Predators plague the whales making them wary of other creatures in the water nearby. To deal with this threat, gray whales use their flukes like a gigantic karate chop to deliver a blow with awesome power and precise accuracy. The whale that attacked me was preoccupied with courtship activity and didn't sense my presence until we came eye to eye with each other. This sudden confrontation with an unknown creature frightened the animal and so it attacked. The bright semicircular arch that I saw just before the lights went out was the vortex left behind as the fluke was swung sideways.

There is one final addendum to my unpleasant encounter in San Ignacio Lagoon (that I am too often reminded of). Several months after our trip, Mr Lazi came to San Diego filled with enthusiasm and congratulations. "You must see the film", Lazi crowed. "We have mating, we have mating". Marty and I looked at each other and shrugged. We had no idea what he was talking about. But when the film was projected, the image of an enormous, pink, prehensile penis twelve feet long appeared fleetingly on the screen! Neither Marty nor I was quick to claim credit for the image. Neither of us remembered seeing the thing underwater (and it would have been difficult to forget). But our producers were quite beside themselves with pleasure. This was mating underwater - a first! Suddenly it dawned on me. It was just possible that the scene was mine and that I had done my very best work while drifting unconscious with a camera dangling from my wrist.

HONEYMOON

"The serenity in Tonga will captivate your senses... This is the bona fide South Pacific as depicted in postcards with its strings of coral islands, dazzling lagoons and reefs, and endless solitary white beaches fringed by coconut palms..." That the eulogies of the travel guide are not an exaggeration already becomes apparent during the landing approach. The author journeyed to the distant kingdom of Tonga in order to observe the Humpback Whales during their honeymoon.

Puffing noisily the impetuous lover surfaces.

The largely uninhabited islands and islets of Tonga are a true paradise rarely encountered elsewhere on the globe. The breathtaking and almost kitschy "South Seas idyll" found here is the perfect ingredient for every vacationer seeking peace and relaxation. Fortunately, only a few tourists, usually honeymooners, have made their way to this paradisiacal kingdom so far.

The idea of spending a honeymoon in these picturesque lagoons and their bordering solitary isles is really not new. Whereas only a few privileged people will ever be able to afford such a luxurious pleasure trip, Humpback Whales of the southern latitude have been coming to Tonga for thousands of years to frolic in its protected bays between June and November. Every year they come all the way from the Antarctic to celebrate their "honeymoon" here, to mate, give birth, and rear their young. When the long winter nights begin in the Antarctic and the ice starts to spread, they end their four-month feeding orgy and head for warmer latitudes in order to satisfy other bodily needs.

The whales need a thick layer of fat around their bodies when they embark upon their long journey because they will have to fast the whole way. Whereas the generally equally corpulent human visitors have little more than their own bodily pleasure to worry about, the whales first have to take care of some very strenuous business. The whale cows give birth to their young in the warm bay waters of the Tongan isles. Although the recently born calves may appear somewhat delicate and small at first, they can already be 4 to 5 metres long and weigh up to 1 or 2 tonnes - or approximately as much as 3 to 4 compact cars together!

In order to put on a thick layer of insulating fat, without which the calves would not be able to survive in the Antarctic, they have to drink enormous amounts of their mothers' rich milk. The "tiny tots" gain a lot of experience during the first months of their lives. They have to look on as passionate lovers make mad passes at their mothers. They also get to observe those curious and uncoordinated little beings splashing about with their snorkels, masks and fins. Whenever they hear strange noises under the water they anxiously seek the comforting nearness of their mothers. Is what they are hearing a battle cry or a love serenade?

The melodious whistling, clicking, growling, moaning, sighing and squeaking sounds that we are even able to hear behind the walls of the ship's cabins are all for the benefit of the females. Burned on CDs, these sounds have become known all over the world. Every whale bull that manages to touch his beloved's heart with one of these melodies has good prospects of founding a new family. If the mother likes what she hears, she will keep her eyes peeled for the worthy composer.

Suddenly he makes his appearance. Large as a locomotive, the singer floats head down in the water with widespread flippers. After a brief foreplay, he wants to get down to business as quickly as possible. Impatient, he begins to press his chosen one hard, circling her with an ostentatious display of power. In the course of their wild courtship games, the whale bulls come dangerously close to our ship. Once they nearly rammed us. Adroitly, the unwilling whale cow manages to keep her suitor at a distance - for the time being at least. Again and again she manoeuvres herself around so that our boat stands between her and the frenzied suitor.

The snorkellers in the water also seem to serve the anxious mother as a welcome distraction for her impetuous lover. Curious, she closes in on us several times and seemingly gives us the once over. We had already seen several Humpback Whales swimming next to our ship in the perfectly clear

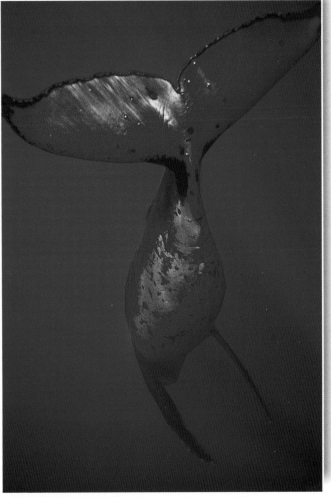

The lonely singer floats head down in the water with widespread flippers.

water. But their grandeur and grace can only be truly appreciated by a snorkeller in the water.

The calf snuggles up to its mother whenever she glides past us. The second time around, the calf finally dares to move a little ways from the protective fold of its mother in order to get a closer look at the "strange and somewhat uncoordinated beings with fins, masks and snorkels." It looks us over briefly and then decides to return to its mother just to be on the safe side. Young whales need to stay very close to their mothers for their own safety as well as to effectively communicate with them.

The calf proves to be more courageous than the once so determined lover. The bull keeps a low profile some distance behind the mother as if he were hiding from us. He probably needs to cool down a bit so that he can think things over. His patience finally wears thins, however. Ignoring the scary snorkellers in the water, he takes heart and begins to pursue his beloved as adamantly as before.

Both snorkellers and the calf had better keep their distance now. The undertow from the giant fluke even whirls the five- to six-metre long whale baby around. A veritable wall of bubbles blinds us momentarily. When two lorry-sized four-ton creatures become oblivious to everything around them in their frenzied love play and the water begins to churn, it is best to withdraw and watch what goes on from the deck. In the meantime several other love-hungry bulls have detected the prospective "bride and groom" and try to butt in. Their puffing and panting can be clearly heard on the surface. Gigantic!

Once the heated contest over melodic virtuosity and prospective fatherhood has been settled, things tone down again and the whales proceed to enjoy the pleasant warm waters as much as their human counterparts. The "tiny tots" still don't need to earn their keep. With great relish they

The baby anxiously snuggles up to its mother.

partake of their mothers' rich milk. Their only concern now is to grow as quickly as possible and to put on as much weight as they can. Soon they will need to be large and strong enough to undertake the long and arduous journey to the cold waters of the Antarctic.

Our boat slowly approaches the spot where a Humpback Whale and its calf have just sounded. The circular pattern made by the bubbles on the surface, or footprint, clearly demarcates where the whales went down. As we lean over the gunwale to take a look we can hardly believe our eyes. In the clear water beneath the hull we can make out the white underside of the mother's fluke. Hectic activity breaks out on board.

Everyone grabs mask, snorkel, fins and camera and slides into the warm South Pacific water with as little commotion as possible. The mother is still there. She hovers motionless about 15 metres below us with her head turned towards the bottom. Either she is resting there and not aware of our presence yet, or she is simply ignoring us. I can clearly see that the tip of her "nose" is almost brushing the white sandy bottom about 40 metres below. Incredible! Like a formidable submarine, she poises vertically in the water with her flippers spread wide open.

Only now do I detect the calf. It takes a cautious peek at us from under-

Above: A rare document: The whale cow floats head down just above the seafloor and nurses her baby.

neath its mother's right flipper. It seems to be unable to make up its mind about whether these strange lilliputian beings with their gaudy flippers are potential playmates or not. Next to its stately mother, the calf appears very small and delicate. As it has to surface for air more often than its mother does, the calf finally summons up all of its courage and begins to ascend towards us. Slowly and with a barely perceptible thrust of its fluke, the calf rises to the surface. Now I am also able to appreciate its true size. The "tiny tot" measures no less than 5 to 6 metres from head to tail! It continues to swim in our direction. At the last moment the calf veers off and surfaces a few metres away from us. It takes a quick breath and immediately sounds again to the safety of its mother's huge flippers. After the calf has repeated this procedure a few times, the colossal body of its mother suddenly begins to move. With a single stroke of her outspread flippers she brings herself up to a horizontal position and then glides effortlessly to the surface to take a breath. Her fluke barely moves, but we are unable to keep up with her and her calf.

Back on board we are still stunned by this encounter when Captain Keith sud-

Mother and calf surface.

denly kills the engine and informs us that the whale mother and its baby are directly under our boat. Quickly we get back into the water. Sure enough, there she is again, floating head-first in the water with her "wings" outspread.

During our first encounter I was practically paralysed with emotion and amazement. Words can hardly describe what I feel now. I have to pinch myself to make sure I am not dreaming. I even forget to take pictures for a moment. There is nothing that can adequately prepare one for the sight that now unfolds before me. Rather than swimming by in one fluid motion as expected, she hovers motionless beneath me with her head facing the bottom and nurses her young. An undescribable surge of admiration and elation courses through my body.

About 15 metres below us, I can see the whale calf open its mouth repeatedly. After a while the calf tries to assume a vertical position

When the snorkeller tries to film cow and calf with her video camera, the baby hides beneath its mother.

At the surface the youngster dares to leave the safe perimeter of the cow...

like its mother - in vain. The whole procedure is obviously not as easy as it would seem. Again and again the calf topples over on its side, circles its mother's head and tries once more.

Finally, the calf glances up and decides to swim in our direction even though it has just recently surfaced to take a quick breath before going down again. Apparently the strange "midgets" have caught its attention after all. It seems as if it wants to get to know its new "playmates" better. It swims around us several times, rolls on its side and proudly displays its wrinkled white belly.

"Big Mama" remains unmoved by the whole episode. She continues to hover headfirst in the water. Only when she feels the need to breathe again does she rise slowly to the surface. She takes a shallow breath and then swims leisurely before us. The calf follows her unwillingly. Its new "playmates" are obviously much too interesting. But we don't have to pursue the mother very far.

I spot the two whales floating on the surface a short distance from us. The mother waves its powerful fluke and gradually sinks to the bottom. When I stick my head under water I realise that they are not that far away. The visibility must be at least 40 to 50 metres. Once again the mother takes up a vertical resting position and doesn't seem to mind if her baby spends some more time with us.

That day we spent almost 7 hours in the water with these two Humpback Whales, as our sun-burned shoulders, backs and legs painfully attest. Not one of us is able to articulate the feelings that well up after this remarkable encounter. I am surrounded by sparkling eyes and beaming faces.

During the next two days the mother lets its calf swim along with us several times. The same procedure repeats itself again and again. The mother floats in the accustomed headfirst position below us and allows the nursing calf to come to us whenever it wants to. Whenever she runs out of air she surfaces briefly to take a short breath and then sounds again. Every time I meet "our" whale mother again my reaction remains the same: Wide-eyed I try to soak up every precious minute of the magic experience. On the third day the whale mother and her calf are nowhere to be seen.

A few days later, another whale cow and her calf surface next to our boat, circle it once and then submerge again. Eager, we try our luck once more. Strangely enough, she also hovers motionless with outspread flippers at a depth of about 20 to 30 metres. Only this whale mother maintains a horizontal rather than a vertical position. Just as it had happened earlier, the calf takes a cautious peek at us from under its mother's flippers. It is probably debating whether or not to surface for a breath of air. Finally, it takes heart just like "our" previous baby and swims to the surface, where it catches a quick breath and then dives right back down again to seek protection under its mother's massive body. Once again, however, curiosity prevails over caution. Resting on its mother's head now, it keeps looking up at us. As the mother surfaces for air she practically noses her baby in our direction.

The ascending whale cow veers off slightly and then surfaces next to us. She takes several deep breaths and then sounds again a little farther on. Once more she positions herself horizontally under water. Surely she has spotted us by now. At any rate, she seems to have no qualms at all about our

...to take a look at its new "playmates".

presence. During the next few days she also permits us to spend many happy hours in the water with her young one.

In the course of our numerous encounters with these two wonderful creatures we nearly had a collision with the mother. Surprisingly, however, she did her best to avoid hitting me with her right flipper. Apparently unintentionally (or did she allow it?), we move so close together that I can look directly into one of her gentle eyes. I can clearly make out the dark-light pigmentation that bisects the eye vertically. The anterior section of her eye is grey, the posterior is white. She has turned slightly sideways, perhaps to have a better look at me as well.

Now that she is obviously about to veer back again, I notice that I am directly in the way of her right flipper. I can see the approximately five-metre long fin heading directly towards me. "If she keeps moving in this direction, then she will surely hit me," I think to myself and try to avoid the impending collision as best as I can. But this "Big Mama" has already appraised the situation correctly and arches her fin underneath and then behind me so that it turns up above my head without ever having touched me. Then she calmly proceeds with her turning manoeuver and swims away with regular and hardly perceptible strokes of her fluke until I lose sight of her in the turquoise-blue waters.

It is almost as if the Humpback Whales were here on a vacation, as they spend most of their time in Tonga sleeping, singing, playing and making love. The young obviously learn all about these pleasantries from their parents. As far as the whale-watcher species is concerned, it is a wonderful spectacle whenever the "big boys" heave their 40 tonnes out of the water while breaching. With outspread "wings" they seem to defy gravity for a brief moment before their massive bodies come crashing down on the water's surface like thunder.

We witness several such spectacular performances from the deck of our ship. Not far from us, an ambitious calf aspires to imitate its mother and breaches about 50 times. Again and again it attempts to launch itself clear out of the water with outspread flippers just like its mother had demonstrated earlier.

High-spirited like a child in a bathtub, it romps around in the water as if it were unable to contain its unbounded energy and joy of living. In between leaps it slaps the surface of the water with its tail and flippers. It is obviously enjoying itself as much as the passengers on board, who cheer loudly every time one of its attempts to breach is crowned with success.

The heavenly "South-Seas feeling" has evidently captivated both travellers and "honeymooners" with its mysterious life-affirming force.

Distinguishing Characteristics of this Family

The family of rorqual whales encloses some of the world's largest whales. Blue Whales, Fin Whales, Bryde's Whales and Sei Whales belong to this family along with the much smaller (up to 7 m long) Minke Whales and Humpback Whales.

The most common characteristic of this family is several longitudinal throat grooves. The throat grooves, which gave the family its name, begin directly at the tip of the chin and extend past the flippers, sometimes even as far as the navel. The number of throat grooves will vary with each species: Humpback Whales have 20, Sei Whales have 50 and Blue Whales have 90. Throat grooves enable the whales to inflate their ventral throats like an accordion. This in turn allows them to ingest huge amounts of water and nutrients. The nutrients, like krill, are then filtered out of the water by the baleen.

All rorquals have short and wide baleen plates, the right and left sides of which run together at the tip of the upper jaw. In addition, rorqual whales have streamlined bodies with a pointed head and a well developed dorsal fin. Their flukes are slightly bent at the tips and have a median notch. All rorqual whales are sexually dimorphic: The females are slightly larger than the males.

SUBFAMILY Rorqual Whales, Balaenopterinae

5 species: Minke Whale, *Balaenoptera acutorostrata*
                 Sei Whale, *Balaenoptera borealis*
                 Bryde's Whale, *Balaenoptera edeni*
                 Blue Whale, *Balaenoptera musculus*
                 Fin Whale, *Balaenoptera physalus*

Distinguishing Characteristics of this Subfamily

All members of this subfamily have a conspicuously long and streamlined body, along with the throat grooves that are the earmark of the family. All have crescent-shaped dorsal fins, but no tubercles on their heads or flippers. All members of this subfamily also have midlines running from the tip of their rostrums to the blowholes. Only Bryde's Whales have two additional ridges on their heads, which run parallel on either side of the midlines. Small bulges situated in front of the paired blowholes of each member of this subfamily function as splash guards.

The largest rorqual whale species in the world is the Blue Whale. Azores, Atlantic.   Ralf Kiefner

Minke Whale, *Balaenoptera acutorostrata*

Minke Whale at Australia's Great Barrier Reef.   Doug Perrine

Distinguishing Characteristics
The most conspicuous features of a Minke Whale are its relatively small size, the narrow and tri-angular head, the characteristic colour of its flippers (with a white band or patch) and its inquisi-tiveness.

Description
Like all rorquals, Minke Whales are very slender and streamlined. They are the smallest members of this family. Minke Whales measure between 8.5-10 m in length and weigh between 4-7.5 t. The individuals living in the Northern Hemisphere appear to be somewhat smaller. As with all rorquals, Minke Whale females grow larger than the males (sexual dimorphism).

Viewed from above, a Minke Whale's head is very narrow and nearly triangular in shape. It has a clearly demarcated midline that runs from the tip of the snout to the blowholes. An L-shaped pattern is frequently discernible behind the whale's head, as in the case of Fin Whales. Curiously, its lower jaw projects further than its upper jaw.

The crescent-shaped dorsal fin is set about two thirds of the way along the back. It is markedly curved and immediately recognizable on the surface. In proportion to their body size, Minke Whales have the largest dorsal fins of all rorquals. Their slim flippers are pointed at the end and relatively short, making up about 1/8 of their total body length.

A Minke Whale's back is grey to black, but turns paler along the sides. The underside of its body and fins range from white to pale-grey. Minke Whales are unique among the baleen whales in that each flipper usually bears a bright white band or patch on the upper side. A few Minke Whales of the Southern Hemisphere do not have this characteristic white band, in which case the topside of the flippers will be entirely dark. This may be an indication for a different subspecies altogether. The underside of a Minke Whale's fluke is always pale-grey to white with a dark bor-der. The tip is slightly concave with a median notch.

The 50-70 white throat grooves can occasionally be light-pink in colour. They do not terminate behind the navel as is the case with all other rorquals, but just short of it. Minke Whales have 260-360 yellowish to white baleen plates on each side of their upper jaws, which attain a maximum length of 23 cm and are no wider than 10 cm. The blow is about 2-3 m high and difficult to spot.

Easily Mistaken For

Beaked Whales, Pygmy Right Whales and younger specimens of Sei, Fin and Bryde's whales.

The most conspicuous characteristic that distinguishes a Minke Whale from all other whales is the white band or patch on the upper side of its flippers. Its uncommonly pointed and triangular-shaped head with a single median line and its usually unblemished skin distinguish it from Beaked Whales. Its straight jawlines set it apart from Pygmy Right Whales.

Although the markings on a Minke Whale's back are similar to those found on Fin Whales, the difference in size makes any confusion unlikely unless the Fin Whale is still very young. Fin Whale calves, however, will never make an appearance unaccompanied by their mothers.

A Minke Whale is easily distinguishable from afar because its surface behaviour differs some-what from that of Fin, Sei and Bryde's whales. When it surfaces, the tip of its snout clears the water at a sharp angle. It often begins to exhale before its blowholes reach the surface. The blow and dorsal fin become visible at the same time.

Other Names

Little Piked Whale, Pike Whale, Sharpheaded Finner, Lesser Rorqual, Little Finner, Lesser Finback (English); Zwergwal, Minkwal (German); Petit Rorqual, Rorqual à Museau Pointu (French); Balenottera Minore (Italian); Rorcual Enano (Spanish); Baleia Minke, Baleia Anã, Roal (Portuguese); Dwergvinvis (Dutch); Vågehval, Minkehval (Norwegian); Lahtivalas (Finnish); Vikval (Swedish); Vågehval, Sildepisker (Danish); Minku, Koiwashi Kujira (Japanese); Malyy, Polosatik, Minke (Russian); Ballena Minke, Ballena Enana, Rorcual Pequeño (Latin American Spanish).

Meaning of the Scientific Nomenclature

Balaenoptera acutorostrata Lacépède 1804 – The generic name *Balaenoptera* is composed of the Latin *balaena* (whale) and the Greek *pteron* (wing), with the latter referring to the relatively large dorsal fin. The Latin species name *acutorostrata* denotes "with a pointed snout."

Behaviour

Minke Whales normally live singly or in groups of 2-3 individuals. In exceptionally rich feeding grounds one may encounter up to several hundred animals.

Male and female Minke Whales migrate separately. Whereas the females tend to seek shelter in the fjords, the males usually remain out on the open sea. Minke Whales spend the winter months in subtropical and tropical waters, where they mate, calve and nurture their young. During the summer months they remain in their feeding grounds in temperate and polar waters.

Not much is known about their social behaviour. The fact that they usually live as solitary indi-viduals or in small groups and nurse their young for only a very short period leads to the assump-tion that they are less gregarious than other whales.

Their reaction to boats varies from inquisitiveness to shyness, depending upon how intensely they are being hunted in the region. They often surface close to boats in order to look them over briefly. Occasionally they will also swim alongside a vessel for a while. The younger and inexperi-enced Minke Whales are the most inquisitive.

Minke Whales are fast swimmers and often change their course under water. Apparently they are not as fond of breaching as their larger relatives. When they do breach, they normally break the surface at an angle of about 45° and then do a belly flop without twisting their bodies. In breaching their bodies nearly come completely out of the water.

Diving

During migration Minke Whales only breathe 1-2 times between dives and spend about 1-10 min under water. In a relaxed state the frequency will change to about 5-8 breaths between dives. They can remain under water for up to 20 min.

The diving sequences of a Minke Whale are unmistakable. As it ascends its pointed snout breaks through the surface of the water at a sharp angle. It will often begin to exhale before its blowholes clear the surface and thereby produce a lot of bubbles under water.

Blow and dorsal fin will become visible on the surface simultaneously. Just before a Minke Whale sounds, it will bend its back and tail stock much further than a Sei Whale does. Like a Sei Whale, however, its fluke will remain submerged.

Feeding Habits

Minke Whales are known as swallowers. They occasionally jump out of the water while feeding, much like a lunge-feeding Humpback Whale. Their preferred diet is euphausiids (krill) and shoaling fish like capelin, cod and herring. They will also take various other species of shrimp and fish (mackerel, shellfish, coalfish, redfish, sand eel) as well as free-swimming molluscs. Those living in the Southern Hemisphere feed primarily on krill, those in the Northern Hemisphere on shoaling fish.

General Information

This species was first classified by Lacépède in 1804. The scientific name he gave the species back then is still valid today.

As their features vary considerably, some systematists have divided Minke Whales into 4 sub-species: a northern variant, two southern variants and a pygmy variant that lives off the coast of South Africa and Australia. The latter grows no larger than 7.5 m.

The Minke Whale population is isolated in three distinct geographical areas: the Northern Pacific, the North Atlantic and the Southern Hemisphere. The baleen plates of the Northern Pacific population are yellowish, those of the North Atlantic population are white. The animals living in the Southern Hemisphere have white baleen plates that turn dark-grey towards the upper parts of the jaws.

The age of a Minke Whale can be determined quite easily by counting the number of growth layers on its ear plugs. Their longevity is 30-50 years.

Whalers have various designations for Minke Whales. Their common English name is of Norwegian origin and gained official recognition at a special convention of the International Whaling Commission (IWC) in Montreal in 1975.

Because of their relatively small size, Minke Whales were not hunted commercially until the decimation of larger whales made it economically worthwhile. Today Minke Whales are the most hunted species of whale because of their relatively large population. Among whalers it is known that an 8-metre-long Minke Whale will yield about 2,500 kg of meat and 1,000 kg of blubber.

Minke Whales emit grunts, clicks and pulses when they communicate. Their frequency range is 20-80 Hz. A few of their auditory signals have a duration of less than 30 ms.

Facts & Figures Minke Whale

Size: 7-10 m
Weight: 4-7.5 t
Longevity: approximately 30-50 years
Sexual maturity: at 7 years, females with a
   length of 7.3 m, males 6.7 m
Mating season: Northern Hemisphere: Oct-
   Mar; Southern Hemisphere: Jun-Dec
Gestation period: about 10 months
Calving interval: every 2 years
Size at birth: 2.4-2.8 m
Weight at birth: 200-300 kg
Nursing period: 4-5 months
Dive depth: max 200 m
Dive time: max 20 min
Maximum speed: 30 km/h
Baleen plates: 260-360 on each side of the jaw,
   max. 23 cm long and 10 cm wide
Blow: 2-3 m high, inconspicuous
Throat Grooves: 50-70, usually terminate right
   behind the flippers
Group (Pod) size: individuals or pairs, occa-
   sionally larger congregations with up to 100
   animals in rich feeding grounds
Population: about 400,000-900,000; still being
   hunted for "scientific purposes"!

Quick ID-Check Minke Whale

A white band or patch on the topside of each flipper

Blowholes and dorsal fin visible simultaneously

Tip of snout is pointed and triangular

Snout breaks the surface first

Lower jaw extends farther than upper jaw

Low and inconspicuous blow

Usually unblemished skin

Often easy to approach

Exhales while still under water

Minke Whale at the surface. Maledives, Indian Ocean. A distinguishing characteristic of this species is the white band on the topside of each pectoral fin.   Helmut Debelius

Where & When

Minke Whales can be encountered in just about all of the seas in both hemispheres. They tend to live inshore and frequent all tropical, temperate and polar waters between the Arctic and the Antarctic. Their range extends all the way to the northern and southern polar caps. They seem to prefer colder waters.

Their migration patterns vary. During the summer months they congregate in the northern latitudes, in the winter they tend to gather in the southern latitudes. In the North Atlantic they seem to prefer spending the summer in the shallower waters of the continental shelf. During the summer months one will frequently encounter feeding Minke Whales near smaller islands and peninsulas.

Some populations are apparently sedentary, while others wander about the same regions. Occasionally they also move into bays or inlets.

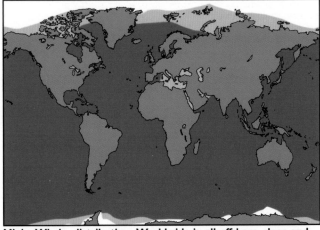

Minke Whale, distribution: Worldwide in all offshore, deep and temperate waters.

Sei Whale, *Balaenoptera borealis*

Sei Whale at the Azores, Atlantic.   Doug Perrine/Seapics.com

Distinguishing Characteristics
Sei Whales can easily be identified by their dark, slender and streamlined bodies, as well as their conspicuously large dorsal fin. Another distinguishing feature is the manner in which they swim. They will usually swim directly underneath the surface without changing their course and leave behind perfectly round footprints.

Description
Sei Whales have very slender and streamlined bodies. Their average length is 15-18 m, but they can reach up to 21 m. Like all rorquals, Sei Whale females grow slightly larger and heavier than the males (sexual dimorphism). The average weight of a Sei Whale is 20-25 t.

Its head and jaws are rather narrow and slightly arched. Viewed from above, a Sei Whale will have single median line that extends from the tip of the snout to the blowholes. There are 20-30 short hairs growing on the tip of its lower jaw, which probably have a sensory function.

Its slim flippers are dark on both sides. Making up about 10% of a Sei Whale's total body length, they are shorter than those of Fin or Blue Whales. The slightly-falcate dorsal fin is well defined and located about two-thirds back along the body. Topping 61 cm, it is comparatively large for a rorqual. As the exceptional size of its dorsal fin already suggest, a Sei Whales is an excellent swimmer. With top speeds ranging from 50-60 km/h, it is the fastest of the large whales.

Sei Whales can vary considerably in colour. Their backs usually range from dark-grey to black. At times their sides will also have a bluish hue. Their undersides are markedly lighter. Their bodies are often covered with white pock marks caused by lampreys and parasitic copepods. In contrast to Fin Whales, their lower jaws are not asymmetrically coloured.

A Sei Whale's fluke is dark on both sides and rather small in proportion to the size of its body. It is pointed at the tips and nearly straight in between, but with a median notch.

The anterior baleen plates are white- to cream-coloured, sometimes also striped. There are 300-400 silky baleen plates on each side of a Sei Whale's jaw, which can be up to 77.5 cm long.

The 38-60 well-defined throat grooves are pale-grey to whitish in colour and usually terminate behind the flippers. In contrast to Bryde's Whales, there is no gap between a Sei Whale's throat grooves.

Easily Mistaken For
Sei Whales can easily be confused with Bryde's Whales. From a distance, they may also be mistaken for smaller specimens of Fin and Blue whales.

For a long time Sei Whales and Bryde's Whales were thought to be one and the same species. They are very similar in size and appearance. The primary distinctions are diving behaviour, range and the shape of the head. A Sei Whales has a single median line running from the tip of its snout to the blowholes. A Bryde's Whale, though nearly alike in size and colour, has two ridges on either side of its median line.

Whereas Sei Whales are found in the temperate zones of all the world's oceans and seas, Bryde's Whales prefer the tropical zones of the Pacific, Atlantic and Indian oceans. Sei Whales favour water temperatures ranging from 8-25° C, while Bryde's Whales like 20-30° C. Unlike Sei Whales, Bryde's Whales will bend their tails when they sound.

Sei Whales can be differentiated from Fin Whales by the symmetric and dark colouration on either side of their heads. In contrast to Fin and Blue Whales, the crescent-shaped dorsal fin of a Sei Whale is more clearly defined and higher. Fin and Blue Whales also differ from Sei Whales in size (they are larger) and behaviour. Moreover, Fin and Blue Whales have smaller flippers.

Other Names
Rudolphi's Rorqual, Pollack Whale, Japan Finner, Coalfish Whale (English); Seiwal (German); Rorqual de Rudolphi, Rorqual Boréal (French); Balenottera Boreale (Italian); Rorcual del Norte (Spanish); Baleia Sardinheira, Baleia Boral, Baleia Sei, Espadarte (Portuguese); Noordse Vinvis (Dutch); Seihval (Norwegian); Seitivalas (Finnish); Sejval (Swedish); Sejhval (Danish); Iwashi Kujira (Japanese); Ballena Boba, Ballena Boreal (Latin American Spanish).

Meaning of the Scientific Nomenclature
Balaenoptera borealis Lesson 1828 – The generic name *Balaenoptera* is composed of the Latin *balaena* (whale) and the Greek *pteron* (wing), with the latter referring to the relatively large dorsal fin. The Latin species name *borealis* (northern) refers to one of the global regions in which the animals are found.

The typical silhouette of a Sei Whale at the island of Pico. Azores, Atlantic.   Ralf Kiefner

Facts & Figures Sei Whale

Size: 15-20 m
Weight: 20-25 t
Longevity: approximately 54-70 years
Sexual maturity: at 8 years & min. length 13 m
Mating season: April-August
Gestation period: 11-12 months
Calving interval: every 2 years
Size at birth: 4.5-4.8 m
Weight at birth: 780 kg
Nursing period: 6 months, until they attain
  8.5 m in size and 3.8 t in weight
Dive depth: max 300 m
Dive time: 20 min or more
Maximum speed: 60 km/h
Baleen plates: 300-400 on each side of the jaw,
  max. length of 77.5 cm
Blow: high and narrow column up to 4-5 m
Throat Grooves: 38-60, usually terminate
  directly behind the flippers
Group (Pod) size: 2-5, occasionally up to 30
  animals in rich feeding grounds
Population: estimated at about 30,000; consid-
  ered vulnerable

Quick ID-Check Sei Whale

Blowholes and dorsal fin simultaneously visible
  on surface

Well-developed, high and crescent-shaped dorsal fin

Single median line

Symmetrically dark colouration on either side
  of the head

Usually dive just below the surface

Rarely raise flukes when sounding

No change in direction or speed

Behaviour

The manner in which a Sei Whale swims is very typical. When chased they usually dive just below the surface. Their footprints are consequently visible for quite a distance. They will rarely ever change their course.

With speeds up to 50-60 km/h, Sei Whales are the fastest of all large whales. They rarely raise their flukes when sounding. As long as they are not being chased they pay little attention to approaching vessels. Even though their footprints are conspicuous and they usually maintain their course, Sei Whales are difficult to follow by boat because of their extraordinary speed.

During migration and while in their mating grounds they live in groups of 2-5 animals. Groups are generally formed by age, sex and stage of fertility, whereby the individual needs of the animals may also play a role. These groups will disband and then regroup once they arrive in their feeding grounds. In richer feeding grounds the groups can be composed of up to 30 animals.

Sei Whales are known as long-distance travellers and dwellers of the open seas. They are not generally found in coastal waters and thus do not strand very often. They prefer water temperatures of 8-25° C.

While feeding, Sei Whales swim at a measured pace of 2-6.5 km/h, but they can average between 5-30 km/h when they migrate. Their top speed lies around 50-60 km/h.

A Sei Whale's surface behaviour is fairly inconspicuous for a baleen whale. Communicative activities such as lob-tailing have rarely been observed among them. When they breach, they break through the surface at a sharp angle and land flat on their stomachs. They usually dive immediately after breaching.

Sei Whales produce very few sounds. According to some reports, they emit "metallic" tones with a maximum frequency of 3 kHz. Each tone lasts about 4 milliseconds (mS).

Footprint of a Sei Whale fluke on the surface. Azores.   Ralf Kiefner

Sei Whale cow with her calf. Azores, Atlantic.   Doug Perrine/Seapics.com

Diving

Experienced whalers recognize Sei Whales on the basis of their extraordinary speed and unpre-
dictable manoeuvres. Whale watchers, on the other hand, have it easier as long as the Sei Whales
are going slow. Normally they dive just below the surface and rarely change their speed or course.
Their regularly spaced footprints are easy to spot from a boat. They seldom raise their flukes
before sounding.

The normal respiratory rate of a Sei Whale at rest ranges from 0.7-1.4 breaths per minute.
After each dive this frequency will increase to 1-2 breaths per minute. Its dive time will normally
not exceed 5 min, but it can last up to 20 min. Its maximum dive depth is probably around 300 m.

Feeding Habits

Sei Whales are primarily dependent on shoaling prey for sustenance. Their fine baleen plates can
filter out minute shrimp and shoaling fish up to 30 cm in length. They also take copepods,
euphausiids (krill) and squid.

A Sei Whale's daily nutritional requirements total about 4% of its own body weight. An animal
weighing 20 t will thus need 800 kg of nourishment each day. Like a Bryde's Whale, it will swim
sideways while feeding.

A Sei Whale's feeding technique ranges somewhere between "gulping," as is typical for all
rorquals, and "skimming," as is practised by right whales. The application of either technique will
depend upon the shape of its jaws, the form of its baleen plates and the stretching capacity of its
throat grooves. So-called "skimmers" intake food by swimming through the water with their
mouths wide open, while "gulpers" ingest large amounts of water and then filter the nutrients
through the baleen plates with their mouths closed. The "gulping" technique is more efficient
when there is a thick concentration of food stuffs in the water; the "skimming" technique is more
appropriate for a lesser abundance of nutrient. Sei Whales are the only baleen whales that make
effective use of both techniques.

General Information

This species was first described in 1822 by Rudolphi, who examined the skeleton of a young animal
that stranded in a bay located in the vicinity of Gormitz (Baltic Sea, Germany) on February 21, 1819.
He named it *Balaena rostrata*. It soon became evident, however, that this particular name had been
given to another species earlier and needed revision.

The following year Cuvier described a Sei Whale skull that was housed in the Berlin Museum.

He recognized the distinction between it and the genus *Balaena,* or whales without throat grooves, and named it "Northern Rorqual." Thus it wasn't until 1828 that this species was given its current name by zoologist René Lesson. Lesson based his diagnosis on the descriptions provided by Rudolphi and Cuvier, comparing them with his own examination of a specimen that stranded in Ile d'Oléron (France) on March 10, 1827.

The scientific designation currently in use is based on the earliest find in the Northern Hemisphere (Baltic Sea, Germany) and thus erroneously limits the range of Sei Whales to the northern half of the globe. Sei Whales are actually found in both hemispheres.

It is astonishing how little is known about Sei Whales today, even though their average size of 15-18 m clearly places them among the larger whales and they can be encountered in nearly all of the world's oceans and seas. This may be due to the fact that they are somewhat difficult to identify (easily mistaken for Bryde's Whales) and rank among the fastest of all baleen whales.

It is generally believed that northern and southern Sei Whales should be divided into two distinct subspecies as there is little, if any, contact between the two populations. In this case the subspecies *Balaenoptera borealis borealis* would comprise the animals living in the Northern Hemisphere and *Balaenoptera borealis schlegelii* those living in the Southern Hemisphere.

The southern Sei Whales can grow to a maximum of 21 m in length and are thus somewhat larger than their northern relatives, which attain a maximum length of 18 m. Northern Sei Whales have 320-340 baleen plates on either side of the upper jaw, while their southern relatives have about 300-410.

The age of a Sei Whale can easily be determined by the number of growth layers on its ear plugs. The longevity of northern Sei Whales is at least 54 years. Their southern relatives can live up to 70 years.

The milk of a Sei Whale cow has a fat content of 26%, which insures the rapid growth of its calves.

During the 1960s and 1970s Sei Whale stocks were reduced to a critical level. It appears as if the species has recuperated somewhat since then.

Where & When
Sei Whales are a pelagic species that range over nearly all of the world's oceans and seas. They are especially numerous in the temperate latitudes of both hemispheres, where water temperatures range from 8-25° C. The rarely move inshore. The species can occasionally be sighted in subtropical latitudes, at times even around the equatorial belt. They are not found in the Mediterranean. The northern Sei Whales are essentially open-water dwellers, while their southern relatives occasionally come close to shore.

Like all rorquals, Sei Whales migrate to their cooler feeding grounds during the summer and then return to warmer waters in the winter. Little is yet known about the migrating habits of Sei Whales, which may well be irregular. Since their seasonal migrations take place at the same time, there seems to be no contact between the northern and southern populations.

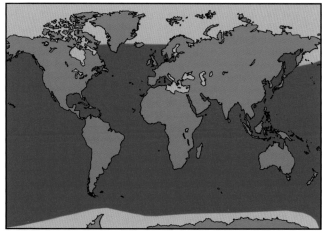

Sei Whale, distribution: Worldwide in all offshore and deep waters with moderate temperatures.

THE FIRST TIME

The first encounter with a whale is a memorable and moving experience for every whale watcher. Regardless of how much one has read or thought about it in advance, the actual confrontation with the size and beauty of these animals is beyond words. The author shares his impressions of his first meeting with a leviathan.

When Right Whales catapult their 40-ton-bodies out of the water, they show their true power.

I will never forget how excited I was after the extremely long and arduous journey. Would the whales really be there as my friend Henry had promised? I could hardly believe it. What was it going to be like, to meet face to face with one of these legendary marine giants?

Thanks to my friend Henry, I was able to obtain a special whale-watching permit from the Argentinian environmental protection bureau. The whales were placed under the official protection of the Argentinian government in 1977. Since then, only tourists participating in controlled whale-watching tours are allowed to come near them.

Far out at sea a high-spirited whale breaches repeatedly. The thunderous crash of its 40-tonne body on the surface can be heard for many kilometres across the bay. Is it giving us a demonstration of its tremendous size and power or is it just in a good mood?

Before we can make up our minds whether or not to head out to where the breaching whale is, we spot a whale cow with its young close by. The v-shaped blow rising high above both whales is momentarily visible on the horizon. The wind carries the smell and the mist of the blow over to us, covering our cameras with a thin, moist and oily film.

A whale's blow is primarily composed of condensed air, or steam. Whenever a large amount of warm air is discharged under pressure and comes into contact with cold air, it will condense into dew. In addition, the blow also carries small amounts of salt water that has accumulated above the whale's closed blowhole as well as tiny particles of an oily binding substance that coats the whale's lungs, sinuses and respiratory tract. This substance reduces the surface tension within the lungs in order to speed up the process of gas exchange. Some of the early whale hunters erroneously believed that the blow itself was poisonous.

At an appropriate distance we kill the engine of our rubber dinghy and wait for the gentle breeze to carry us slowly towards the two whales. We try to be as quiet as possible. But before we can get within 30 metres of them, they evidently notice our presence.

The "smaller" one is about 7 metres long. It keeps raising its head out of the water, or spy-hopping, to see what we are up to. They keep coming closer to us. "Hopefully they have really seen us," I think to myself as the 15-metre-long whale cow weighing no less than 40 tonnes elegantly plunges under our dinghy at the very last moment.

As her huge body gradually submerges in one slow and seemingly never-ending motion, I realise for the first time just how small we really are in comparison to this mighty creature. Its head alone is larger than our dinghy!

As its fluke lightly touches the bottom of our dinghy, I feel as if I were sitting on top of an outsized fly swatter. Its flukes extend a full metre on either side of us. What incredible dimensions.

With a single stroke of its mighty fluke the whale could easily pulverise us and the dinghy.

But we have little time to worry. Now it is the calf that approaches us with the intention of playing with the tiny rubber dinghy. At first it subjects us to a firm but apparently well-meant bunt with its head. Then it gently heaves us out of the water for a little ways. "Please don't turn us over," runs quickly through my mind as its head scrapes against our dinghy once more.

Touching a whale is usually forbidden, but this baby whale seems to like being caressed.

Again and again the calf rubs its head along the dinghy's gunwale until it begins to squeak like some child's rubber toy.

Although I know that one should never touch a whale, I stretch out my hand to caress its head. It is hard to believe, but the little fellow actually seems to appreciate it. Evidently it is also quite pleased when we remove a few bothersome whale lice from its head, as it keeps butting its head against our dinghy. Whale lice are thumbnail-sized copepods (Crustacea) that thrive on the whales like the minuscule inhabitants of a roving planet. The whale's skin feels like a hard rubber car bumper.

As if wanted to show its gratitude, the whale calf suddenly opens its mouth wide enough for us to admire its huge tongue embedded in rows of baleen plates. It even allows Henry to touch its tongue. Incredible! Every time the baby whale closes its mouth again a surge of water floods our dinghy.

After a while the whale mother, which had been scrutinising our doings from a distance until now, nudges her body between us and the calf. "Enough play for today," she seems to be

signalling. The calf's half-hearted show of defiance has little effect on the mother. In this sense at least, all babies are alike. Slowly, without the slightest indication of haste, the pair moves on again. The calf gives the skill of breaching a few more clumsy tries before its mother presumably leads it to some secluded spot to spend the night.

Curiously the whale looks at the rubber dinghy.

SEAGULL ATTACKS

It is no secret that whales are threatened by humans. But that seagulls can also be a threat to them is known to only a few. Nature photographer and biologist Armin Maywald brings light to the matter.

As soon as a Southern Right Whale shows up, the seagulls lie in wait for them along the shore.

Fascinated, we move ahead. The creature raises its monstrous head and water pours down the thick folds along its neck. We look straight into its right eye, which is tucked away in a white depression located at the corner of a dauntlessly curled upper lip. The creature scrutinizes us, roars and spews fountains of water out of its head. The spray brushes against my face, and I smell salt and decay. Slowly the creature sinks back into the water. The contours of its blue-black head finally dissolve in the deep, leaving no trace of our unexpected encounter with a giant other than a flimsy pool of bubbles.

As I look into the faces around me I detect joy and amazement. Shivering with cold, but grateful for the experience, we head back to Puerto Piramides. We are a group of whale fanatics who have just seen their first Southern Right Whale, an eighty-ton creature with a three-kilo brain and a tonne of testicles. A species of baleen whale that approaches humans with curiosity, but whose behaviour still remains a partial mystery despite several decades of intensive research. A gentle giant that has managed to recuperate somewhat from the bloodletting days of the whale hunt and now supposedly has to face the danger of seagull attacks. We plan to sail out to where the Southern Right Whales are every day in order to observe and photograph them. And perhaps even to dive with them, should they allow it.

If the Antarctic Sea can be likened to a Southern Right Whale's pantry, then we are currently cruising through what might be described as its nursery. The first whales make their appearance at one of the many bays off the Argentinian peninsula of Valdes in May, where they wallow in the warm water and seek out the more quiet and secluded bays when they need a rest. In August the first whale calves are born and begin to suckle their mothers' milk. September marks the

Even as the Southern Right Whale breaches it is being eyed by a hungry seagull.

arrival of the early whale watchers at Puerto Piramides, the start and finish line for all whale watching tours in the Golfo Nuevo. It is also a god-forsaken hole. A few years ago, the Lord even saw fit to have a tornado blow away the local church. Everything in Puerto Piramides is simple but functional. Two hotels take care of guests like us, and a petrol station helps those who are anxious to move on again once they have seen enough whales and supplied them-selves with sufficient T-

One of the culprits in action: As soon as this whale surfaces it is joined by an unwelcome escort...

shirts and other nicknacks from the scattered wooden stalls.

Alacran, our captain, stands behind the helm of the "Cormoran" as if nothing in the world could ever unsettle him, that is if it weren't for the gaps and the decayed stumps in his mouth. These have made him somewhat taciturn, especially when there are women on board. Rather than talk, he prefers to point his chin to the starboard and then to the port side with a questioning glance at me. I am supposed to decide where we are going. There is only a weak breeze blowing in from the land and the water is perfectly calm. It is a fine day for snorkelling. I point to the west, which is where we had spotted the mother whale and its calf the day before.

Alacran steers the "Cormoran" around the Loberia, a large table rock on which hundreds of male Southern sea lions congregate every December. At the present there are just a few young bulls dozing alongside a number of bored cormorants. A Southern Right Whale lies peacefully in the water, but we sail past it. The water is so calm that we can spot every whale and every blow in the distance. There, a breaching whale. We watch as the spray collapses. Everyone on board is suddenly busy changing lenses, stowing away submersible camera housings. Alacran gets the hint - we want to photograph rather than snorkel - and pushes down the throttle down. The twin outboard motors with 200 horses each practi-cally lift the "Cormoran" out of the water as we speed towards the spot where the breaching whale sounded. Its footprint is almost perfectly round and smoother than the surrounding water.

We stop and wait. The whale breaches again about 300 metres away from us. It swims quickly along the surface, blows heartily, spy hops briefly and then sounds again. Suddenly its mighty fluke is up in the air, drawing a curtain of water behind it as it slips back into the ocean at a steep angle. We are well aware, of course, that when a whale flukes like that it is preparing for a sounding dive. Although Alacran remains on course, we can see no trace of the whale. But Alacran knows what he is doing. We wait, 10 sec-onds, 15 seconds... "Perfecto!" Alacran suddenly cries into the wind. I watch as the whale materialises out of the turbid water no more than 30 metres from the boat, its huge body rising slowly and at an odd angle, the flippers spread wide on each side. The colossal crea-

...which begins by pecking at the countless parasitic crustaceans infesting the whale's upper body.

ture ascends higher and higher, revealing its white underside to us, then bends over backwards and comes crashing down upon the water with a vengeance. Fountains of water shoot up several metres high to the left and right of it, and then collapse into a curtain of spray that barely disguises the sinking body of the whale.

Twenty seconds later the scene repeats itself no more than 100 metres away from us. The whale breaches, twists and comes crashing down on the water's surface, all seemingly in slow motion - a tremendous spectacle. Southern Right Whales can breach up to ten times consecutively. Why do they do this? It can't only be for the simple joy of it as each time they breach they expend a lot of energy. Alacran tells us that the whales jump most frequently in September. That might have something to with it, because each September the number of Southern Right Whales in Valdes increases noticeably. The bulls arrive then and the mating season begins. Breaching may well be an acoustic signal for a marine rendezvous. "Listen up, here I am!" the breaching

That the clever bird is not just out to perform a cleaning service is clearly evident from this crater-like wound. There is great danger that such wounds will become inflamed and that the Southern Right Whales will eventually move elsewhere as a result.

whale seems to be heralding. At any rate, the crashing of the bodies on the water's surface can be heard for many kilometres. Scientists take a more pragmatic view of the matter, however. According to them, Southern Right Whales breach so often in order to rid themselves of the whale lice infesting every nook and cranny of their bodies. Could this not be a pleasant side effect of a much more complex social behaviour? Our supposition seems to be confirmed as we watch a flock of Kelp Gulls swoop down to the whale's footprint and frantically peck for parasites and shreds of skin. Are these the birds that pose such a threat to Southern Right Whales? We are loath to believe it.

According to a study by Roger Payne, a female Southern Right Whale will generally calve every three years. In spite of its strapping 5 metres, the "tiny tot" is still quite insecure and breathes irregularly at that point in its life. It always stays close to its mother, swimming around her in tight circles, touching her incessantly with its lower jaw or resting on her broad back. If it wants to suckle it has to dive down to the mother's underside. It is quite likely that the mother actively squirts milk into the calf's open mouth. When it is about three years old, the calf will venture to swim a little ways from its mother. Its early forays are quite brief, however, as it will return to its mother almost immediately. As the weeks go by the calf becomes more lively and impetuous. Swimming away from its mother and back

Sounding is the whale's only means of defence: The seagulls are forced to take to the air. But they have left ugly wounds behind that are a clear signal to other hungry seagulls.

again becomes a form of play. Now it also learns how to turn over on its back. By the time the calf is one and a half months old it will have mastered this skill to perfection. The art of fluke slapping and splashing about with flippers soon follow.

A few days later we come upon another whale mother and its calf. The little fellow is but a few weeks old and already covered with small scratches. On its back there are also two plate-sized wounds, each about two to three centimetres deep. Pecking wounds caused by seagulls, Alacran explains. That same afternoon we get to observe the evildoers in action. A Southern Right Whale surfaces and almost immediately two Kelp Gulls land on its back and start hacking away at its skin. The whale raises its head as if it wanted to look over its shoulder and then sounds. The gulls take to the sky, but every time the whale surfaces again they land on its back and start tearing away pieces of its flesh with their strong beaks. Ugly wounds appear on the whale's back that look like shredded whale flesh - an unmistakable signal for other seagulls to join the feast.

The wounds can easily become infected and then the danger is great that carriers will spread disease. In addition, the permanent molestation by seagull might someday cause the Southern Right Whales to migrate elsewhere. The Kelp Gulls are not really at fault. Attacks such as these have been recorded since the eighties, but they were not nearly as fre-

Here are two Kelp Gulls that have landed on a whale's broad back and are pecking away frantically at its skin.

quent as they are today. Since then the human population in this region has increased dramatically and with it the number of seagulls. The latter thrive in the vicinity of human settlements, where they can pick scraps from rubbish heaps. Accordingly, the local population of seagulls has increased threefold. Like the Herring Gulls living in our regions, Kelp Gulls are intelligent, robust and highly adaptable birds. Consequently, they are not slow to take full advantage of any new source of nourishment. It is very likely that they have always fished for scraps of dead whale skin floating on the water's surface. At one point they must have learned how to land on the whale's back. The next step, namely to peck at the live skin of the whale, could not have been that difficult for them after that. Younger birds soon learned the trick from their experienced parents.

Recently born whale calves are particularly helpless against such attacks. They can neither swim for long distances nor have they learned the skill of sounding. Thus they are an easy target for the hungry seagulls. Young whales pitted with festering peck wounds have become a common sight these days. "We are worried that more and more whale calves will die because of the seagulls," writes Roger Payne of the Whale Conservation Institute, who is currently investigating the problem. The whales spend about twenty per cent of their time trying to get away from the seagulls. Whale cows need to maintain a certain amount of fat in order to insure the proper growth and development of their young. But now the whales are burning up too much energy dodging the seagulls. This is why there is an acute danger that the whale cows might someday be forced to abandon the place where they have been rearing their young long since.

We have learned much at Valdes. Whales can really affect people. To observe and to be so near them is a unique experience for all of us. Such wonderful encounters have become possible because whale hunting has been prohibited and the population of Southern Right Whales has increased accordingly. But the increased attacks of the Kelp Gulls have also taught us something important: For us to rest assured that the Southern Right Whale is safe forever is obviously a grave mistake.

Bryde's Whale, *Balaenoptera edeni*

Bryde's Whale off the Pacific coast of Mexico.   Doc White/Seapics.com

Distinguishing Characteristics
The earmarks of a Bryde's Whale are its range, manner of swimming and, especially, the three distinct ridges on its head.

Description
Bryde's Whales attain an average length of 12-15 m. Their average weight is 14-20 t. Like all rorquals, female Bryde's Whales grow larger than the males.

The chief characteristic of a Bryde's Whale is the two ridges found on its head. No other rorquals have these ridges, which can only be seen from a top view of a Bryde's Whale's head. The thick median line that extends from the blowholes to the tip of the snout is flanked on either side by two parallel-running, 1-2 cm thick ridges.

The dark colouration on the back and sides of a Bryde's Whale's slender body can have a brown or golden shimmer to it when the light strikes it in a certain way. Its underside is cream or blue-grey in colour. Like Sei Whales, the underside of a Bryde's Whale is often covered with pock marks, which give it a mottled appearance. These pock marks are caused by parasites and possibly by smaller sharks like the Cookiecutter Shark *(Isistius brasiliensis)*.

The falcate dorsal fin can be up to 45 cm high and is located far down the dorsal ridge. The slender and pointed flippers are dark on both sides. Making up no more than 10% of the the whale's total body length, they are relatively short. The edge of the wide fluke is slightly concave at the back and has a conspicuous median notch. The top side is dark, the back side can be a dirty-white.

The 40-70 yellowish to whitish throat grooves extend down to the navel. The 250-360 baleen plates on each side of the upper jaw are 40 cm long, coarsely textured and grey in colour. The tips may be paler. There is a small gap between the baleen plates on both sides. The blow is 3-4 m high and narrow.

Easily Mistaken For
Due to their similarity in size and colour, its is easy to confuse a Sei Whale with a Bryde's Whale. Once they were even thought to be the same species. Nevertheless, they can be distinguished by their range, different manner of swimming and, especially, the ridges on their heads. Bryde's Whales are the only rorquals with two ridges on either side of their median lines. Bryde's Whales prefer water temperatures ranging from 20-30° C, while Sei Whales favour 8-25° C.

From a distance it is also possible to mistake a smaller Fin Whale or Blue Whale for a Bryde's Whale. In contrast to a Fin Whale, both sides of a Bryde's Whale's head are uniformly dark. Unlike Fin and Blue whales, Bryde's Whales and Sei Whales have crescent-shaped dorsal fins.

Bryde's Whales also differ from the much larger Fin and Blue whales in colouration and behaviour. Other features distinguishing them from Fin and Blue whales are the smaller flippers and the position of the dorsal fin.

Other Names
Tropical Whale (English); Brydewal, Brideswal (German); Rorqual de Bryde, Rorqual Tropical (French); Balenottera di Bryde (Italian); Rorcual Tropical (Spanish); Baleia de Bryde, Baleia de Brinde (Portuguese); Bryde-vinvis (Dutch); Brydehval (Norwegian); Brydenvalas (Finnish); Brydes Fenval (Swedish); Brydeshval (Danish); Nitari Kujira (Japanese).

Meaning of the Scientific Nomenclature
Balaenoptera edeni (Anderson 1858) – The generic name *Balaenoptera* is composed of the Latin *balaena* (whale) and the Greek *pteron* (wing), with the latter referring to the relatively large dorsal fin. The Latin species name *edeni* honours Eden, British Commissioner of Burma, who brought Anderson the first specimen ever examined in 1858.

Behaviour
Little is known so far about the behaviour of Bryde's Whales even though they rank among the larger whales. Vessels occasionally draw their curiosity, in which case they will circle them a few times or swim alongside for a short while. They usually live singly or in pairs. On rare occasions and in especially rich feeding grounds one may come across groups of up to 20 animals.

Bryde's Whales breach often and nearly vertically. Their bodies will not always come completely out the water, however. The hind quarters up to the dorsal fin will usually remain submerged. At times they bend backwards while breaching and either twist their bodies forward again or land flat on their backs. They often breach 2-3 times, occasionally up to 12 or more. A Bryde's Whale that was observed off the coast of Ogata (Japan) broke the record with 70 consecutive breaches.

Bryde's Whales are the only species of baleen whale that feeds all year round. Unlike other rorquals, their feeding habits are not tied to the seasons. While feeding they will change course frequently and unpredictably. It is also thought that a few regional populations may not have a mating season either. This atypical mating behaviour probably has something to do with the tropical climate of the regions in question. Bryde's Whales favour temperatures ranging from 20-30° C.

Diving
Bryde's Whales breathe and dive more irregularly then Sei Whales do. The way they sound is very conspicuous: They will bend their tail stocks at a sharp angle and rarely raise their flukes out of the water. Their diving sequences, course and breathing frequency become even more irregular when they are feeding. Normally they will breathe 5-10 times before sounding. Their dive time will usually not exceed 2-5 min, but can take up to 20 min. Bryde's Whales can dive to 300 m.

Facts & Figures Bryde's Whale	Quick ID-Check Bryde's Whale
Size: 12-15 m	
Weight: 14-20 t	Two ridges parallel to the median line
Longevity: approximately 50 years	
Sexual maturity: fem. at 10, males at 9-13 years	High, crescent-shaped dorsal fin
Mating season: all year	
Gestation period: 11-12 months	Underside dark, sometimes mottled
Calving interval: every 2 years	
Size at birth: 3.5 m	Dorsal fin and head not visible simultaneously
Weight at birth: 800-900 kg	
Nursing period: 5-7 months	Usually do not raise flukes when sounding
Dive depth: max 300 m	
Dive time: max 20 min	Curves back when sounding
Maximum speed: 25-30 km/h	
Baleen plates: 250-370 on each side	Irregular swimming and diving behaviour
Blow: 3-4 m high and narrow	
Throat Grooves: 40-70, usually terminate behind the navel	
Group (Pod) size: individuals or in pairs, up to 30 animals in rich feeding grounds	
Population: 40,000-80,000; endangerment under dispute	

Stranded Bryde's Whale in New Zealand.   Ingrid Visser/Seapics.com

Feeding Habits
Shoaling fish like herring, mackerel, anchovies and sardines are their preferred food along with krill and shoaling calamari. Like Sei Whales, Bryde's Whales turn on their sides while feeding.

General Information
Because of their similarity in size and colour, Bryde's Whales and Sei Whales were long regarded as one and the same species. It wasn't until 1913 that Olsen recognized the difference and gave Bryde's Whales the scientific name of *Balaenoptera brydei*. This was later changed to the currently valid designation of *Balaenoptera edeni*.

Offshore and inshore populations with differing feeding and mating habits have been observed around South Africa. It appears that these are actually two subspecies with diverging migration patterns and mating habits. The offshore population apparently prefers to wander about on the open sea, while the inshore group tends to be more sedentary. The inshore animals are usually smaller, with fewer pock marks and shorter baleen plates. Whereas the offshore animals have been protected since 1930, the inshore group was still being hunted by some seafaring nations as recently as 1987. Rumours about the discovery of a "pygmy version" of a Bryde's Whale off the Solomon Islands have apparently not been substantiated.

Like all other rorquals, the age of a Bryde's Whale can best be determined by the number of growth layers on it ear plugs. Their longevity is about 50 years.

Where & When
Bryde's Whales can be found in all tropical and warm temperate waters. Preferred water temperature is 20-30° C. This is why most of them are found between 30° N and 30° S. Sometimes they will follow warm currents to 40° N or S. Best chances for inshore sightings in South Africa, Sri Lanka, Japan, Fiji and West Australia.

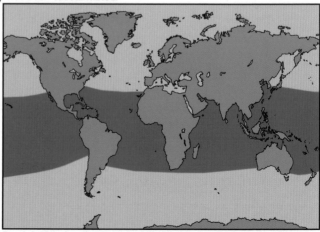

Bryde's Whale, distribution: Worldwide in all tropical, subtropical and warmer temperate waters.

DEATH OF A BLUE PRINCESS

The Bay of Prony is located on the Western coast of New Caledonia's main island, some 50 km Southwest of Noumea. Its splendid coastal dry vegetation covering steep hills that encompass a jade-coloured lagoon within the island's great barrier reef offers the most appealing set-up for whale watching. Unexpectedly, in the middle of summer, a beautiful Blue Whale appeared in this bay. While Sperm Whales are commonly encountered all year round outside the barrier reef , the appearance of a Blue Whale in the summer season can only mean trouble. Biologist/UW-cinematographer Eric Clua and Vanessa Top witnessed a heartbreaking tragedy.

The young blue whale chose the enchanting Bay of Prony - just off the southwest coast of New Caledonia's main island - to live its last days.

Wednesday, January 2, 2002: An elegant long body is spotted in a confined and small inlet of the lagoon in the Bay of Prony. Species and approximate length of the animal can only be determined by using a helicopter to follow the whale's concentric movements. Calmly, the whale draws its circles within the confined space. Each circle measures several hundred metres in diameter. Every 10 to 15 minutes it changes the axis of its clockwise (rarely ever anti-clockwise) rotations. It surfaces and breathes at regular intervals, inhaling and exhaling 2 to 3 consecutive times after diving for very short periods. The top of its flat skull appears first, followed by its impressive splash guard protecting the blowhole. Prior to each dive, the whale releases a quick and straight blow. Its long back surmounted by a small dorsal fin disappears under water with the smooth and elegant motion of a giant snake, a comparison that is fostered by its malnourished condition. Its fluke never clears the water, but leaves an impressive footprint behind.

We, a team of French scientists and UW-photographers, search for a possible explanation: What is a Blue Whale (Balaenoptera musculus) doing in this very confined and small inlet in the south of New Caledonia in mid summer season? At this time of the year Blue Whales normally forage on krill in feeding grounds that are located in higher latitudes. They are definitely not found in tropical regions. With the little knowledge that we have about this particular individual, we decide to concentrate on what has been already published elsewhere about Blue Whales and their behaviour. As a result of our study we come up with four possible hypotheses:

Firstly, we believe that although out of season, it is possible that this whale is a pregnant female. The Bay of Prony and surrounding waters are used as a birthing place by other whales, so it may also serve the same purpose for a birthing blue whales, providing adequate protection for its offspring from predators such as orcas *(Orcinus orca)*.

Secondly, we also assume that, for whatever reason, this Blue Whale has strayed from its habitual course of migration and is now desperately searching for food. Sickness is another possible explanation.

Thirdly, we consider the possibility that this whale may be trying to escape from predators

Above: The kayak allowed the scientists to get close enough to the whale to collect DNA samples, using a crossbow.
Left: Because of its poor condition, the emerging dorsal portion of the whale looked more like a snake slipping through the water than the back of a well-fed whale.

like pelagic sharks, orcas, etc.

Fourthly, it may be that this whale is still relatively young and has lost its mother for some reason.

Our quest for explanations calls for further investigation. First of all, we try to determine the length and size of the whale, which may help to estimate its age. However, this task turns out to be more difficult than expected because of the lack of appropriate reference points and the extremely poor condition of the creature. Finally, we agree to settle on a probable length between 15-18 m. This rules out or first hypothesis. Blue Whales are weaned by the time that they attain a length of 15 m. However, they are not sexually mature until they average 21-22 m in length. It should be remembered that a mature female is about 30 m long and weights between 140-160 tonnes. Its tongue alone already weighs 4 tonnes. The heart of a mature Blue Whale cow is the size of a car. Its fluke spans 7 m in width and has a surface area of tens of square metres. Thus we can safely conclude that what we are dealing with here is a teenage Blue Whale that has already been weaned. Even though we can't determine its sex, we know that it cannot possibly be pregnant. Therefore, its appearance in the Bay of Prony has nothing with the search for a protected birthing place. All of our attempts to determine the gender of this individual fail because of the turbidity of the water and the whale's restless movements and avoidance of any approaching divers.

January 17, 2002: We have observed the whale for more than a week now. From the day it was first sighted it has never shown any inclination to feed or search for food. Neither can we detect signs of bowel movement. In order to find out more about this particular aspect, we install some aggregating lights in order to attract anchovies and other small potential prey. Unfortunately, this experiment does not produce any positive results. There are no visible signs of abnormalities or deformations on the whale's body. Its behaviour is that of a young, calmly-breathing and circling whale. If it were suffering from any kind of disease we could expect a much quicker deterioration of its overall physical condition. Consequently, we also rule out our second hypothesis.

Another couple of days pass by (January 22) and the Blue Whale continues to draw its habitual circles.

"Blue Princess" escorted by a fleet of remoras.

It is still breathing calmly and regularly, and it is not showing any visible signs of sickness. But it is also not feeding at all and has consequently reached an alarming stage of malnutrition. It becomes apparent to us that the animal is starving to death, being either indecisive about what to do or simply accepting its fate. Our hypothesis that it might be trying to escape from large predators can also be discarded. The shelter provided by the Bay of Prony can't possibly offer a long-term solution to the problem. This Blue Whale is definitely running out of time.

As time goes by we become more and more convinced that our last hypothesis is the most probable. Considering its young age, we assume that it has never migrated unaccompanied by its mother. We don't have a clue where it was born, nor do we know where its feeding grounds are. However, the nearest possibility lies south of Tasmania, where krill is in rich supply at this time of the year. Losing its mother at this stage in its life is a crucial matter as it has no notion whatsoever where the feeding grounds are located, nor where to rejoin its mates. Disoriented, it may somehow have found this sheltered location, where it will await the end of its short life.

There are no more than one thousand specimens of this subspecies of Blue Whale (Balenoptera musculus intermedia) in the entire Southern Hemisphere. Consequently, each loss is tantamount to a small ecological disaster that contributes to the diminishment of this ancient genetic pool. In addition, there are another one thousand individuals of a distinct subspecies (Balenoptera musculus brevicauda) in the Southern Hemisphere, as well as an equal number of both subspecies in the Northern Hemisphere, including the northern "true" Blue Whale (Balenoptera musculus musculus). In total, there are probably less than four thousand Blue Whales left in the world.

But what can we do? Is there any chance to interfere and if so would that change the young whale's fate? Our options are slim. The animal does not permit any divers to come near it, it never stops swimming in circles, and it is impossible to establish any visual contact with it for longer than just a few seconds at a time.

The only alternative that we come up with is to transmit recorded Blue Whale songs from on board a vessel and thus lead the Blue Whale out of the Bay of Prony. The specialist for whale communication that we contacted informed us that, unfortunately, the songs of Blue Whales are much less studied than those of Humpback Whales. The chances that the UW-transmission of any fragment of recorded Blue Whale songs could lead to success are practically nil. A Blue Whale's communication songs are produced in very low frequencies ranging around 20 Hertz. The advantage is that such low frequencies can travel through water for thousands of kilometres. The disadvantage, however, is that they are almost impossible to detect with the human ear. Furthermore, devices for their detection and recording are highly sophisticated and not readily available in places like New Caledonia. It is quite likely that this Blue Whale is also intoning songs, trying to establish contact with its relatives to obtain guidance or protection. But no matter how much we may wish for it, there no evidence that it is being answered. In time it becomes painfully evident to us that we cannot possibly help this whale. It cannot live autonomously and if left alone it will become an easy prey for large sharks and orcas. Its only chance would be the protection of a mature

Blue Whale willing to accept its company on their joint way to the feeding grounds. Considering that the approximately one thousand surviving specimens are dispersed over millions of square kilometres of ocean and definitely not closer than the south of Tasmania, this chance is also practically nil.

We are now in the middle of our third week (January 25) in the Bay of Prony. The Blue Whale has changed its location but is still within the lagoon. It continues without to circle clockwise, and its state of undernourishment is becoming acute. I have not seen it during the last 3 days, but my colleagues continue to monitor its whereabouts from their vessels.

As usual, I slip into the water, carefully planning to wait on the surface for its approach. I discovered that observing the Blue Whale from a distance of about 400 m will not disturb its behaviour. This time, however, we seem to accept each other's presence in a way that hasn't happened before. I try to move in closer. Recognizing its acceptance, we also move our boat towards the centre of its circular route in order to gain easier access its current position. While free diving to a depth of 8-10 m, I am finally able to get close enough to determine its sex: It is a female. I am also close enough to look over her body for any signs of illness, discolouration, or abnormalities. Again, except for its obvious emaciated appearance, the only thing that catch-

The young whale had been attacked during the night and was living its last hours under a sad and rainy sky.

es my eye is a dozen remoras clinging to its tail. I close my eyes and try to store the majestic imagine in my mind forever. As I am ascending to make my way back to the boat, a chill constricts my blood vessels: A huge bull shark (Carcharhinus leucas) looks me straight in the eye. The frightful apparition is intensified by the poor visibility in the water. I keep facing the shark, trying to avoid swimming and exposing my back. When it turns, it becomes obvious to me that I am not the object of its interest. The shark is shadowing its sole target: the emaciated

The tail was the first target of the sharks.

The whale undoubtedly sends out the signals of an easy prey and bull sharks are known to roam in this kind of environment...

Blue Whale. Indeed, it comes as no surprise to me that the presence of increasingly weaker whale should have attracted predators. The whale undoubtedly sends out the signals of an easy prey. Furthermore, bull sharks are known to roam in this kind of environment as they are well adapted to cope with a wide range of salinity found in various mixtures of salt and fresh water. I am sure that the young whale is aware of the shark's presence. Since it continues to stay in the bay, we can now definitely discard our third hypothesis stipulating that the animal may have been trying to flee from predators.

Now tiger sharks that were already in the vicinity a few hours earlier chase away the bull sharks and take over their business.

While we were still wondering how long the still surprisingly strong Blue Whale would be able to keep predators at bay, the first attacks occurred. On the night between January 26-27, at least two bull sharks commenced their deadly work. The sea is calm but the visibility poor due to a constant and heavy downpour. At a depth of approximately 4- 5 m, the sharks first set upon an easier target, namely the whale's tail, inflicting profusely bleeding bite wounds on it. Part of the whale's spine, particu-

No other shark species were allowed to approach the carcass, and there was fierce competition within the group of dominant tiger sharks.

larly the space between dorsal fin and tail, is another preferred target. The Blue Whale's soft belly is attacked next and soon bleeding from several open wounds as well. I can't resist entering the water to watch this cruel but fascinating battle between prey and predators. The Blue Whale is still alive, but it has ceased moving for the first time since its appearance in the bay. I notice the many gaping wounds with large chunks of flesh missing. They are bleeding profusely, discolouring the surrounding waters. The whale's eyes are closed as I approach its head. I touch it tenderly, receiving but a gentle stir in return. Suddenly, as if determined to mobilize the last ounce of its strength, the whale begins to work its injured tail and dives to the bottom of the lagoon, leaving a bloody trail behind.

However, once the bull sharks have tasted success their confidence rises and they keep on slamming into the whale as a pack. A total of 15 hours elapse from first shark attack to the moment when the Blue Whale finally dies, on January 27, 2002, and sinks to the bottom. The carcass shows up again 36 hours later (January 29) at 8 AM, close to the place where it sank. This is when the feeding frenzy really begins. Now two tiger sharks (Galeocerdo cuvier) that were already roaming around in the vicinity a few hours earlier chase away the bull sharks and take over their bloody business. Undisturbed by any competitors, the two tiger sharks feed on the carcass for another 36 hours. Great quantities of blood and lipids ooze out of the carcass and are diluted by the outgoing current. Then another 15-20 tiger sharks arrive, including two massive 4.5-m-long females, that were presumably attracted by the blood. With the arrival of more tiger

A tiger shark with a mouthful of whale blubber.

sharks, the feeding frenzy intensifies. It is as if the additional competition only whets the sharks' craving for more food. During the next three days and nights about 20 tiger sharks rip into the carcass of the whale. The feeding frenzy peaks when the predators appear collectively in the early morning and late afternoon. At other times, tiger sharks approach the carcass individually, tearing off a mouthful of flesh and bone. At the end of the fifth day (February 2, 2002), little is left over for any latecomers. The tiger sharks managed to keep all other shark species away from the carcass, including the bull sharks that killed the whale and a sandbar shark (Carcharhinus plumbeus).

I was asked by many people present to kill the "Blue Princess," as she was named by local whale watchers, in order to end its suffering. Besides the fact that appropriate means are necessary to comply with such a request, it is also illegal as Blue Whales are protected by international convention. Official permission is always required in such a case, which would hardly have been granted under the conditions at hand. As tragic or even cruel as this event may seem to many, it is a part of nature. The short life story of the "Blue Princess," whose violent demise we witnessed, demonstrates that it is our duty and responsibility to preserve and protect the habitats of whales. We not only need to understand the importance of natural balance in the marine ecosystem, but also learn to respect rather than interfere whenever nature takes its own course.

A couple of vertebrae remain the only trace of the blue princess who visited New Caledonia's lagoon.

Blue Whale, *Balaenoptera musculus*

Breeching Blue Whale. Sea of Cortez, Mexico.   Francois Gohier

Distinguishing Characteristics
The most typical characteristic of a Blue Whale is its immense size. Its mottled appearance is another identifying feature.

Description
The average length of a Blue Whale is 25 m, but they can grow up to 30 m. Their average weight is 90-125 t. Like all rorquals, female Blue Whales are somewhat larger than the males.

Their bodies are very long, slender and streamlined. Viewed in profile, they have conspicuously wide and flat rostrums, which differentiates them from other rorquals. Well-defined median lines run from the tip of their snouts to their blowholes.

A few hairs grow on the tip of a Blue Whale's lower jaw, which may have a sensory function. The paired blowholes are protected in front by a conspicuous splash guard.

There are 260-400 baleen plates on each side of a Blue Whale's upper jaw, which can be up to 1 m in length and therefore the longest of all rorquals. They are 85 cm thick at the base, giving them a quasi-triangular appearance. The 70-120 throat grooves extend from the chin almost all the way down to the navel. These allow the animal to fill its mouth with up to 1,000 l of water and nutrients at once.

The width of a Blue Whale's fluke can be equal to 1/4 of its total body length. The fluke itself has a smooth and slightly concave edge with a small median notch. Its slender flippers can equal 1/7 of its total body length. The flippers are often paler than the rest of the animal's body.

In proportion to its huge body, the 45 cm-high dorsal fin of a Blue Whale appears much smaller than those of other rorquals. The dorsal is located about three-quarters of the way along the back. It can be crescent-shaped, with or without a rounded tip, or nearly triangular.

The individual colouration of Blue Whales is remarkably varied. The backs and sides of most animals are blue-grey to light-blue in colour and have a mottled appearance. Occasionally they are uniformly dark-grey. In contrast to the much smaller Fin Whales, a Blue Whale's head is also uniform in colour.

The undersides and throat grooves range in colour from a pale blue-green to white. Blue Whales that live predominantly in colder polar waters can also be yellow-brown in appearance. This colouration is not produced by pigmentation, but by minuscule diatoms *(Cocconeis ceticola)*, a colonial algae that thrives in colder waters and can attach itself to a Blue Whale's body. When a Blue Whale is covered with these diatoms it is appropriately designated "Sulphur-Bottom."

A pilot radioed to underwater filmer Howard Hall that he was watching Blue Whales eating krill off the Californian coast. Within two hours the film team was there to dive with the whales near the Los Coronados islands.

Above:
Pierre Larue
Left:
Mark Conlin

Easily Mistaken For

From a distance it is possible to mistake Fin Whales for younger Blue Whales. In contrast to Fin Whales, a Blue Whale's back is usually mottled. In addition, a Blue Whale's head is not asymmetrically coloured. While the right side of a Fin Whale's lower jaw and occasionally also the baleen plates are white, both sides of a Blue Whale's head are uniform in colour.

Both species can also be distinguished by their response to vessels. Whereas Fin Whales generally pay little attention to them, Blue Whales can be quite inquisitive. Confusion with Sei or Bryde's whales is very unlikely because of the obvious difference in size, colour and manner of diving.

A mix-up is possible in the tropical waters of the Southern Hemisphere, where Sei, Bryde's or Fin whales might actually be mistaken for Pygmy Blue Whales *(Balaenoptera musculus brevicauda)*. Pygmy Blue Whales are a much smaller subspecies and thus more likely to be identified incorrectly.

Other Names

Sulphur-Bottom (English); Blauwal, Großer Nördlicher Furchenwal, Sibbald's Furchenwal (German);

Baleine Bleu, Rorqual Bleu, Grand Rorqual (French); Balenottera Azzurra (Italian); Ballena Azul (Spanish); Baleia Azul (Portuguese); Blauwe Vinvis (Dutch); Blåhval (Norwegian); Sinivalas (Finnish); Blåval (Swedish); Blåhval (Danish); Shiro Nagasu Kujira (Japanese); Blyuval, Goluboy Kit (Russian).

Meaning of the Scientific Nomenclature
Balaenoptera musculus (Linnaeus 1758) – The generic name *Balaenoptera* is composed of the Latin *balaena* (whale) and the Greek *pteron* (wing), with the latter referring to the relatively large dorsal fin. The Latin species name *musculus* (muscular) refers to the enormous size of this species.

Behaviour
Blue Whales usually live singly or in groups of 2-3. In especially rich feeding grounds one may occasionally come across groups of 5 or more animals. Sometimes they share their habitat with Fin Whales.

Statistics compiled by whaling stations show that 75% of all Blue Whales were dispatched in deep waters. This means that they are rarely seen near the coast. Instead, they prefer a pelagic mode of existence.

Like all rorquals, Blue Whales migrate seasonally. They spend the summer in nutrient-rich polar and subpolar waters. In the winter they head for their mating grounds in warmer subtropical and tropical regions. Due to the inverted seasons, Blue Whales in both hemispheres will migrate north and south at the same time. This means that, in spite of some overlapping ranges, there is little chance that the northern subspecies *(B. m. musculus)* will crossbreed with the somewhat larger southern subspecies *(B. m. intermedia)*.

Whereas mature Blue Whales seldom breach, their young will do so quite frequently. Thereby they usually land on their bellies or sideways. Their response to vessels varies considerably. Some animals become fairly receptive once they have gotten accustomed to the presence of a boat. Others are extremely shy and will disappear as soon as a boat approaches them. Underwater encounters with Blue Whales are extremely rare.

Diving
In a relaxed state Blue Whales normally breathe every 10-20 sec and then dive down to a max depth of 200 m for 5-10 min. Diving and breathing patterns can change radically depending upon the whale's activity. While feeding Blue Whales normally maintain a speed of 2-5.5 km/h. When they migrate they average 5-35 km/h. If threatened they can temporarily speed up to 45 km/h. If they are moving at a fast pace they will breach at a sharp angle. In a relaxed state they tend to breach fairly level with the surface.

Facts & Figures Blue Whale
Size: average 25 m, max 33.58 m
Weight: 90-125 t, max 190 t
Longevity: 80-90 years
Sexual maturity: at 5-6 years, 23 m in length
Mating season: Northern Hemisphere: Fall-Winter; Southern Hemisphere: Winter
Gestation period: about 11 months
Calving interval: every 2-3 years
Size at birth: about 7 m
Weight at birth: 2.5 t
Nursing period: 7 months
Dive depth: max 200 m
Dive time: max 30 min
Maximum speed: max 50 km/h
Baleen plates: 260-400 on each side, up to 1 m in length
Blow: slim vertical column up to 10 m
Throat Grooves: 70-120, terminate just before the navel
Food consumption: up to 4 t of krill per day in the summer
Capacity of maw: up to 1,000 l
Group (Pod) size: normally 1-3 animals, occasionally 5 or more in rich feeding grounds
Population: about 3,000 in the Northern Hemisphere, 10,000 in the Southern Hemisphere; extremely vulnerable

Quick ID-Check Blue Whale
Huge, slender body

Back and sides uniformly blue-grey and mottled in appearance

Tiny dorsal fin, far down the back

Slender blow up to 10 m high

Large and conspicuous splash guard

Wide, flat, U-shaped head, uniform in colour

Dorsal fin and head not visible simultaneously

Seldom raises fluke when sounding

Mouth wide open a Blue Whale enters a swarm of krill.   Mark Conlin

With a full mouth and widely extended throat grooves it returns to the surface.   Mark Conlin

A Blue Whale will begin breathing as soon as its head clears the water. Its blow is high and narrow. The head disappears under water immediately after the whale has taken a breath and its seemingly endless back becomes visible on the surface. Dorsal fin and head rarely clear the water at the same time. When the dorsal fin appears and the whale's back begins to curve it is about to sound. Blue Whales usually sound without raising their flukes, but they do leave a huge footprint behind on the surface. The backwash from the powerful fluke forms a visible circle of up-welling water.

Feeding Habits

Blue Whales primarily feed on euphausiids, tiny plankton commonly known as krill that appear in thick concentrations close to the water's surface at dusk. Blue Whales feed in polar and subpolar waters during the respective summer seasons of their northern and southern ranges. Krill consume certain organisms that are in turn dependent upon nutrients released by the melting ice. Blue Whales rarely take up nourishment in their warmer mating grounds.

A mid-sized Blue Whale can consume an average of 4 t of krill per day. By expanding its throat grooves, it can increase the volume of its maw sixfold. A fully-grown Blue Whale can swallow nearly 1,000 litre of water and nutrients at once.

General Information

Everything about a Blue Whale is exaggerated. It is the largest living being that has ever existed on our planet - larger even than the mightiest dinosaurs. Its heart alone weighs about 600 kg, or nearly the equivalent of a compact car. The largest Blue Whale on record is a 33.58-m-long female that was caught in Antarctic waters off Grytviken (South Georgia) in 1909. Such colossal specimens are rarely encountered today. The heaviest Blue Whale on record is a 27.6 m long female weighing 190 t that was killed in Arctic waters in 1947. Its total weight is equal to that of 48 elephants, or more than 2,000 men.

Blue Whale calves are born with a length of about 7 m and a weight of 2.5 t. They are nursed for 7 months, initially consuming up to 190 l of milk daily. Blue Whale milk has a fat content of 35-50%, which greatly accelerates the growth rate of the calves during the first months after birth. They can put on 3.3 kg per hour, or a strapping 80 kg per day! Blue Whale calves increase 30 times in size during the first year of their lives. By the time they are weaned, after about 7 months, they already weigh 23 t and average about 12.8 m in length. Blue Whale cows lose about 1/4 of their original weight while nursing.

Like all other rorquals, the age of a Blue Whale is best determined by the growth layers on its ear plugs. Their longevity is about 80-90 years. On calm days, their slender blows can rise up to 10 m in the air.

During the heyday of whaling, Blue Whales were hunted almost to the point of extinction because of their great size and commercial value. Some populations will probably never recover. It is estimated that 6,000-14,000 Blue Whales exist today, but they are still considered to be an extremely vulnerable species.

Three distinct subspecies with different ranges are recognized today. Even though their respective areas of distribution overlap, there is no interbreeding between them due to the inverse seasonal migration patterns:

1. *Balaenoptera musculus intermedia:* Southern Hemisphere, largest member of the species.
2. *Balaenoptera musculus musculus:* Norhtern Hemisphere, somewhat smaller than its southern relatives.
3. *Balaenoptera musculus brevicauda* (Pygmy Blue Whale): Tropical waters of the Southern Hemisphere. Smallest Blue Whale with an average length of 21 m. Calves average about 6 m in length. There are only a few hundred specimens of this subspecies.

Blue Whale, distribution: Offshore waters all over the world, preferably colder water temperatures.

Where & When

With a lot of luck, Blue Whales can be sighted in waters all over the world. Usually they migrate on the open sea independently. In the Pacific they range as far north as the Aleutian Islands and the Bering Strait. In the Atlantic they range as far 80° latitude north, to the waters around Spitsbergen. During the summer months they follow their main source of food as far north as the pack ice will permit.

Most Blue Whales live in the Southern Hemisphere. During the summer months they are often sighted in the Sea of Cortez (Mexico), off

In the photo above one can clearly see the two blowholes sitting side by side. In front of them there are the so called splash guards, those of the Blue Whale being very large when compared to other rorqual whale species. Also visible is the mottled appearance of the skin.
Left:
The impressive fluke of the largest living animal on earth.

Francois Gohier

the coast of California and in the Gulf of St. Lawrence (Canada). They frequently range for great distances between the lower latitudes in winter and the upper latitudes in summer. A few Blue Whales in the northern Indian Ocean are apparently sedentary.

BARRIER TO THE NORTH

Most baleen whales migrate to cold polar seas to feed on rich plankton blooms in the summer. They then migrate back to warm temperate and tropical seas to breed in the winter. But there are exceptions to this simple pattern. The bowhead whale, which spends its entire life in Arctic waters, is one. And what happens in the North Indian Ocean? Marine biologist Charles Anderson traces the paths of whales.

PHOTOS: CHARLES ANDERSON

Head and blow of a Blue Whale in the Arabian Sea.

Of all the three great oceans, the Indian Ocean is the only one that does not extend to Arctic latitudes. The great landmass of Asia is in the way, so there is no cold northern part to the ocean. And yet baleen whales are found in the North Indian Ocean, most frequently in the western part, or Arabian Sea.

Blue whales, Bryde's whales and humpback whales all occur in good numbers in the Arabian Sea. Bryde's whales are known to be permanent residents of tropical seas, but blue and humpback whales are renowned for their long-distance migrations. What are they doing in the Arabian Sea, and where are they feeding? The idea that baleen whales must migrate to polar seas to feed is so well entrenched that for decades it was assumed that Arabian Sea blues and humpbacks must be doing the same thing. Two rival theories emerged.

Most cetologists believed that Arabian Sea blues and humpbacks migrated across the equator to feed in Antarctic waters during the southern summer. But why should whales that feed in the South Indian Ocean bother to swim so far north (while those in the South Atlantic and South Pacific do not)? This was never adequately explained.

Other (mostly Dutch) cetologists believed that Arabian Sea blues and humpbacks migrated to the North Pacific to feed in Arctic waters during the northern summer. It was thought that these whales migrated through the Indonesian Archipelago (formerly the Dutch East Indies). Again, why these whales should bother to swim so far was never explained. Furthermore, as the Dutch themselves pointed out it was a "remarkable fact that this migration has never been observed in the comparatively narrow passages of the Indonesian Archipelago".

Only since the 1980s has a completely different story emerged. In January 1982 scientists aboard the tiny research yacht *Tulip* recorded a singing humpback whale off the coast of Oman. Only male humpbacks sing, and only during the breeding season. So January must be the breeding season for humpback whales in the Arabian Sea. January is the height of the Antarctic summer, so Arabian Sea humpbacks cannot be migrating to the Antarctic to feed. Furthermore, an analysis of blue whale strandings in southern Asia (Maldives, India and Sri Lanka) has shown that most dead blues wash up during January to April. Again this is the Antarctic summer, so Arabian Sea blues cannot be migrating to the Antarctic to feed.

It is also now known that blue whales in the Arabian Sea and the North Pacific Ocean belong to different subspecies. On top of this, a major migration of blue and humpback whales through the Indonesian islands has never been discovered. Indeed, there are very few confirmed records of any humpback or blue whales from Indonesia. So these whales cannot be migrating from the Arabian Sea to feed in the North Pacific Ocean.

If the Arabian Sea baleen whales are not migrating to the nearest polar regions to feed the question remains, where are they feeding? The answer is that they are stay-

A Bryde's Whale in Maldive waters.

ing year-round in the Arabian Sea where they both feed and breed. In the North Indian Ocean there are two main seasons or monsoons. These are named for the prevailing winds. Thus the northeast monsoon (which lasts from about December to April) has mainly northeasterly winds. During the southwest monsoon (which lasts from about May to October) the winds blow mainly from the southwest.

This reversal of prevailing winds is unique to the North Indian Ocean. It is caused by the seasonal heating and cooling of the great landmass of India and central Asia. In the northern summer (starting in about April-May) the Indian subcontinent heats up. Air over the land rises, so moist air is drawn in from the ocean to replace it. As this air blows over the land its cargo of moisture is dropped as rain. In the Indian subcontinent the arrival of the rain is awaited with eager anticipation and celebrated with festivals and merrymaking. For the coming of the rains, normally in June, brings an end to the oppressive summer heat and regenerates the land for a new crop of life-sustaining rice.

Out in the Arabian Sea the wind blows with gale force towards India. It blows especially strongly from southern Arabia and the Horn of Africa. In these areas the wind blows offshore with such strength that it pushes the surface water away from the coast. Replacement water wells up from the deep. This upwelling water is cold but full of nutrients such as nitrates and phosphates. As the nutrient-rich water

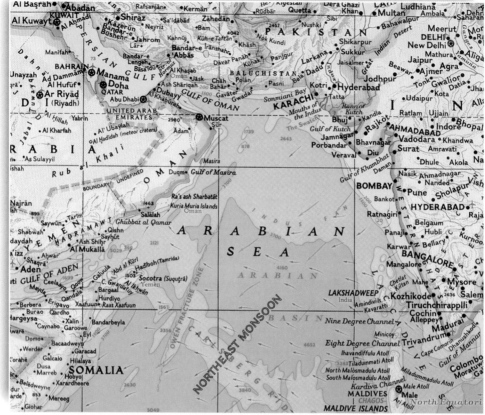

Map of the Arabian Sea.

rises from the dark depths and reaches the surface it is suddenly bathed in sunlight. Nutrients and sunlight are all that the microscopic marine plants known as phytoplankton need to flourish. They bloom in prodigious quantities. Tiny marine animals, the zooplankton, graze on the phytoplankton and flourish too. These are perfect conditions for a whale banquet.

Blue whales, humpback whales and Bryde's whales all feast on this seasonal harvest of zooplankton. From May to October the upwellings continue and so does the supply of zooplankton. It is assumed that the whales are feeding in this area throughout the period May to October. There are indeed many sightings of baleen whales in the area off southern Arabia and Somalia in September and October. However, there are very few from earlier in the season. This is due to the ferocious weather conditions in June-July, when enormous seas limit research vessel operations in this area, and prevent observers from seeing even the largest whales.

In effect, the summer upwellings and associated plankton bloom off southern Arabia and the Horn of Africa are the equivalent of a polar summer plankton bloom. Certainly to the baleen whales that feast on the plankton there may be little difference between the two.

The upwellings continue right throughout the northern summer, for as long as the sun is heating the Indian subcontinent. As autumn arrives, and India cools, the wind dies and with it the force driving the upwellings. By October the summer is spent, and the upwellings suddenly stop. Without a constant supply of fresh nutrients the phytoplankton bloom fades to nothing and the zooplankton die out.

Once their food supply dries up, the blue, humpback and Bryde's whales fan out across the Arabian Sea looking for little patches of plankton wherever they can find them. By November they can be found on the far side of the Arabian Sea, in Maldivian and Sri Lankan waters. They stay throughout the calm of the northeast monsoon season, making this the very best area in Asia to see them.

In April, as the northeast monsoon season comes to an end, the baleen whales around Sri Lanka and the Maldives head west in search of food. The Somali coast may be roughly 3.000 km from the central Indian Ocean, but a blue whale cruising at just 10 km per hour could make the journey in under two weeks. And so as the southwest monsoon picks up strength and the upwellings commence, the seasonal cycle of the Arabian Sea baleen whales starts again.

PELAGOS

In 1990 the Italian TETHYS Research Institute proposed the "Pelagos Project," envisaging the creation of a sanctuary in the Corso-Ligurian Basin, which has the highest sighting frequency of cetaceans and possibly represents the richest area in the Mediterranean Sea. The Basin is most likely to be the principal feeding ground for Fin Whales in the region. Underwater-cinematographer Dieter Paulmann visited these Fin Whales many times and followed up on the development of this proposal.

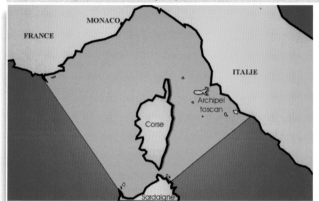

ACCOBAMS

The region comprising the Corso-Ligurian Basin is characterized by very high levels of primary productivity, in contrast to the widespread oligotrophy of the Mediterranean Sea. All cetaceans regularly observed in the Mediterranean can be found in the region, including pelagic species such as the Fin Whale (*Balaenoptera physalus*). Results from previous surveys had emphasized that cetaceans in this region are significantly more abundant than in all other seas surrounding Italy, including the rest of the western Mediterranean basin. The coasts surrounding the area are basically rocky, with the exception of the eastern coasts of Corsica and the Tuscan coasts, where there are plains. These steep coasts are the result of recent tectonic movements that are still in action. The rivers bring down water that is essentially torrential and most of the streams drain water from short, steep slopes. The continental slope is generally very narrow along the rocky coasts, though better developed along the coasts of the plain (Tuscany and eastern Corsica). The Corsican-Provencal basin is highly bathymetric (2,500-2,700 m). All the rocky coasts are deeply eaten into by underwater canyons, which increase the morphological and hydrodynamic diversity. It is in this vast pelagic realm that the cetaceans, this area's main subject of protection, develop in all their diversity.

However, considerable threats exist for cetacean populations living in the region, including, among others: by-catch in driftnet fishing activities; presence of substantial concentrations of toxic xenobiotics in the trophic chain, which accumulate in the cetaceans' fatty tissues; and, last but not least, high levels of maritime traffic, including fast ferries, ships transporting hazardous chemicals to and from the region's commercial harbours, and offshore speedboat races. The research conducted by TETHYS has highlighted the need that a conservation structure such as the Sanctuary be created in the area. Fin Whales living in the Ligurian Sea during summer were found to be genetically distinct from their North Atlantic relatives, and most likely belong to a reproductively isolated population that resides in the Mediterranean the year round. At an estimated 1,000 individuals, the population in the western Mediterranean is small and potentially vulnerable, particularly since the contribution from the eastern basin to the total Mediterranean population is likely to be negligible.

Three years later (March 22, 1993) the French and Italian Ministers of the Environment, and the Minister of State of the Monaco Principality, signed a joint declaration in Brussels calling for

FOTOS: BORIS PAULMANN

After trying for three hours, UW-cinematographer Dieter Paulmann finally manages to float alongside of a Mediterranean Fin Whale.

the institution of a Mediterranean Sanctuary for marine mammals. In the future Sanctuary all direct takes and intentional harassment of marine mammals will be forbidden, potentially invasive research activities and whale-watching will be regulated, large-scale pelagic driftnet fishing will be banned, offshore speedboat races will be limited and eventually forbidden and a special

The Fin Whales, rather than us, always decide just how close an encounter will turn out to be.

effort will be devoted to control and curb pollution harmful to cetaceans.

This project was also actively promoted by such diverse organizations as the WWF Mediterranean program or, in France, the RIMMO Association, which has been organizing annual seminars on the protection of the western Mediterranean since 1992. Responsible for the sustainable management of the natural resources is the Monaco-based ACCOBAMS (Agreement for the Conservation of Cetaceans of the Black Sea, Mediterranean Sea and Contiguous Atlantic Area).

On September 29, 1998, the Ligurian Sea Cetacean Sanctuary came one step closer to materializing after the Italian Government officially agreed on a proposal that will be shortly forwarded to France and the Principality of Monaco. The proposal involves the establishment of an international protected area for cetaceans in the Mediterranean Sea, approx 100.000 km_ in size and situated between the continental coast of Italy, Monaco and France, Corsica, and northern Sardinia. A permanent frontal system is the cause of primary production levels exceptional for Mediterranean offshore waters, which support a major biomass of krill, Meganyctiphanes norvegica. Eight cetacean species inhabit the area, including a large population of Striped Dolphins and more than a thousand Fin Whales (most of the Mediterranean population), which congregate there during summer to feed. Aims of the Sanctuary will be, among other things, to monitor cetacean population trends, facilitate the enforcement of existing legislation to curb pollution, regulate a budding whale watching industry and increase awareness among the general public.

On November 25, 1999, representatives from Italy, France and Monaco met in Rome to sign an agreement creating the Ligurian Sea Cetacean Sanctuary, which is hosted by the Principality of Monaco. For the first time in Europe, three Mediterranean countries joined efforts to create, survey and manage an area largely located in international waters. The Agreement creating the area described in detail aims at coordination between the three countries to implement concerted measures that will reduce the threat hanging over the cetaceans. It entered into force on February 21, 2002. It is hoped that this will present a model for the creation of other areas of this kind in the Mediterranean Sea.

My encounter with Fin Whales began in a very mysterious way. One early summer we were sailing from Antibes to Sardinia and had been underway for less than four hours - we could still see the mountains lining the southern coast of France - when our cook announced that lunch was ready. Now, as all sailors know, mealtime is a serious business that should never be interrupted carelessly. For some reason unknown to me, I suddenly stood up in the middle of the meal and excused myself with the following words: "I'm going to the bow to look for whales." My friends' laughter accompanied as I made my way to the fore of the ship. But after sitting there for about 10 minutes, I was startled by the sight of a blow dead ahead about a mile off. As soon as I spotted a second vertical blow I was certain that it was a Fin Whale. As I had never heard of the presence of Fin Whales in the Mediterranean before, I assumed that it must be a wayward solitary individual. After three hours, I finally managed to float alongside of it.

My second encounter with Fin Whales, which occurred in the same area a few weeks later, was even more curious. This time a Fin Whale headed directly towards our craft, circled it twice and disappeared. Then came the evening of July 14, when a lot of fireworks were going off along the coast. In the light cast by the fireworks we suddenly recognized the blow of a Fin Whale

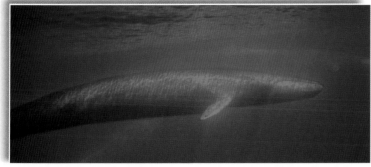

The Fin Whales got so used to us that we were even able to photograph them under water.

about 20 m away. As we reduced speed, this animal also circled our boat and then swam away again. I couldn't stop thinking about it and told my family and friends at 7 o'clock the next morning that I would not be going home with them as planned. Instead, I had decided to load the boat with fuel, 10 fried chickens and sufficient bread for 8 days and immediately set sail with only a cook and a boatswain on board - in other words, without an adequate crew for a whale watching expedition.

We headed out to sea again, but I was very disappointed when we failed to sight a single Fin Whale after two days. On an impulse I marked the three places on the sea chart where we had come across the whales previously, which were no less than 150 miles apart. Then I picked a point at the centre of the three sites and steered for it. Off course there was no logical reasoning behind such a decision, but when we arrived there 20 Fin Whales were lying in wait for us. My intuition had brought us directly to the very place where most Mediterranean Fin Whales congregate in July/August. We remained there for 4 days, during which I filmed "Pelagos" all by myself. The weather was perfectly calm and the shipping traffic was light enough so as not to disturb us or the whales. In those 4 wonderful days I was not only able to take beautiful shots of the whales from atop the ship's mast, but also under water. I made it back home safely shortly thereafter.

At the end of August I was out searching for Fin Whales once again, this time with a group of Italian photographers affiliated with the protective association THETYS on board my ship. We noticed that the Fin Whales were communicating with each other and obviously enjoying the presence of divers and vessels. We were able to document how two Fin Whales approached us, followed by two more 10 minutes later, which were joined by an additional pair a quarter of an hour after that. The we got into the water with the whales and all six of them remained in our immediate vicinity for two hours. In this particular situation it became quite obvious that they wanted to play with us. They were just as enthusiastic and astonished about this encounter with strange beings as we were. Why are there so many Fin Whales in this region in July/August, and why are there such large quantities of nourishment available to them at this time of the year? The Mistral, a strong northerly Mediterranean wind, is the answer. Especially in spring and fall, and to a lesser degree in summer, it pushes the surface water of the Mediterranean in a southwesterly direction. This in turn creates

Dieter Paulmann on board his ship the "Foftein" filming a Fin Whale in the Ligurian Sea.

an upwelling current that brings up nutrient-rich water from the bottom of the 2000 m deep basin - a veritable banquet for Fin Whales.

Unfortunately, we also had to look on as speedboats headed directly towards the whales resting on the surface and their skippers failed to take note of the animals in spite of cruising at speeds exceeding 30 knots. But the Fin Whales always managed to submerge in time and they should be capable of judging the correct distance to the oncoming craft. After all, we did not come across a single Fin Whale with external injuries caused by a ship's propeller.

As we drifted along on the calm seas at night, a Fin Whale would come and rest next to our boat for an hour, looking it over from a distance of about 10 m as if it were trying to figure out what we were up to in the light of our petroleum lamps. Isn't it wonderful when whales watch the whale watcher rather than the other way around?

Fin Whale, *Balaenoptera physalus*

Also Fin Whales regularly visit the Azores in the Atlantic.　　　　　　　　Ralf Kiefner

Distinguishing Characteristics
Besides their impressive size and very pronounced dorsal fin it is the characteristic asymmetrical pigmentation on the head that distinguishes the Fin Whale from all other whale species. Also the high swimming speed is a good distinguishing characteristic. The Fin Whale is the only rorqual whale species which can be found in the Mediterranean.

Description
Fin Whales average about 18-21 m in length, but can grow up to 25 m. They weigh between 40-70 t. Like all rorquals, female Fin Whales are larger than the males.

A Fin Whale has a narrow rostrum with a conspicuous median line running from the tip of the snout to the blowholes. Its 56-100 throat grooves usually terminate at or just behind the navel. There are 350-400 baleen plates on each side of the upper jaw, which can be up to 70 cm long. Like all rorquals, a Fin Whale has a splash guard in front of its paired blowholes. Its blow is narrow and 5-6 m high.

The crescent-shaped dorsal fin of a Fin Whale is very well developed and can grow up to 70 cm. Its slender and pointed flippers appear somewhat short in relation to the body. The topsides of the flippers are dark, the undersides white. Its fluke is broad and triangular with a median notch. Its underside is white, while the topside is the same colour as the back. The edge of the fluke is slightly concave and sometimes a little irregular.

A Fin Whale's slender, streamlined and very long body is dark-grey, silver-blue or brownish black on top and white underneath. Behind its head there will often be a pale-grey angular pattern that points towards the blowholes.

Fin Whales have a rather remarkable feature: The right underside of their heads (right lower lip, sometimes also the right upper lip and maw) along with the anterior right baleen plates are white. The remaining baleen plates as well as the right lower jaw are dark-grey. It is assumed that this colouration has something to do with the fact that Fin Whales prefer to feed on their sides. On either side of their bodies, between the head and the flippers, there will often be a varying, pale-grey and angular pattern that is usually more pronounced on the right side.

The skin of a Fin Whale is often covered with round or elongated pock marks that may be caused by Sea Lampreys *(Petromyzon marinus)* and Suckerfish *(Remora* spp.). Similar to Blue Whales, the underside of those Fin Whales that spend most of their time in colder waters can be coated with a yellowish layer of diatoms.

Easily Mistaken For
Fin Whales are easily confused with smaller Sei Whales. In the tropics it is also possible to mistake Bryde's Whales and smaller Blue Whales for Fin Whales. Nevertheless, Fin Whales clearly distinguish themselves from all other whales by virtue of their asymmetrical colouration on the right side of their heads and backs. Their absolute disinterest in vessels also sets them apart from the other rorquals. In contrast to Bryde's Whales, a Fin Whale only has a single median line running from the tip of the snout to the blowholes.

Other Names
Finback, Finner, Razorback, Herring Whale (English); Finnwal, Gemeiner Furchenwal (German); Rorqual, Rorqual Commun (French); Balenottera Comune (Italian); Rorcual Común (Spanish); Baleia Comum, Baleia Fina, Rorqual, Rorqual de Aleta (Portuguese); Gewone Vinvis (Dutch); Finnhval (Norwegian); Sillivalas (Finnish); Sillval (Swedish); Finhval (Danish); Nagasu Kujira (Japanese); Sel'Dyanoi Kit, Finval (Russian); Ballena de Aleta, Rorcual Común (Latin American Spanish).

Meaning of the Scientific Nomenclature
Balaenoptera physalus (Linnaeus 1758) – The generic name *Balaenoptera* is composed of the Latin *balaena* (whale) and the Greek *pteron* (wing), with the latter referring to the relatively large dorsal fin. The Latin species name *physalus* refers to a curious behaviour: Fin Whales occasionally inflate their throat grooves, reminding one of a frog's throat sack.

Behaviour
Despite their enormous size Fin Whales are not awkward or ponderous, but very fast swimmers. They can cover long distances and still average more than 35 km/h without much effort. The fact that they rank among the fastest baleen whales prompted old whalers to nickname them "Greyhounds of the Seas."

    Fin Whales are not very gregarious. They roam the world's oceans as solitary animals or in smaller groups of 2-3. In particularly bounteous feeding grounds one might encounter groups of up to 100 animals. Such congregations are only temporary, however. The only stable social relationship is the one that exists between a Fin whale cow and its calf during the nursing period. Fin Whales often appear in the company of Blue Whales, occasionally also with Long-Finned Pilot Whales and Striped Dolphins.

Facts & Figures Fin Whale	Quick ID-Check Fin Whale
Size: 18-22 m, max 25 m	Asymmetrical pigmentation on the head (right side white)
Weight: 45 t, max 70 t	
Longevity: about 75-90 years	
Sexual maturity: at 6-7 years, as of 17.5-18.5 m in length	Conspicuously slender, long and streamlined body
Mating season: Northern Hemisphere: January-February; Southern Hemisphere: May-Septem.	High, well-developed, crescent-shaped dorsal fin set far down the back
Gestation period: 11 months	
Calving interval: every 2 years	
Size at birth: about 6 m	Pale-grey angular pattern laterally behind the head
Weight at birth: 1-1.5 t	
Nursing period: 11-12 months	
Dive depth: max 300 m	Slender blow, 5-6 m high
Dive time: 3-10 min	
Maximum speed: over 35 km/h	Dorsal fin visible shortly after blow
Baleen plates: 350-400 on each side, max length 70 cm	
Blow: high thin column, up to 5-6 m	Seldom raises fluke while sounding
Dorsal fin: 70 cm high, crescent-shaped	
Throat Grooves: 56-100, usually terminate at or just behind the navel	Indifferent towards boats, unpredictable surfacing
Group (Pod) size: 3-7, occasionally up to 100 in rich feeding grounds	
Population: about 120,000, vulnerable	

Typical for Fin Whales is the asymmetrical pigmentation on the head: Its right side is white and ➤

Fin Whales are a pelagic species and usually remain beyond the continental shelf. On rare occasions, such as when they are chasing after shoaling fish, they can be seen close to shore.

Tests performed with transmitter-bearing Fin Whales off the coast of southeastern Alaska and Greenland revealed certain breathing and movement patterns among them. One specimen was kept under steady observation as it covered a distance of 2,000 km between Greenland and Island. During its voyage the Fin Whale dove for longer intervals during the day and then spent more time resting on the surface at night.

Fin Whales emit loud and relatively simple (for baleen whales) low-frequency moans and grunts, which range from 20-80 Hz and are therefore inaudible for the human ear. Higher frequency tones up to 200 Hz probably have a social connotation. Although there is no concrete evidence for the use of echolocation among Fin Whales, the 16-228 kHz clicking sounds they emit make it seem very likely.

When Fin Whales breach they generally land on their sides with a tremendous splash. Occasionally they will twist in the air and come down on their sides or backs. As far as vessels are concerned, they are neither shy nor curious, but rather indifferent. Regardless of whether they are feeding or migrating, it is usually difficult to predict when they will sound or surface. Consequently, close encounters with them from the deck of a boat or under water are extremely rare.

Each winter the populations in both hemispheres migrate to lower latitudes and then move back to higher latitudes during the summer. Within their respective areas of distribution they apparently live in casual reproductive groupings. It is not known to what extent these populations interbreed or remain isolated from one another.

Diving

The surface behaviour of a Fin Whale is difficult to predict. It frequently changes direction while diving and then resurfaces in some unforeseeable place. Being relatively shy, it tends to avoid coastal waters.

Under normal circumstances Fin Whales take 2-5 short breaths before diving to depths of up to 200 m for about 3-10 min. They rarely raise their flukes while sounding. When they go for deeper dives, they merely arch their backs more than usual and occasionally allow their flukes to barely clear the surface.

its left side is dark. Azores, Atlantic.   Ralf Kiefner

As long as they are not being hunted, Fin Whales will glide through the water at a regular pace and rarely come up to breathe. Their average speed is 9-15 km/h. When in haste they can maintain a top speed of 35 km/h for long distances.

Depending upon how deep it went, a Fin Whale usually breaches at a fairly flat angle to the surface. In that case the white asymmetrical colouring on the right side of its head will be clearly visible. The crescent-shaped dorsal fin appears shortly after the blow. Its head and dorsal fin will not reach the surface at the same time, however.

Feeding Habits

Fin Whales have a variable feeding spectrum. With their fine baleen plates they filter out masses of small (2-3 cm) euphausiids and other pelagic crustaceans. But they also consume smaller shoaling fish like herring, capelin, mackerel, European hake, cod and coalfish, as well as various smaller species of shoaling squid.

Like all rorquals, Fin Whales feed during the summer and fast in winter mating season. Fin Whales have developed an amazing peculiarity: They like to turn on their right sides while feeding. No explanation has been found so far for this phenomenon. It is likely that the typical asymmetric head colouration of the species has something to do with this curious habit.

General Information

After Blue Whales, Fin Whales are the second largest beings that ever inhabited our planet. They were probably first described by Frederick Martens in 1675, followed by Paul Dudley in 1725. Based on their findings, Linnaeus classifed the species as *Balaena physalus* in 1758. Later on Lacépède applied the designation *Balaenoptera* to all northern baleen whales with a dorsal fin. The original name given by Linnaeus was subsequently modified and retained until the present.

Prior to the advent of commercial whaling, Fin Whales were probably the most common species. Their size, however, made them equally profitable for whalers as Blue Whales and their numbers soon decreased accordingly.

Fin Whales are still found in all oceans, but in various genetically isolated populations. The Mediterranean Fin Whales, for instance, appear to be genetically isolated from the Atlantic population. The animals living in northern waters are an average 1.5-2 m shorter and have smaller but wider flippers than the animals living in southern waters. Consequently, some systematists prefer

This photo clearly shows the splash guards in front of the blowholes.   Ralf Kiefner

to speak of two distinct subspecies: *Balaenoptera physalus physalus* in the Northern Hemisphere and *B. physalus quoyi* in the Southern Hemisphere.

Like all rorquals, the age of a Fin Whale can best be determined by the number of growth layers on its ear plugs. Their longevity is approximately 75-90 years.

Where & When

Fin Whales are found in all colder and temperate waters. They are the only rorquals frequently encountered in the Mediterranean.

They prefer deep open waters or deep coastal waters. They are most frequently spotted in the Southern Hemisphere and in waters with moderate temperatures. Seldom seen in tropical waters. The ice barrier apparently hinders the species from spreading further in the colder polar waters. Here they are less populous than Blue and Minke whales.

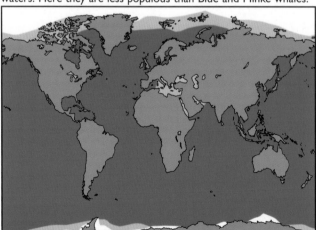

In spring Fin Whales migrate to their feeding grounds in colder regions, in the summer they migrate to their mating grounds in warmer waters. There appear to be a number of sedentary populations in the Sea of Cortez.

Fin Whale, distribution: Worldwide in all deep offshore waters, usually in temperate latitudes.

HUNTING HUMPBACKS

Feeding, feeding, feeding...a more or less continuous feeding binge is keeping Humpback Whales busy for about four months each year. These whales are far more innovative in their hunting methods than any of the other baleen whales. For that they have developed varied, unique hunting techniques in order to capture even fast-swimming prey, like shoals of herrings. Ralf Kiefner has visited Humpback Whales in their feeding grounds off Alaska.

Among these behavioural innovations, so-called 'cooperative feeding' and 'lateral lunge feeding' represent particularly clever and ingenious capture methods for securing an adequate food supply. This methodology requires high intelligence as well as extraordinary acrobatic capabilities. 'Cooperative feeding', that is, the communal hunt for food is one of the most complex and amazing types of behaviour known in the Animal Kingdom. Moreover, another surprising aspects of this is the fact, that up to now little has been known about it and even less has found its way into print.

'Cooperative feeding' conveys the impression of a precisely timed and choreographed manoeuvre. All the animals in one particular pod of Humpback Whales usually dive in the same sequence and with the same alignment (relative to each other). Up to 1,200 finely tuned feeding manoeuvres of this kind have been observed among various pods. Only through total cooperation can a loose aggregation of individual animals turn into a complex, social unit with a common goal: A successful and energy-conserving hunt for food. Such cooperation then facilitates the capture of shoals of fishes that are much faster than whales and also more agile and alert. Other advantages derived from of such cooperative behaviour are a common defence against predators, better reproductive opportunities and easier access to food.

Straining large volumes of water for tiny krill certainly requires much less complex social skills; however, the populations of these small crustaceans can be highly variable in size and so they are not always available to whales in sufficient quantities. Consequently, their hunting methods needed to be refined in order to widen the menu for these leviathans of the sea. Moreover, the nutritional value of shoaling fishes is considerably higher than that of krill, a factor that is of enormous significance to Humpback Whales since they feed only during a four-month period of the year.

One particularly fascinating hunting strategy of Humpback Whales is the so-called 'bubble net feeding'. As soon as a shoal of herring has been detected, the whales do not immediately pursue it, but instead first dive underneath it and then - slowly rising - gradually close-in in ever-decreasing circles. While there are thus ascending, the whales release a continuous stream of air from their blowhole. As this cloud of air rises to the surface, it breaks up into millions of tiny bubbles that spread out, thus creating an opaque bubble curtain. With this technique

PHOTOS: RALF KIEFNER

The so-called 'cooperative feeding' requires high intelligence as well as special acrobatic capabilities.

69

the whales can 'construct' many different air bubble traps, such as nets, curtains or clouds, depending on how they position themselves while releasing the air. Fishes that become entrapped in such 'nets' can no longer escape, and the noisy, bubbling air holds the fish shoal together. Innate instincts prevent the fish from swimming against barriers or penetrating such a bubble curtain. Once the net has been completed, the whales dive down again and then come up inside the 'bubble tube', rising rapidly towards the surface with their mouth wide open. The diameter of the 'bubble tube' can vary widely, depending on how many whales participate in such a communal feeding venture.

Since bubble curtains are not always deployed during this particular hunting technique, the simultaneously emitted 'hunting songs' seem to be more important. The purpose of such sounds, which have no similarity to the mating calls of males in tropical breeding grounds, has not yet been fully resolved. In any event, in response to these whale songs the frightened herring tend to

In all baleen whales the baleen plates hang from the upper jaw and serve in straining food organisms like krill and small fish from the water.

One particularly fascinating hunting strategy of Humpback Whales is the so-called 'bubble net feeding'.

This photo clearly shows the circle of bubbles and the hungry Humpback Whale rising in its centre.

move closer together yet, until the Humpback Whales, side-by-side and with their barn-door-size mouths wide open, rise swiftly to the surface. When this happens and the herrings are pushed to the surface like a bubbling mass - all trying to get away - the sea churns like a boiling kettle. At that point the water seems to consist of nothing but twisting and splashing fish bodies. The next whale in line rising to the surface automatically gulps up the herrings that overflow from the mouth of the first whale and so on, ...a virtual feeding orgy until their throat grooves bulge out grotesquely. And what appears at first sight total chaos is in reality a precisely executed, almost choreographed manoeuvre. This becomes clear when watching the whales for days, always coming up in the same formation and with the same relative position to each other. With this technique Humpback Whales take advantage of the (normally) effective defensive strategy of all shoaling fishes: When threatened the members of a shoal tend to draw closer together and so form a dense mass of fish bodies, which makes it difficult for a predator to recognise and target a specific individual.

The preferred and most-frequently used hunting technique of Humpback Whales appears to be what is called 'lateral lunge feeding'. This is generally seen during the evening hours, when krill has risen to just below the sea surface. While executing this manoeuvre, a Humpback Whale normally turns onto its right side and ploughs along the sea surface with its mouth wide open. This tendency towards dextral orientation is not limited to Humpback Whales. Other baleen whales, such as grey whales and fin whales, also turn over preferentially onto their right side when feeding. In fact, 'lunge feeding' has even lead to the development of an asymmetrical head colouration in fin whales.

If several Humpbacks are participating in such a richly provided for evening meal, they tend to form a feeding formation, referred to as 'echelon'. In an obliquely displaced row they ascend sequentially with such precision timing, so that the whales rise sequentially (one-immediately-

The most-frequently used hunting technique of Humpbacks appears to be 'lateral lunge feeding'.

If several Humpbacks are participating in a richly provided for evening meal, they tend to form an 'echelon' feeding formation.

after-the-other) to the surface. Sometimes up to eight whales make up such a diagonal squadron (hence the name 'echelon'), that ploughs through the krill 'soup' like a row of trawling nets. When swimming in such a feeding formation, obviously each successive whale takes advantage of the briefly condensed mass of prey as it glides along the body of the whale in front. It appears to be more of a significant advantage than a disadvantage to the whale that such a lateral swimming position, with the giant mouth being wide open, has a detrimental effect on the hydrodynamics involved. Because of the turbulence created, krill is then being concentrated and so becomes trapped and more easily available in large quantities to each subsequent whale. Often also krill drifting at the surface is concentrated by slapping the water surface heavily with the giant fluke.

The entire food intake of Humpback Whales is designed amazingly consistent by concentrating the prey within the smallest possible confine, before commencing the actual hunt. With that nearly 24 hours per day are involved in food gathering. The daily food intake per whale is up to 1 ton in order to accumulate sufficient fat reserves for the long migrations to the breeding grounds.

Certain environmental signals, such as length of day light, water temperature and lunar cycles are responsible for the onset of the migration of Humpback Whales to their mating and nursery grounds in warm seas. Such migrations take place twice a year, and they are beyond doubt among the longest in the entire Animal Kingdom. With this, Humpback Whales spend nearly one-third of their life to crossing the world's oceans, from their feeding grounds off Alaska or the Antarctic to the subtropical breeding areas. The cold, food-rich seas provide the enormous caloric requirements of these giants of the sea, and the warm water regions of the tropics are needed for calving. At birth, a Humpback Whale calf does not yet have an adequate blubber layer to protect it against the cold water of high oceanic latitudes.

In coastal waters Humpback Whale can easily orient themselves using topographic features, such as mountains and islands. Yet, how they are able to orient themselves during their long migrations in the open ocean has remained - to this day - their very own secret. It is being assumed that iron oxide crystals (magnetite) in the lobes of the brain of these whales act like magnets. With the aid of such an inbuilt 'compass' they could detect and then follow the magnetic field of the earth. Apparently Humpback Whales orient themselves in a similar manner as is known from birds and bats.

SUBFAMILY Humpback Whales, Megapterinae
A single species: Humpback Whale, *Megaptera novaeangliae*

Distinguishing Characteristics of this Subfamily
Humpback Whales are similar to other rorquals in many ways, but various anatomical differences have prompted numerous systematists to place them in a separate subfamily. Although they are closely related to rorquals of the genus *Balaenoptera*, Humpback Whales distinguish themselves by virtue of their stockier bodies and outsized flippers. In place of the well-developed dorsal fin commonly found among other rorquals, Humpback Whales have a slight elevation there- their name-giving "hump." Another obvious distinction is a series of raised lumps, or tubercles, on their broad heads.

Humpback Whale, *Megaptera novaeangliae*

Humpback Whales are relatively easy to watch. Tonga, South Pacific.   Ralf Kiefner

Distinguishing Characteristics
The two most conspicuous earmarks of a Humpback Whale are its stout, nearly barrel-shaped body and oversized flippers covered with tubercles. The flippers can be up to 5 m long and irregularly shaped in front because of the lumps and bumps on it. Its head and fluke are also covered with these characteristic tubercles.

    Instead of a dorsal fin, Humpback Whales have a small hump to which they owe their common name. Their flukes have irregular edges covered with bumps. The underside of each fluke bears an individual black-and-white pattern.

    Humpback Whales are one of the most active species of large whale. Their most spectacular activities are acrobatic breaching, lob-tailing and singing, along with highly sophisticated feeding techniques.

In Hawaiian waters Humpback Whales are breaching directly in front of the hotels.   Ed Robinson

Description

In contrast to all other rorquals, Humpback Whales have a stocky body. This in turn means that they are also among the slowest of the rorquals. They average between 13-16 m in length, but can grow up to 18 m. Like all rorquals, female Humpback Whales are larger than the males. Their average weight is 35-40 t, with some animals weighing up to 65 t. Newborn calves are 4.5 m in length and weigh 1-2 t. They double in size during the first year of their lives.

Humpback Whales have rounded and relatively flat heads that make up to 30% of their total body size. Unlike other rorquals, they lack a distinctive median line. A Humpback Whale's head appears somewhat narrow in profile and its lower jaw has a downward-pointing bulge.

The most conspicuous feature of a Humpback Whale's head is the rows of lumps, or tubercles, along the upper and lower jaws, as well as in front of the paired blowholes. Each one of these tubercles is a golf-ball-sized follicle with a coarse bristle in the centre about 1-3 cm in length and 0.6-0.8 mm in circumference. These bristles may have a sensory function. Barnacles often grow on the head and, especially, the lower jaw.

Humpback Whales have very conspicuous, up to 5-m-long flippers with irregular edges in front. They are only mobile at the base. The pigmentation on the flippers varies geographically: Those of the Atlantic Humpback Whales are white on both sides and only occasionally of a darker hue; those of the remaining populations are uniformly dark on top and more or less white underneath.

Instead of the typical well-developed dorsal fin of a rorqual, Humpback Whales have a characteristic small hump after which the species was named. The hump itself sits upon a low and fleshy dorsal ridge midway down the body.

The edge of fluke is irregular and covered with lumps. Its underside has a distinctive black and white pattern. This pigmentation is permanent and, like a human fingerprint, it is used to identify individual animals. In some rare cases the underside will be uniformly white. The fluke is wing-shaped and has a conspicuous median notch.

The pigmentation of a Humpback Whale varies with each individual animal. Back and sides are usually blue-black, black or dark- to pale-grey. The underside can be completely dark, white or partly white.

Right: "Half Tail" is a mature female living in the South Pacific. She has been sighted repeatedly in Tonga during the mating season. It is easy to recognize her because half of her fluke is missing. Perhaps the missing part of her fluke got tangled up in a fishing net somewhere. But the loss of half her fluke doesn't seem to bother "Half Tail" too much, as she has since managed to raise two healthy calves.

Below: The typical fluke of a Humpback Whale.

Ralf Kiefner

Since Humpback Whales are slow swimmers, barnacles (ecto-parasitic crustaceans, *Coronula* spp.) will often attach themselves to their heads, flippers and flukes. In the summer, when the whales are in their colder feeding grounds, their flukes will occasionally be covered with yellow spots. These are caused by the same diatoms that cover Blue and Fin whales.

Humpback Whales have 12-36 noticeably wide throat grooves that run down to their navels. Their 250-400 relatively long and wide baleen plates average 70-100 cm in length and 15 cm in width. Their big and bushy blows can be up to 3 m high.

Easily Mistaken For

Thanks to their stocky bodies, tiny humps and outsized flippers Humpback Whales can easily be identified from afar. Their active surface behaviour, the individual patterns on the underside of their flukes and the tubercles on their heads clearly distinguish them from all other large whales as well.

Ectoparasitic barnacles (cirripeds) settle on the front rims of the characteristic long flippers of the Humpback Whale.

Silver Banks, Dominican Republic.   Ralf Kiefner

Other Names

Buckelwal (German); Baleine à Bosse, Mégaptère, Jubarte (French); Megattera (Italian); Rorcual Jorobado (Spanish); Baleia Corcunda, Baleia Jubarte, Baleia de Bossa, Baleia de Corcunda, Baleia Preta (Portuguese); Bultrug (Dutch); Knølhval (Norwegian); Ryhävalas (Finnish); Knölval (Swedish); Pukkelhval (Danish); Zatô Kujira (Japanese); Gorbatyi Kit (Russian); Ballena Jorobada (Latin American Spanish).

Meaning of the Scientific Nomenclature

Megaptera novaeangliae (Borowski 1781) - The scientific name *Megaptera novaeangliae* can be translated as "Big-Winged New Englander." The generic name *Megaptera* is made up of the Latin word *mega* (large) and the Greek word *pteron* (wing). The Latin species name *novaeangliae* means "from New England."

Behaviour

Since Humpback Whales spend the greater part of the year in proximity to the shore and always frequent the same places, the feeding and mating grounds of most populations are as well known as their habits. More is actually known about their behaviour than most other species of whale. Historical records show that Humpback Whales also spend a lot of time along the continental shelf in depths of 200-1,500 m.

Humpback Whales usually appear in large casual groups that are subdivided into smaller pods with strong social ties. Depending upon the abundance of food, 10-20 individuals may form temporary pods when they reach their feeding grounds. These pods lack a stable social structure because they are strictly opportunistic and only occur whenever the food supply is plentiful. Nevertheless, these annual feeding associations will apparently regroup in the same constellation every year. The only stable group one is likely to see in the mating grounds is that of a whale cow and its calf. Mother and calf are occasionally escorted by one or more males.

Humpback Whales are by far the most active species of large whale. In addition, they are not at all uneasy about the presence of vessels. At times they will even approach a stationary boat in order to do some "whale watching" of their own. This explains why they are so popular among whale watchers. They will frequently perform their entire repertoire of acrobatic surface activity: breaching, lob-tailing, flipper-slapping, fluking-up and spy-hopping.

A Humpback Whale's annual cycle is divided into three phases: a **summer phase**, a **migrating phase** and a **winter phase**. Each one of these phases is associated with certain characteristic forms of behaviour.

Summer Phase

Since Humpback Whales fast while they are in their mating grounds or in the process of migrating, they will be in fairly poor shape by the time they arrive in their feeding grounds and immediately begin feeding. During the next four months their sole concern will be the procurement of food. The partially aggressive and competitive comportment manifested in the mating grounds now makes room for more cooperative behaviour. Two basic forms of cooperation will take place at this time, both of which are connected to the availability of food:
1. Shifting bonds between individuals while gulping krill.
2. Stable bonds while feeding on shoaling fish. These stable affiliations, which can last for months and even years, provide the most effective way to herd shoaling fish together and consume them with a minimum expenditure of energy.

Of all the baleen whales, Humpback Whales have undoubtedly developed the most variable, specialized and efficient hunting techniques. The most spectacular of these is bubble-netting. Usually a single Humpback Whale will circle krill or shoaling fish under water while blowing bubbles. The rising bubbles form a funnel around the shoaling fish, which holds them in confinement much like a net would. One or more Humpback Whales will then swim through this funnel of bubbles vertically with their mouths wide open until they reach the surface. There is no escape for the shoaling prey. Depending upon the size of the prey and the number of whales participating in this joint effort, this funnel of bubbles can measure up to 25 m in circumference.

There are two basic ways in which Humpback Whales feed:
1. The technique generally used by baleen whales known as skimming. It does not require any specialized technique like bubble-netting and is primarily used with slow-swimming krill. Hereby the whales simply swim through the water with their mouths open. In so doing they imbibe large amounts of nutrients and water before closing their mouths again. This method is most effective when there is a low concentration of food in the water.
2. The technique generally used by rorquals known as gulping. The whales can take up huge amounts of food at once by stretching their throat grooves. Hereby they swallow great portions of nutrients along with the water, continually closing their mouths again in the process. This method is most effective when there is a thick concentration of food or fast-moving prey in the water.

Only recently has it become known that Humpback Whales intone regular "hunting songs" in their feeding grounds. It may well be that this singing, which is unlike any of the mating songs performed by the males in their mating grounds, helps to herd the shoaling fish together.

Migrating Phase

Humpback Whales spend the summers in their cool Arctic/Antarctic feeding grounds. At the end of the feeding season they migrate to their respective winter mating grounds in warmer waters. Some populations cover up to 19,000 km (both ways) in the course of their migrations - almost as for as the Gray Whale. The whales will not take up food during their migrations from the feeding to the mating grounds.

While migrating their average swimming speed will vary between 3-15 km/h. When threatened, Humpback Whales can speed up to 27 km/h. Females are forced to move at a slower pace on their way from the mating to the feeding grounds because of their recently-born young.

Winter Phase

During the winter season in their respective hemispheres, Humpback Whales will congregate in shallow tropical waters with temperatures ranging between 25-28° C. Here they will mate, give birth and nurture their young. During this four-month sojourn they will take little, if any, nourishment. Observations of them feeding at this time are extremely rare. During this phase the whale cows are solely preoccupied with nurturing their young. The bulls, on the other hand, are busy posturing, courting and rivalling. Fierce struggles break out between the males as they compete for a mate. They will put up a bitter fight in order to gain access to a rutting female, as an observation made off the coast of Lahaina (Maui, Hawaii) on February 9, 1996, attests. According to it, a group of 4 rowdy males fought so hard over a female that one of the contenders died as a result.

Rivalries between whale bulls can best be observed whenever two or more of them are courting the same female. Their aggressive behaviour entails lob-tailing, flipper-slapping, ramming and blowing bubbles under water. At times they practically pave the surface with their bubbles. The bulls try to move in close to females and maintain their "escorting" privilege for as long as possible, often up to 7 hours. In many cases escorting bulls will suffer bleeding wounds as a result of physical contact with their rivals.

The temporariness of these unions and the lack of communication between mature bulls lead to the assumption that they are polygynous. Males will compete with each other for a certain female and try to keep all rivals away from her. Both sexes subsequently mate with several partners. This kind of mating behaviour is typical for all species with relatively small testicles.

A breaching Humpback Whale is truly an imposing sight. Breaching is a common posturing gesture among them during their mating season. Sometimes the whales catapult their massive bodies completely out of the water and execute elegant pirouettes with their flippers extended before they come crashing down again.

A snorkeller who witnessed a breaching Humpback Whale from very close up made the following observation: The whale began to twist its body even before it actually breached, during its run-up under water so to speak. Its flippers were also spread wide prior to surfacing and basically functioned as a rudder for the pending pirouette.

Sometimes Humpback Whales only propel half of their bodies out of the water and land flat on their bellies. Whenever a whale breaches for the benefit of a rival, it is intended as a threatening gesture. The same holds true when Humpback Whales confront rivals with posturing exhibitions like lob-tailing and flipper-slapping.

Such aggressive behaviour becomes more noticeable at noon or when the seas are rough. Perhaps the loud sounds created by these activities serve as a means of communication whenever the noise made by the wind and waves threatens to drown out any other signals.

Courtship songs are only intoned by the males when they find themselves alone in their mating grounds. They are obviously intended to impress a female. Such "songs" are composed of a complex series of sounds in a wide frequency range and can last from 6-30 min. The individual sounds usually only last for a few seconds, but together they create a recognizable pattern. These sounds have been variously described as "snoring," "moaning," "grunting," "growling," "whistling," "uhs," "ohs," "uihs," "oihs," and "ahs." The singing can be heard up to 30 km under water.

Facts & Figures Humpback Whale	Quick ID-Check Humpback Whale
Size: 13-16 m, max 25 m	
Weight: 35-40 t, max 65 t	Lumps (tubercles) on head and lower jaw
Longevity: about 40-60 years	
Sexual maturity: at 4-5 years, as of 11 m in length	Conspicuously large flippers
Mating season: winter in both hemispheres	Underside of fluke has individual patterns
Gestation period: 11.5 months	
Calving interval: every 1-3 years	Wing-shaped fluke with irregular edge
Size at birth: 4.5 m	
Weight at birth: 1-2 t	Stocky body
Nursing period: 10.5-11 months	
Dive depth: rarely over 50 m	Raises fluke high into the air while sounding
Dive time: 15-30 min	
Maximum speed: 27 km/h	Often inquisitive
Baleen plates: 250-400 on each side, fairly long (70-100 cm) and wide (15 cm)	Very active on surface
Blow: very conspicuous, wide and bushy, 3 m high	
Throat Grooves: 12-36, wide gaps between them, reach the navel	
Flipper size: 5 m	
Group (Pod) size: 1-3 in mating grounds, hunting packs up to 20 animals in feeding grounds	
Population: estimated at about 10,000-15,000, vulnerable	

The breaching of Humpbacks is often associated with dominance behaviour. Alaska.   Ralf Kiefner

Humpback Whales of one region intone fairly identical songs that will only change slightly throughout the years. Segments of "songs" from previous seasons are left out and new compositions added. Studies conducted by Payne and Guinee in 1983 showed that animals in different mating grounds (Hawaii and California) used similar melodic patterns even though they were 4,800 km apart. Two years later members of both populations made similar changes in their style of singing. Darling and Jurasz concluded that a certain exchange must have taken place between these animals in their summer grounds and that the changes in the melodic patterns were the result of a learning process.

Diving
Humpback Whales tend to feed within 50 m of the surface. Their dives rarely last longer than 15 min, but in their winter feeding grounds they can remain under water up to 30 min. After surfacing they breathe deeply 4-8 times with an interval of 15-30 sec between each breath. They often raise their flukes so high while sounding that the undersides become clearly exposed. Scientists are able to identify individual whales by the patterns on the undersides of their flukes, which are as unique as human fingerprints.

Feeding Habits
Humpback Whales have coarse baleen plates that are hardly suitable for filtering out minute plankton. Consequently, and in contrast to all other rorquals, Humpback Whales prefer to feed on small shoaling fish and larger zooplankton.
    Their main source of food is krill and shoaling fish (herring, capelin), which they herd together in great masses and literally shovel into their gaping maws. Occasionally they also take sand eels, mackerel, cod and salmon. Even birds have been found in the stomachs of Humpback Whales, which were undoubtedly swallowed by accident as the whales were lunge-feeding (swimming up through a shoal of pray and breaking the surface with their mouths wide open).

During courtship, a male Humpback releases a string of air bubbles to tickle a female from below.

Also during courtship and prior to the copulation itself the male Humpback extends his penis.
Both photos Hawaii.   Doug Perrine/HWRF, NMFS research permits 633 & 882
Facing page: The photographer clearly heard this Humpback Whale singing in an upside down position.
Photo Silver Banks, Dominican Republic.   Howard Hall

RORQUAL WHALES   BALAENOPTERIDAE

General Information

The two earliest scientific names for this species, *Balaena boops* and *Balaena novaeangliae,* were introduced by Fabricius in 1780 and Borowski in 1781 respectively. In 1846 Gray coined the currently valid species name of *Megaptera.*

There is a northern and a southern population of Humpback Whales, which are regarded as one and the same species. Both populations migrate from their respective Arctic and Antarctic feeding grounds to their tropical mating and nursing grounds. Due to the inverse hemispherical seasons, however, there is no interbreeding between the two populations.

Hundreds of thousands of Humpback Whales were slaughtered during the days of commercial whaling. Although the species has since recuperated, its current population is only a fraction of what it once was.

Like all rorquals, the age of a Humpback Whale is best determined by the number of growth layers on its ear plugs.

Where & When

Humpback Whales are found in all oceans from the tropics to polar waters. They prefer shallower coastal waters. Northern and southern populations migrate annually but do not interbreed. They spend the summer in their respective polar feeding grounds:

- North Atlantic: Gulf of Maine (New Scotland), Labrador (Newfoundland) and West Greenland.
- Northern Pacific: Alaska.
- Southern Hemisphere: Antarctic.

Humpback Whales are noted for their long winter migrations to their respective mating grounds:

- North Atlantic: Caribbean; the largest population of Humpback Whales frequents the Dominican Republic (Samaná Bay, Silver Banks) and Puerto Rico between December and April.
- Northern Pacific: In Hawaii between December and April.
- Southern Hemisphere: From June to October Humpback Whales congregate in the protected bays of numerous South Sea islands as well as Australia, the Abrolhos Islands (Brazil), Mozambique, Tanzania and Madagascar.

A small group of Humpback Whales living north of the equator in the Indian Ocean are an exception to the rule. The Asian landmasses prevent these animals from migrating north. Consequently, they either range along the equator all year round or move across to the higher latitudes of the Southern Hemisphere. They are the only Humpback Whales known to cross the equator from one hemisphere to the other. A few of these animals are occasionally sighted in the Red Sea.

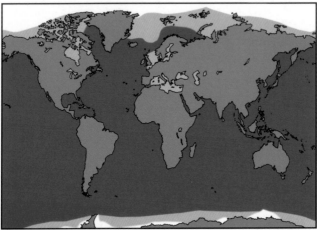

Humpback Whale, distribution: Worldwide in all oceans, from the tropics to coastal polar waters.

LAS BALLENAS JOROBADAS

Most North Atlantic Humpback Whales spend the winter, calve and mate in the warm tropical waters off the coast of the Dominican Republic. This Caribbean nation can rightly claim to be the homeland of the "ballena jorobada." Bernd Peyer, travel book author and scuba diving instructor, describes his encounter with Humpback Whales in the Bay of Samaná and outlines the restrictions that have recently been applied to whale watching there.

PHOTOS: BERND PEYER

The Bay of Samaná provides a safe haven for North Atlantic Humpback Whales after their long migration from the north.

"Whale at 3 o'clock!" All eyes turned to the starboard side and scanned the horizon for the telltale sign of a whale's presence. "There she blows again!" This time we all saw it. Two or three fountains of water, looking much like thin wisps of smoke, could be made out in the distance. The skipper turned the boat in the direction of the spouting whales and then let the engine idle, allowing the craft to cut its way almost soundlessly across the smooth waters of the bay.

Suddenly two glistening black masses welled side by side from the depths just beyond our boat and seemed to swell upwards into the blue sky where they crashed into each other like thunder and then came tumbling back down again in an explosion of white foam. The entire episode only lasted a few seconds and yet I had the distinct impression of having witnessed the birth and death of an island.

"Part of a rowdy group," our Canadian whale expert on board explained. "Obviously two bulls vying with each other for a mate."

And then the rest of the herd made its way past us, their slightly angled humps gliding in an elegant arch over the surface of the membrane-like water. The dark silhouettes briefly superimposed the similarly shaped hills beyond the bay and then disappeared again, all in one smooth motion. Here and there a spout peaked into a misty spray that the ocean breeze blew across our eager faces. Afterwards, all that remained were large, round pools of slick water into which the graceful giants had seemingly melted away.

We had obviously picked a perfect day for whale watching in the Bay of Samaná with a clear blue sky and a calm sea. After departing from the tiny peer in Samaná city we were briefed about the habits of the Humpback Whales and the fact that most of the North Atlantic representatives of this second-large whale species were full-blooded "Dominicanos." About 80% of the Humpback Whales living in the North Atlantic (estimated at about 6,000) spend the winter months from mid-January to mid-March in the warm waters of the Greater Antilles after having migrated all the way from Iceland and Greenland by way of the New England coast.

A Humpback Whale sounds close to the bottom. One can clearly recognise the typical gorgonians of the Caribbean.

Among their favourite mating and calving grounds in this region are the remote Silver Banks, a long and shallow reef lying approximately 150 km to the northeast of Puerto Plata, and the Bay of Samaná, one of the largest protected harbours of the West Indies. "It can be likened to a huge singles' bar," our tour guide bantered, "where everyone is looking for a date." The otherwise gentle leviathans will often forget their manners here in the heat of their competition for a mate, frequently butting in between other "couples" and showing off by heaving their colossal bodies way out of the water.

Our whale-watching boat continued past the tiny island of Cayo Levantado and headed out towards the mouth of the long-drawn bay. It did not take long until someone spotted a spout again, this time on the port side. Something that looked like an oversized leaf fluttering in the wind turned out to be the pectoral fin of a playful calf slapping the water and basking in the sun under the ever watchful eyes of its mother. Apparently not at all interested in the fragile creatures craning their scrawny necks over the gunwale and making strange clicking noises with shiny objects, the mother nudged its calf forward and both calmly swam out to the open sea. It was only after the whales had disappeared along the horizon that I remembered my own camera hanging uselessly from my shoulder.

As our boat made its way back to the peer in Samaná and most of the passengers stretched themselves out on deck to enjoy the Caribbean sun, I sat down on the very tip of the bow and kept my eyes glued to the water. For some reason I was sure that one more encounter was still due - I just needed to be patient. It came as we were almost level again with Cayo Levantado on the starboard side, no more than 50 metres from where my legs were dangling from underneath the railing. The ridged back of a solitary whale traced a nearly perfect crescent over the calm surface and, just as I thought that was it, its huge fan-like fluke unfolded to reveal an intricate black and white pattern framed by the azure sky for the duration of a heartbeat. An original imprint, never to be reproduced again. A whale's unique signature, its unmistakable "fingerprint."

In the split second that the mirror blocked out the light in the prism of my SLR camera I had a most disturbing vision. A man, like myself, stood on the bow of a ship. In his hands he held not a camera, but a harpoon made of shiny steel. When the light flooded the prism once again, all I could see through the viewfinder was the empty sea.

Later that afternoon, as I was enjoying a cup of coffee at one of the restaurants lining the harbour, or malecón, I happened to overhear a discussion going on among a group of young marine biology students who had also been on the whale watching tour. One of them expressed strong doubts about the merits of such ventures, arguing that excessive whale watching activities in Hawaii had already led to a decline in the local whale population. Such

Would the reader care to go whale watching in one of these Samaná "cruisers"?

disturbances undoubtedly had an influence on the whales' behaviour, and this during the vital mating and calving season. Another basically agreed, but thought that restrictions alone could not ameliorate the situation either. To see a whale in its natural environment was a very moving experience that could awaken a deeper concern not only for whales, but for nature in general. Whale watching activities needed to be conducted by qualified and responsible personnel under strictly controlled conditions. After all, whale watching also provided a commercial incentive to keep the whales alive, he concluded.

A delicate question. Whale watching is still a relatively undeveloped activity in Samaná, but it didn't take the owners of all kinds of sea-going vessels long to recognise its financial potential. Could one make it plausible to the less solvent residents that only organised tours on large boats should be granted official permission to exploit this profitable tourist attraction - especially if most of the organisers turned out to be foreigners? Controlled whale watching can only be effective if the local fishermen, for instance, who pride themselves for not having a whale hunting tradition, are somehow incorporated into the plan.

A positive development in this direction is the establishment of the *Centro para la Conservación y Ecodesrrollo de la Bahía de Samaná y su Entorno, Inc.* (CEBSE), a local organisation that is actively dedicated to the conservation and ecologically sound exploitation of the natural resources in Samaná and its surroundings. With its assistance, the following restrictions have recently been implemented: Whale watching tours can only be conducted with the official permission of the *Dirección Nacional de Parques* (central office of the National Parks Bureau). No more than one large vessel (over 9 m) and two smaller ones (less than 9 m) are to approach a solitary whale or a herd of whales at the same time. All approaching vessels have to maintain a minimum distance of 80 m to the whales; those awaiting their turn should come no closer than 500 m. Once the minimum distance has been reached, the skipper has to let the engine idle (not shut it off). The maximum time allowed for the observation of individual whales or groups of whales is 30 minutes. The maximum speed in the area lying beyond the Cayo Levantado and wherever else whales are encountered is 5 knots. Swimming or diving in the vicinity of the whales is **strictly prohibited.** Although the last restriction will prove frustrating for some, it probably has more in mind than just the protection of breaching love-crazed thirty-ton leviathans!

One thing is certain: More and more tourists coming to the Dominican Republic will want to go whale watching and it is doubtful whether all providers will always mind the new regulations. Looking out over the many types of vessels anchoring in the beautiful Bay of Samaná, I wondered to myself just how much space there really is between a man with a camera and a man with a harpoon.

EYE TO EYE

Although whales tend to shy away from snorkellers, at times there is an unexpected and very intensive meeting between them. The author was fortunate enough to experience one of these rare moments when he had an "eye-to-eye" encounter with a Southern Right Whale in the Golfo Nuevo, along the coast of Patagonia (Argentina).

Eye to eye with a Southern Right Whale *(Eubalaena australis)*: I am entranced, caught in space and time.

"Apparently it wants to play with us," I think to myself as a Southern Right Whale suddenly breaches next to our rubber dinghy. Quietly I slip into the icy water. Its 10° Celsius almost take my breath away.

Before I can change my mind and climb back into the dinghy, the whale begins to swim leisurely towards me in the turbid water. I can see it eyeing me curiously just a few metres away. As it swims by me at a slow pace I take first notice of its imposing size. It keeps moving closer to me. Under water it looks even larger. Then I notice that its huge six-metre-wide fluke is heading straight for me. While I am paddling desperately to get out of its way, the whale casually moves its fluke under and around me without the slightest touch.

After we have swum side by side for a few minutes, the whale decides to make a turn and head directly for me once again. My efforts to paddle away from it are as futile as the last time. "Has it failed to see me? Can't it tell that I am directly in its way?" I wonder nervously. When its enormous head is just a few metres away I try to move to one side of it. In vain. The whale notices comprehends my efforts to escape and simply shifts its direction so that we are on a collision course again. I try to dodge to the other side. Nothing doing.

Fear suddenly takes hold of me and I can feel my heart beating madly. About 40 tons of living flesh are about to crash into me and I am unable to get out of its way. The whale's head is no more than an arm's length from my body. I can clearly make out the stubble on its lower jaw. If I want to avoid a collision there is little more that I can do other than to hold out my hand in the hopes of keeping the whale at a safe distance that way. I touch its lower jaw. I expect the worst, but what happens next catches me totally unprepared. The whale just keeps right on swimming, pushing me gingerly before it.

Its calm and gentle movements make me confident again. My initial anxiety has given way to a feeling of familiarity and trust. I have the definite impression that the whale is enjoying my company as well. It rolls over on its back right beside me. I can detect a twinkling in its eye. "What is it trying to tell me?"

I can clearly see its small eye wandering back and forth inquisitively. It appears to be looking me over from top to bottom. Its head is still an arm's length away. But now its eye is practically right before my face. I recognise the barnacles growing above it like an eyebrow.

Our glances meet. For a brief moment I am lost in space and time. Its docile gaze reflects a comforting warmth. "Wonder what it is thinking," crosses my mind at that moment. I respond to its tender gaze with the proper respect and admiration. I hope it has understood.

I am certain that I will never have such a remarkable encounter again. Curious, the whale eyes its own image reflected in my camera lens. I nearly forget to take a picture. Calmly, as if there were only the two of us left in the whole world, I set my aperture at 0.3 m and hold the 15 mm lens close to its brown eye. The reflection in the lens really seems to have caught the whale's attention. I notice that the movement of its eye gradually slows down.

At the moment it appears to be fully concentrated on its reflection. I allow the whale ample time to look. After a while, its warm and gentle gaze shifts back and forth between me and the lens, as if it were saying: "Well, get on with it." The whale

About 40 tons of living flesh are on a direct collision course.

hovers next to me absolutely motionless. Now it is finally time to take a picture of its eye.

When the icy cold finally forces me to swim back to the dinghy, my "chubby chum" seems reluctant to let me go. The whale places itself directly between me and the dinghy so that I am unable to reach it. I try to swim around it repeatedly, but each time the whale anticipates my move and blocks me off again. At last, after my third try, it takes pity on me. Shaking with cold, I clamber back on board after having spent almost an hour in the water. And believe me, 10° C is no laughing matter.

Just as unexpectedly as my "chubby chum" had appeared next to my dinghy, it vanished in the depths again. But not before giving me a parting salute with its powerful fluke.

Only after I tried already three times, the whale allows me to return to the boat.

MATING AT VALDES

The Chinese underwater photographer Stephen Wong from Hong Kong had one of his most surreal encounters with wild animals while observing some Southern Right Whales in the sheltered waters of the Golfo Nuevo around the Peninsula of Valdes in Argentina.

PHOTOS: STEPHEN WONG

A pair of Southern Right Whales entwine each other while mating in the quiet waters of the Golfo Nuevo, Argentina.

"They are not mom and calf! These are mating whales!!" I was screaming my lungs off at the direction of our rubber dinghy. I had no clue whether the ranger, the guide, the skipper or other guests on the boat could hear what I was yelling about. Hyperventilating from both breathlessness and excitement, I had completely forgotten how cold the water actually was.

At a water temperature of about 9 degrees Celsius, I was wearing a hooded 7-mm 'farmer John' 2-piece neoprene suit (there would have been 14 mm on chest and body, if the suit was not 5 years old). Despite that I was lucky to have seen these Southern Right Whales during the past few days in the water, I had always felt cold. So cold in fact, that my head and fingers became totally numb, even after a short 5-minute dip, and then I had to thaw my brain to pick up any thoughts. Usually when I finally crawled back on board (sometimes with calf or thigh cramps), I could only slur. My English sounded like Chinese, and my Chinese sounded more foreign. My mouth, tongue, and vocal chords simply were not coordinating with my brain.

Yet, at this moment, bobbing at the surface next to these two whales, I felt warmth. It was not only the adrenaline rush that supplied me with this strength, but it was also the emotional high that kept me forgetting the cold Valdes seas, "I AM WITNESSING MATING WHALES!"

From a distance of 5 metres, I could see this big male copulating with the smaller female. She appeared to be about 9 metres in length and probably was too young to be fertile. Her body was partially exposed at the surface, while the much larger male swam upside down beneath her, belly to belly. Despite poor underwater visibility on this morning, I could clearly see that he had inserted his sex organ inside her. Aware of my presence, the female 'detached' herself from her lover, and swung her head towards me. Apparently, she was more curious in me than in making love.

Coming to within two metres, her enormous head had blocked out most of my sight of the surroundings. Her right eye rolled, as she continued investigating this tiny submarine man. The callosities were prominent and parasitic crabs could be seen milling on her jaws and eye. She pirouetted herself slightly to get a better view. Our eyes met.

I froze, for a special kind of telepathic interaction was radiating from this behemoth. A message was definitely conveyed by this whale. "What are you telling me?" I was asking.

Though I would appear so puny and feeble in her world, the idea of me getting hurt had never crossed my mind.

Her gentleness and the warm communication simply expanded my emotions and engulfed me. There was this bondage between us. However, the eye(s) looked sad, but were simultaneously filled with intellectual curiosities and understanding, like a holy person with expansive knowledge and wisdom. All I could reciprocate back was to watch the

The mighty erectile penis of the male Right Whale on its search for the female's vagina.

whale with the most respectful thoughts and awesome appreciation of this contact.

The male suddenly reappeared from below, and slightly nudged the female's body with his gargantuan snout, like a gentle caress. Slowly, he veered off to the green abyss. The female whale gave a blow. Deciding to follow her male counterpart and to continue their pilgrimage, she banked to her right. Her left pectoral fin gently brushed past my arms, and was lifted from the murky water. As if to bid farewell, the oblong-shaped fin was held in the air for a lingering moment, then the leviathan gracefully dove head first into the deep.

I did not (and today still don't) have any vocabulary that I could use to describe the feelings I had then. The feeling of being closely observed by this 20 to 30-ton gentle giant was plainly unimaginable, a moment of time frozen in awe. For over 100 years, humans have been hunting them, but this whale still came looking at me eye-to-eye, with curiosity and no hatred. I was so indulged in this brief moment of eternity that I did not care whether I was taking photos. It would have been mere stupidity to experience this contact through the tiny viewfinder of a camera. Indeed, this was the most surreal encounter with any wild animal in my life.

Finally the male succeeds to insert his penis. Hopefully, another member of the small Right Whale population will be generated.

3 species: Southern Right Whale, *Eubalaena australis*
             Northern Right Whale, *Eubalaena glacialis*
             Bowhead, *Balaena mysticetus*

Distinguishing Characteristics of this Family

A distinctive characteristic of right whales is that they do not have throat grooves and nor do they have a dorsal fin. Their large and stocky bodies are portly rather than streamlined, which makes them extremely slow swimmers. Another typical feature is the angular placement of the blowholes, which produce a high and V-shaped blow. Southern and Northern Right Whales have a conspicuous growth of white barnacles on and around their heads. All right whales are dimorphic: The females grow substantially larger and heavier than the males.

Right whales will typically have long and narrow baleen plates that are very pliable. The baleen plates of a Bowhead Whale can be up to 5.8 cm in length. All species in this family have two independent rows of baleen plates. Unlike most rorquals, their baleen plates are not joined together at the tip of the upper jaw.

All right whales have wide, more or less triangular flukes with a conspicuous median notch and very large, spade-like flippers.

Southern Right Whale, *Eubalaena australis*

Right Whales very often jump, especially in their mating grounds. Valdes, Argentina.   Ralf Kiefner

The high, V-shaped blow of the Southern Right Whale together with the area of distribution is diagnostic for the species. The two blowholes are placed at a v-shaped angle to each other, hence the peculiar shape of the blow.   Ralf Kiefner

Description

The body of a Southern Right is very large and stocky. Its blubber can be up to 36 cm thick, much denser (but also softer) than that of most other baleen whales. This thick layer of blubber makes up about 40% of its total body weight. Like all members of this family, Southern Right Whales are dimorphic: The females are substantially larger and heavier than males.

Southern Right Whales average about 11-15 m in length, with a maximum of 18 m. Their average weight is 40-80 t. The heaviest whale on record weighed a little over 100 t.

Like all other members of this family, Southern Right Whales neither have throat grooves nor dorsal fins. There is not even a small hump or any other elevation on their backs.

A Southern Whale's head is very large and massive, making up more than a quarter of its total body length. The most noticeable earmark of a Southern Right Whale is the conspicuous horny growth on its head, or so-called callosities. These are beset with a pale-grey growth of barnacles and other organisms. The callosities are already fully developed in the embryonic stage of the whale. The largest of them sits in the middle of the upper jaw and is referred to as a "bonnet" because of its similarity to a lady's headgear. Additional callosities are found above the eyes, in front of the blowholes, and on each side of the upper and lower jaws. Whale lice and numerous barnacles infest these callosities along with certain worms that produce a whitish, yellowish, pink or orange colouration.

The males tend to have more scratch marks and larger and/or more abundant callosities than the females. This gender-based difference has led R. Payne and E. Dorsey to suggest that the callosities might function as a weapon during inner-species altercations, e.g. when the males contend with each other for the favour of females.

South Africa's Peter Best has determined that, in comparison to Northern Right Whales, Southern Right Whales will usually have more callosities on the anterior part of the lower jaw, but fewer of them on the head.

A Southern Right Whale's jawlines are noticeably arched. The lower jaw is wider than the upper jaw. Mature males have up to 300 short bristles on the tip of the lower jaw and up to 100 of them on the upper jaw. These may have a sensory function.

The body of a Northern Right Whale is almost uniformly black or dark-brown with a few dark-brown or dark-grey spots. Only a few, individually varying white markings break up the uniformity of its dusky underside. Newborn calves are often lighter in colour and turn darker as they grow older. Some albinos have been recorded.

The large, spade-like flippers are dark on either side. The bone structure of the flippers is visible through the skin. The powerful fluke is also dark on both sides. Its edge is smooth and concave with a conspicuous median notch.

Another distinguishing mark of Southern Right Whales is their conspicuous V-shaped blow that can be up to 5-6 m high. The left blow is usually somewhat higher than the right one. The paired blowholes sit apart and at an angle, which is why the blow of a Southern Right Whale has the appearance of a V-shaped fountain rather than a cloud.

The 200-270 baleen plates on each side of the upper jaw grow to a max length of 2.5 m. Because of their great pliability they were used to make frames for corsets and umbrellas up until the middle of the 19th century.

Easily Mistaken For

Because of their massive, dusky bodies and the horny growth on their heads Southern Right Whales are easily distinguishable from all other large whales except members of their own family. It is almost impossible to tell them apart from Northern Right Whales. Thanks to their separate areas of distribution, however, a mix-up is hardly likely. The same applies to the somewhat larger Bowhead Whales.

At close range a Southern Right Whale can be identified by the callosities on its head.   Ralf Kiefner

Other Names
Black Right Whale (English); Südlicher Glattwal, Südkaper (German) Baleine Australe, Baleine Franche Australe (French); Balena Franca Australe (Italian); Ballena Franca Austral (Spanish); Baleia Franca, Baleia Franca Austral (Portuguese); Zuidkaper (Dutch); Sørlig Retthval (Norwegian); Eteläinen Mustavalas (Finnish); Sydlig Rätval (Swedish); Sydlig Rethval (Danish); Ballena Franca, Ballena Franca del Sur (Latin American Spanish).

Meaning of the Scientific Nomenclature
Eubalaena australis Desmoulins 1822 – The generic name *Eubalaena* is composed of Greek *eu* (right, genuine, true) and Latin *balaena* (whale). The Latin name *Eubalaena* literally means "the right whale." The Latin species name *australis* means "from the southern hemisphere."

Behaviour
Because of their massive bodies Southern Right Whales are very slow swimmers. As long as they are not being hunted they will move along at a leisurely 7 km/h. In their mating grounds they spend hours floating lazily on the surface, almost as if they were dozing. At times they even get their backs badly burned by the sun. In Valdés (Argentina) Kelp Gulls take advantage of a Southern Right Whale's lethargy to feed on scraps of its exposed skin, which they virtually peck full of holes.

In spite of their portliness, Southern Right Whales can still be remarkably active, if not outright acrobatic. Lob-tailing and flipper-slapping are part of their regular surface repertoire. During the mating season they breach frequently, sometimes up to 10 times consecutively. They are most active in the early morning and evening hours. After breaching they land on their bellies, backs or sides with a tremendous splash that can be heard more than 1 km away. Their breaching activities may be related to mating behaviour and communication, or simply represent an effort to get rid of bothersome parasites.

In general Southern Right Whales are inquisitive and playful. They often show a marked interest in vessels and their passengers. Sometimes they will even nudge a boat or some other floating object. They express their annoyance with a loud and pronounced growling sound while they exhale. Southern Right Whales have an extensive repertoire of low-frequency tones, which they primarily emit during the mating season in connection with courtship or other related social activities. Among the more typical sounds they make are "burping" and clicking, as well as low frequency moaning and grunting. It is assumed that the more complex intonations play a role in social communication within the group. They are often made in conjunction with clamorous surface activities such as breaching, lob-tailing and flipper-slapping. The simpler intonations are probably used for long-distance communication. The "grumbling" sounds remind one of a creaking door.

Facts & Figures Southern Right Whale	Quick ID-Check Southern Right Whale
Size: 11-15 m, max 18 m	
Weight: 40-80 t, max 100 t	Large head, covered with lumps of barnacles
Longevity: 70 years	
Sexual maturity: at 6-14 years, as of 14-15.5 m in length	Highly-arched jawlines, no dorsal fin
Mating season: June-November	Massive, stocky body, conspicuously wide back
Gestation period: 10-12 months	
Calving interval: every 3 years	Irregular white spot on underside
Size at birth: 4-6 m	
Weight at birth: 1 t	Blow V-shaped, high, left blow higher than right
Nursing period: up to 14 months	
Dive depth: max 200 m	Two blowholes set at angle
Dive time: max 22 min	
Maximum speed: 15 km/h	Large, spade-like flippers
Baleen plates: 225-390 on each side, longer on the left	
Blow: V-shaped, 5-6 m high, left blow higher	Large fluke, dark on both sides
Group (Pod) size: usually 1-5, in feeding grounds up to 20	Very slow swimmer
Population: worldwide about 10,000-15,000, extremely vulnerable	Often inquisitive and friendly

Spy-hopping and diving Southern Right Whales. Valdes, Argentina.   Ralf Kiefner

For a mature Southern Right Whale with its thick layer of blubber water temperatures ranging around 10° C can already be much too warm. In order to cool off in their warmer mating grounds, the whales will spend 20 min or longer "sailing," whereby they hang vertically upside-down in the water with their flukes up in the air. Heat exchange takes place in the fine network of capillaries in the fluke which, like the flippers, does not have an isolating layer of blubber. This "air-condition system" functions on the same principles as a countercurrent heat exchanger. The blood vessels transporting warm internal blood are enclosed by a fine network of capillaries carrying blood that has been cooled by the air or cold water surrounding the fluke. Another activity that has occasionally been observed among Southern Right Whales in their nutrient-poor mating grounds could also have a cooling function: The whales swim along the surface with their mouths wide open and wash out the so-called "miracle net" (rete mirabilis) in their throats with cold water. This "miracle net" consists of a thick maze of fine, interconnected capillaries that are gorged with blood. Its function is not clearly understood, but the heat exchange produced by the cold water leads to a reduction in the whale's body temperature.

Up until the present it has been thought that mature Southern Right Whales will not feed during the 3-4-month sojourn in their mating grounds. It was assumed that they sustain themselves solely on their blubber reserves. Observations recently made in their mating grounds in Valdés, however, have shown that mature whales will, if the opportunity offers itself, occasionally feed during the mating season as well.

Right whales have the largest and heaviest testicles of all whales, weighing up to 1 t. By way of contrast, their brains weigh a mere 2.4-3 kg. Because of the great size of their testicles and the relatively unaggressive nature of the whale bulls, successful reproduction among them depends more upon "sperm competition" than "social competition." This means that the whale cows will mate with several males in order to improve the chances of impregnation by receiving greater quantities of sperm.

During courtship the males are more preoccupied with achieving copulation than fending off other suitors. Consequently, sexual activities among Southern Right Whales usually involve groups composed of one female and several males. The males will often assist each other during copulation. Their penises attain a stately length of 1.8 m and can be freely moved in the water in order to facilitate copulation. Copulation can last 1-2 hours. When the females are ready to mate they will turn over on their backs so that their undersides become exposed. The males then have to wait until the object of their desire turns over again to breathe. On the mating of this species also see MATING AT VALDES on pages 88-89.

Diving

When Southern Whales surface to breathe their entire heads and part of their backs will become visible at the same time. They often raise their flukes when sounding. After a long dive their loud snorting can be heard for a great distance. The whales frequently come up in the same spot where they sounded.

Southern Right Whales can dive to depths of 200 m. How long their dives will last depends upon the activity involved. Their average dive time is 4-20 min. While they are feeding they usually dive for 1-7 min. Their average swimming speed is 6 km/h, with a max of 15 km/h.

Feeding Habits

Southern Right Whales primarily feed on concentrations of planktonic crustaceans (copepods and krill) as well as pelagic larvae and Spiny Squat Lobsters. Occasionally they also take small fish. In their feeding grounds Southern Right Whales will consume between 1,500-2,000 kg of zooplankton per day.

Southern Right Whales typically feed by "skimming," whereby they swim through the water with their mouths wide open and ingest enormous quantities of nutrients. Occasionally they close their mouths in order to press the water out again through their baleen plates. This feeding technique is most effective with slow-moving prey. Normally the whales skim the water on or near the surface, where they practically plow through thick concentrations of zooplankton.

General Information

Southern Right Whales were among the first species of whale to be hunted commercially. More than 45,000 were killed in the brief period between 1805 and 1844. The hunting methods used were particularly cruel. First the whalers would harpoon the calves and then kill the mothers as they invariably came to their aid.

A large whale would render up to 25 t of oil, as well as 2 t of baleen plates. The latter, known as whalebone, was an important trade item in the 19th century. It was used to make the frames for corsets and umbrellas, and even boots were tipped with it. In those days the capture of a single Southern Right Whale could already cover the costs of an entire whaling expedition. After most of the whales in a certain hunting grounds had been killed, the whalers would move on and consequently the remaining populations would manage to recover somewhat.

As far as whalers were concerned, right whales were indeed the "right whale" to hunt as the slow-swimming animals preferred coastal waters and the large quantities of blubber kept their harpooned cadavers afloat for a long time. Consequently, Southern Right Whales were slaughtered by the hundreds of thousands. No less than 99% of the original stock of an estimated 300.000 whales before the year 1800 was duly eradicated. As their annual reproductive rate lies around 5-16%, the species is only gradually recovering. Even though its population has grown by 7% in the last few years, this species is still very vulnerable.

For a long time it was believed that the species had become extinct. They were not rediscovered until 1969, when American whale expert Raymond Gilmore anchored his research vessel, the "Hero," in the waters off the Valdés Peninsula and came across an unexpectedly large number of Southern Right Whales. This population was placed under the legal protection of the Argentinian government in 1977. Only controlled whale-watching expeditions are still open to tourists. A recent count made in the Golfo Nuevo, Valdés, showed a slight increase in the population of Southern Right Whales there. The population was estimated at nearly 500 specimens. They regularly return from their colder feeding grounds in the Antarctic and remain here - probably always in the same bays - for a few months.

Whereas little research has been done on Northern Right Whales so far, Roger Payne and his collaborators have been observing Southern Right Whales in Valdés since 1970. Their method of "research by observation" has ushered in a new era in whale research. Paine and his colleagues photographed the whales from cliffs, vessels and aircraft. Payne discovered that Southern Right Whales can be clearly identified by the lumps on their heads. Their appearance and arrangement are as individually unique as human fingerprints. As a result of 20,000 aerial photographs, a total of 557 individual whales have been identified in Valdés so far. Of these 557 animals, no less than 411 have been sighted there repeatedly, in some cases up to 18 times.

The earmark lumps are caused by barnacles that attach themselves to the callosities on a calf's head shortly after its birth. Since unborn Southern Right Whales already have such callosities, Payne concluded that they are hereditary rather than a product of barnacle growth.

Today most scientists consider Southern Right Whales and Northern Right Whales to be two distinct species, even though superficially they are nearly identical in appearance. The distinction between them is based on minor differences in the shape of the head (position and form of the alisphenoid bone) and the geographic separation of the species.

On the basis of a few fossil finds in South Africa, researchers Pilleri and Marcuzzi suspect that both species originated in the Southern Hemisphere. In addition, they assume that right whales migrated to the equator during the last ice age and then moved farther north as the temperatures warmed up again. If so, this must have been a singular occurrence as it is very probable that the two current populations have no contact with each other. This is not only due to the fact that their respective territories are 5,000 km apart, but also because of the inverse seasons on either half of the globe.

There is still some uncertainty today about whether there are 2 or 3 different species (not counting Bowhead Whales) of right whale (see the section on Northern Right Whales). The gestation period for Southern Right Whales is 12 months. The new-born calves are about 4-6 m long. During the first few weeks the calves gain up to 100 kg daily. After 3-4 months they already weigh 8-9 t and attain a length of about 7-8 m, which means that they grow 2-3 cm each day. In order to grow at such a rapid rate, the calves need to suckle more than 100 l of milk per day. The milk of a Southern Right Whale cow has a fat content of 60 %, making it one of the absolute richest kinds of mother's milk. After a few months the calves are large and strong enough to make the long and perilous journey to the cold Antarctic. In 6 years they reach maturity.

Where & When

Southern Right Whales live inshore in cold circumpolar waters and are only found in the Southern Hemisphere between 20-55° latitude south. Only rarely (during migration) are they encountered in open waters.

In the months between August and December they migrate to warmer, protected bays in order to mate, give birth and nurture their young. In South America they prefer the bays around the Patagonian peninsula of Valdés (Argentina) and Santa Catarina (Brazil). In South Africa one will often encounter them in Walker's Bay (near Hermanus and the adjacent bays), as well as in the bays of South Australia. During the other months they remain in their Antarctic feeding grounds.

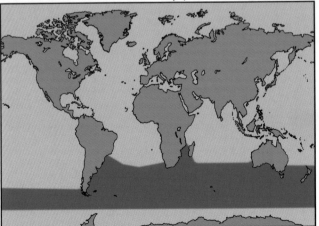

Southern Right Whale, distribution: Temperate cold, cold and subpolar coastal waters, only in the Southern Hemisphere.

TOY STORY

When well-known underwater photographer Stephen Wong from Hong Kong became a toy for a Southern Right Whale baby and some Dusky Dolphins, he experienced that a child is always a child, no matter if human, dolphin, or whale.

A group of the very playful Dusky Dolphins and a Southern Right Whale, both species occur together at the Valdes Peninsula.

In the course of the past few days at Valdes, I had experienced the playfulness of individual juvenile Southern Right Whales - each of different character - and the protectiveness of their mothers. The calves' inquisitiveness was boundless and always resulted in their mothers hurrying to interfere in our encounters. They probably were worried about the possibility of us inflicting any harm on their calves (actually it was vice versa!).

As if there was a timetable for plays and mischief, these baby and juvenile whales certainly knew when to play. They were frolicking, tumbling, and splashing very near to us. Once, I was closely observed by a young individual, and almost became 'sandwiched' by the calf and its mother. At another occasion, I was lifted up by a baby's snout, and then slided back down along its back. At other times, I was simply accidentally hit by their pectoral fins or flukes. Oh yes, they do hurt!

There was another breathtaking experience of a juvenile whale playing with a pod of Dusky Dolphins. The 5-metre-long Right Whale calf was happily chasing the playful dolphins (incidentally, these two species are the friendliest cetaceans that I have encountered so far).

As I entered the water, the dolphins and the juvenile Right Whale converged their mutual attention on me, and immediately recognised me as the better toy. They rushed towards me. The Duskies were all around, streaming bubbles all over me, and whistling loudly. Suddenly, in a haste, the dolphins dove. To my astonishment, the big calf, however, was heading straight for me. It was like opening the curtain of a window and seeing a truck approaching head-on! Staying out of the large and curious mammal's path seemed to be impossible. I kept quiet and held my breath, much like a soccer goalie anticipating a penalty kick but not wanting to save the shot.

Fortunately, the visibility was good on that day, and I could see the approaching calf. When the whale rushed to within 3 metres from me, I propelled myself to one side, avoiding direct collision. When the calf passed me, I pushed myself away using its body as leverage. Luckily, its right pectoral fin was just below my fins. But foam and bubbles had clouded the visibility during the commotion, and now I could not see a thing. Suddenly, I was airborne. I had been completely lifted out of the water by the young whale's powerful fluke, just like a goldfish being netted out of the aquarium by a child.

Things were happening so fast that my mind was not registering until I dropped back into the water. Then I saw the Dolphins once again surrounding me. It did not take long to realise that I had been a toy for both species. Unscathed but more than slightly intimidated, I decided to swim back to the zodiac to sort out my thoughts and bones. My dolphin escort followed. I guess, regardless of species, a child is

always a child: Human, dolphin, or whale, all are mischievous at times and enjoy playing with toys.

Dusky Dolphins are very inquisitive and often associate with other marine mammals and even with people who enter their realm. Here they gayly circle their clumsy distant cousin who is not as swift as his new friends but enjoys childhood play just like they do.

THE MALDIVES WHALE NET

Dead whales or dolphins occasionally wash up on every sea coast in the world. But some coasts receive more than their fair share. One such place is the Maldives. Professional marine biologist Charles Anderson has lived and worked in the Maldives since 1983. He is an authority on the fisheries of the islands, and has also been studying its diverse cetacean fauna. He delves deeper into dead whales and explains why they strand so frequently in these islands.

A Blue Whale carcass on the beach of a Maldive island.

All living things eventually die. This includes the great whales. Some whales are taken by human whalers, but most die of natural causes. Just like us, whales are subject to heart attacks, parasites, cancers and other diseases. When they die their carcasses may initially sink, but as they rot, gas bloats their internal cavities. This, together with their blubber, brings them back to the surface and helps to keep them afloat. They may drift for several days, and wash up on coasts a hundred miles or more from where they died.

Dead whales wash up regularly on the atoll reefs and islands of the Maldives. Some are fresh, and appear to have only just died. Others are rotten, and have probably been drifting for days. In either case, if a giant whale corpse lies on a hot tropical beach for more than a few hours it stinks!

Many islands in the Maldives have been developed in recent years into luxury resorts. Not surprisingly, resort guests are none too happy if a stinking mass of rotten flesh washes up in their pure white sandy beach. The resort management losses no time in getting the offending carcass towed away.

On other islands within the Maldives, however, the arrival of a dead whale is treated not with disgust but with delight. For whale carcasses are an excellent source of oil, which Maldivian fishermen need to treat their wooden fishing boats. The fishermen strip off the blubber, cut it into small pieces and lay it out in the sun, for the oil to drip out. A carcass may also yield teeth, which were traditionally used in handicrafts, and if the men are very lucky, ambergris.

Local fishermen collect the blubber of the stranded Blue Whale.

Maldivians are therefore always on the lookout for whales washed up on their reefs and islands. Recent studies have shown that a surprising number and variety of whales do wash up. There are three reasons for this bounty.

First, whale and dolphins are especially abundant in Maldivian waters. The more living animals there are to start with, the more dead ones will eventually wash up.

Secondly, the Maldivian island chain lies North-South, while the seasonal currents flow East-West. Any drifting dead whale in the latitude of the Maldives is almost certain to be carried onto the reefs or through the atolls. In effect, the Maldives acts like a giant net, catching whale carcasses that drift past.

Finally, Maldivian fishermen keep a sharp lookout for any drifting objects, including whale carcasses. In tropical seas fish tend to aggregate beneath floating objects. The reasons for this are not fully understood, but local fishermen know it happens. They search tirelessly for floating objects, in the hope of landing a good haul of tuna. Fishermen who do find a whale carcass drifting at sea will almost always tow it back to their home island, once they have finished fishing, in order to extract the oil.

Signs of shark attack are visible on many, if not most, of the dead whales washed up or towed in by fishermen. Sharks are a natural part of the tropical ocean ecosystem, and several species occur in the oceanic waters around the Maldives. Sharks rarely attack living whales; the damage is done after they have died.

Maldivian fishermen report that large numbers of sharks often accompany drifting whale carcasses. The tiger shark (Galeocerdo cuvier) is the species most frequently associated with such carcasses. Tiger sharks (known locally as "femunu") are particularly partial to whale meat. They can detect rotting whale meat from miles away, and soon home in on any drifting carcass.

Sharks attack the flukes first. This is not only because the tail section hangs lowest in the water and so is more accessible to sharks, but also because the shape of the flukes facilitates biting. Once a start has been made it is easy for the sharks to continue biting away at the exposed flesh, eating their way forward from the tail. As a result, large whale carcasses drifting in tropical seas lose their posterior parts first. In one study of whale strandings in the Maldives, nine carcasses were reported to have the tail missing or to consist of the head only. In contrast,

not one single stranding of a tail section without a head was reported.

The sharks are unable to eat the whole carcass. As they eat their way forwards, stripping off the blubber and ripping out the guts, the carcass loses buoyancy. Eventually the heavy bones can no longer be sup- ported, and the remains of the car- cass sink down to the depths.

This "whale fall" may be a loss to the sharks of the surface waters, but is a vital gain for the

Above: Precious whale oil drips from the blubber and is collected in a wooden boat.

Right: Even the Blue Whale's bones are not dis- carded but used by the islanders.

creatures of the deep ocean floor, hundreds or thou- sands of metres below.

Most of the deep ocean is charac- terised by a chronic shortage of food. With the exception of animals living in just a few tiny areas (the famous hydro- thermal vents), all the deep-sea animals must survive on little more than crumbs of food dropping down from above. A whale carcass, even a half-eaten whale carcass, falling onto the desert-like abyssal plain is a bonanza indeed. Deep-sea sharks, other fishes, crabs, shrimps, and many others all converge on the feast. In the cold, dark depths things move slowly, but within months the bones may be stripped bare.

Deep-sea bacteria multiply on fallen whale carcasses. These bacteria produce special diges- tive enzymes that can break down the glutinous whale oils, even in near freezing temperatures. Washing powder manufacturers have been quick to realise the potential of such enzymes. So in the not too distant future, your biological washing powder may owe much of its effectiveness to studies of stinking whale corpses.

Northern Right Whale, *Eubalaena glacialis*

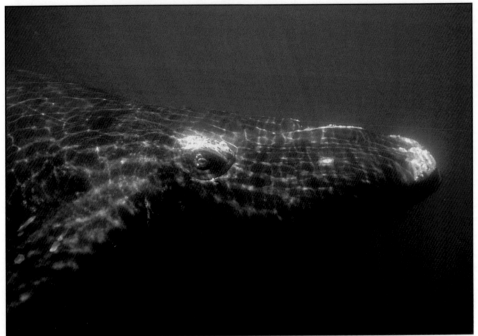

Northern Right Whale off Newfoundland, Canada.   Ralf Kiefner

Distinguishing Characteristics
Like Southern Right Whales, the earmarks of a Northern Right Whale are a massive body with a conspicuously broad back, horny lumps on the head (callosities) with a characteristic growth of barnacles and a high, V-shaped blow. It does not have a dorsal fin or throat grooves.

Description
The body of a Northern Right Whale is very large and stocky. Its blubber can be 36 cm thick, much thicker (but also softer) than that of most other baleen whales. This thick layer of blubber makes up about 40% of its total body weight. Like all members of this family, Northern Right Whales are dimorphic: The females are substantially larger and heavier than the males.

The average length of a Northern Right Whale is 11-14 m, with a maximum of 18.5 m. Their average weight is 40-80 t, with the heaviest on record weighing 106.5 t.

Like all other members of this family, Northern Right Whales neither have throat grooves nor dorsal fins. There is not even a small hump or any other elevation on their backs.

A Northern Whale's head is very large and massive, making up more than a quarter of its total body length. The most noticeable earmark of a Northern Right Whale is the conspicuous horny growth on its head, or so-called callosities. These are beset with a pale-grey growth of barnacles and whale lice. The callosities are already fully developed in the embryonic stage of the whale. The largest of them sits in the middle of the upper jaw and is referred to as a "bonnet" because of its similarity to a lady's headgear. Additional callosities are found above the eyes, in front of the blowholes, and on each side of the upper and lower jaws.

The males tend to have more scratch marks and larger and/or more abundant callosities than the females. This gender-based difference has led R. Payne and E. Dorsey to suggest that the callosities might function as a weapon during inner-species altercations, e.g. when the males contend with each other for the favour of females.

South Africa's Peter Best has determined that Northern Right Whales differ from Southern Right Whales in that the latter will usually have more callosities on the anterior part of the lower jaw, but fewer of them on the head.

A Northern Right Whale's jawlines are noticeably arched. The lower jaw is wider than the upper jaw. Mature males have up to 300 short bristles on the tip of the lower jaw and up to 100 of them on the upper jaw. These may have a sensory function.

The body of a Northern Right Whale is almost uniformly black or dark-brown with a few dark-brown or dark-grey spots. Only a few, individually varying white markings break up the uniformity of its dusky underside. These white spots are not gender-specific. Newborn calves are often lighter in colour and turn darker as they grow older.

The large, spade-like flippers are dark on either side. The bone structure of the flippers is visible through the skin. The powerful fluke is also dark on both sides. Its edge is smooth and concave with a conspicuous median notch.

Another distinguishing mark of Northern Right Whales is their conspicuous V-shaped blow, which cane be up to 5-6 m high. The left blow is usually somewhat higher than the right one. The paired blowholes sit apart and at an angle, which is why the blow of a Northern Right Whale has the appearance of a V-shaped fountain rather than a cloud.

The 200-270 baleen plates on each side of the upper jaw grow to a max length of 2.5 m. Because of their great pliability they were used to make frames for corsets and umbrellas up until the middle of the 19th century.

Easily Mistaken For

Because of their massive and dusky bodies with the horny growth on the head Northern Right Whales are easily distinguishable from all other large whales except members of their own family. It is almost impossible to tell them apart from Southern Right Whales. Thanks to their separate areas of distribution, however, a mix-up is hardly likely.

Due to their similar size and colouration, the structure of their baleen plates and the overlapping of their ranges, early whalers (and older scientific treatises) often confused Northern Right Whales with Bowhead Whales. Bowhead Whales, however, do not have a growth of barnacles on their heads and are markedly stockier than Northern Right Whales.

Other Names

Black Right Whale, Biscayan Right Whale (English); Nördlicher Glattwal, Nordkaper, Biskayerwal, Nordatlantischer Glattwal, Nordpazifischer Glattwal (German); Baleine de Biscaye, Baleine Franche des Basques (French); Balena Franca Boreale (Italian); Ballena Franca (Spanish); Baleia Franca, Baleia Negra (Portuguese); Noordkaper (Dutch); Nordkaper (Norwegian); Mustavalas (Finnish); Nordkapare (Swedish); Nordkaper (Danish); Semi Kujira (Japanese); Ballena Franca del Norte (Latin American Spanish).

Meaning of the Scientific Nomenclature

Eubalaena glacialis Müller 1776 – The generic name *Eubalaena* is composed of Greek *eu* (right, genuine, true) and Latin *balaena* (whale). The Latin name *Eubalaena* literally means "right whale." The Latin species name *glacialis* means "icy" and refers to the whales' range near the northern glacial boundary.

Behaviour

Because of their massive bodies Northern Right Whales are very slow swimmers. As long as they are not being hunted they will move along at a leisurely 7 km/h. In their mating grounds they spend hours floating lazily on the surface, almost as if they were dozing. At times they even get their backs badly burned by the sun.

In spite of their portliness, Northern Right Whales can still be remarkably active, if not outright acrobatic They are most active in the early morning and evening hours. After breaching they land on their bellies, backs or sides with a tremendous splash that can be heard more than 1 km away. Their breaching activities may be related to mating behaviour and communication, or simply represent an effort to get rid of bothersome parasites like whale lice, sucker fish (remoras) and the like.

In general Northern Right Whales are inquisitive and playful. They often show a marked interest in vessels and their passengers. Sometimes they will even nudge a boat or some other floating object.

They express their annoyance with a loud and pronounced growling sound while they exhale. Northern Right Whales have an extensive repertoire of low-frequency tones, which they primarily emit during the mating season in connection with courtship or other related social activities.

Among the more typical sounds they make are "burping" and clicking, as well as low-frequency moaning and grunting. It is assumed that the more complex intonations play a role in social communication within the group. They are often made in conjunction with clamorous surface activities such as breaching, lob-tailing and flipper-slapping. The simpler intonations are probably used for long-distance communication. These "grumbling" sounds remind one of a creaking door.

In order to cool off in their warmer mating grounds, the whales will spend 20 min or longer "sailing," whereby they hang vertically upside-down in the water with their flukes up in the air. A similar cooling effect presumably takes place when Northern Right Whales swim along the surface with their mouths wide open.

Right whales have the largest and heaviest testicles of all whales, weighing up to 1 t. By way of contrast, their brains weigh a mere 2.4-3 kg. Because of the great size of their testicles and the relatively unaggressive nature of the whale bulls, successful reproduction among them depends more upon "sperm competition" than "social competition." This means that the whale cows will mate with several males in order to improve the chances of impregnation by receiving greater quantities of sperm.

During courtship the males are more preoccupied with achieving copulation than fending off other suitors. Consequently, sexual activities among Northern Right Whales usually involve groups composed of one female and several males. The males will often assist each other during copulation. Their penises attain a stately length of 1.8 m and can be freely moved in the water in order to facilitate copulation. Copulation can last 1-2 hours. When the females are ready to mate they will turn over on their backs so that their undersides become exposed. The males then have to wait until the object of their desire turns over again to breathe.

Diving

When Northern Whales surface to breathe their entire heads and part of their backs will become visible at the same time. They often raise their flukes while sounding. After a long dive their loud snorting can be heard for a great distance. The whales frequently come up in the same spot where they sounded.

Facts & Figures Northern Right Whale	Quick ID-Check North. Right Whale
Size: 11-14 m, max 18.5 m	
Weight: 40-80 t, max 106.5 t	Large head, covered with lumps of barnacles
Longevity: about 70 years	
Sexual maturity: at 6-14 years, as of 14-15.5 m in length	Highly-arched jawlines, no dorsal fin
Mating season: June-November	Massive, stocky body with conspicuously wide
Gestation period: 1o-12 months	back
Calving interval: every 3 years	
Size at birth: 4-6 m	Dusky body
Weight at birth: 1 t	
Nursing period: up to 14 months	Irregular white spot on underside
Dive depth: max 200 m	
Dive time: max 2o min	Blow V-shaped, high, left blow higher than right
Maximum speed: 10 km/h	
Baleen plates: 225-390 on each side, max length 2.5 m, width 25-30 cm	Two blowholes set at angle
Blow: V-shaped, 5-6 m high, left blow some-what higher	Large, spade-like flippers
Group (Pod) size: usually 1-5, in feeding grounds up to 30	Large fluke, dark on both sides
Population: worldwide 300-1,000, extremely vulnerable	Very slow swimmer

Like its southern relative this right whale species has pronounced callosities on its head.   Ralf Kiefner

Northern Right Whales can dive to depths of 200 m. How long their dives will last depends upon the activity involved. Their average dive time is 4-20 min. While they are feeding they usually dive for 1-7 min. Their average swimming speed is 2-3 km/h, with a maximum of 10 km/h.

Feeding Habits
Northern Right Whales primarily feed on concentrations of planktonic crustaceans (copepods and krill) as well as pelagic larvae and Spiny Squat Lobsters. Occasionally they also take small fish. In their feeding grounds Northern Right Whales will consume between 1,500-2,000 kg of zooplankton per day.

Northern Right Whales typically feed by "skimming," whereby they swim through the water with their mouths wide open and ingest enormous quantities of nutrients. Occasionally they close their mouths in order to press the water out again through their baleen plates. This feeding technique is most effective with slow-moving prey. Normally the whales skim the water on or near the surface, where they practically plow through thick concentrations of zooplankton.

General Information
The Northern Right Whale continues to be one of the least studied species of whale, even though it was the first large cetacean to be commercially hunted by man. The hunt for Northern Right Whales dates back to the 10th century, when Basque whalers chased them in the coastal waters of the Bay of Biscay, and lasted up until the beginning of the 20th century. More Northern Right Whales were decimated by whaling than any other species of whale and they are still extremely vulnerable today. The currently estimated population of 300-1,000 animals will probably not suffice to save this species from extinction. As the American scientists working with Massami Fujiwara warned in their article in *Nature* (2001), the life of every single female Northern Right Whale is crucial to the preservation of the species. According to their calculations, if only two additional

The straight, finless back of a Northern Right Whale. Newfoundland.   Ralf Kiefner

Most of the times Right Whales are inquisitive and very interested in playmates.   Ralf Kiefner

females were spared each year then the population would begin to recover. Northern Right Whale cows are not sexually mature until they are 10 years old and they only calve every 3 years.

In March of 2001 the radio station "Deutsche Welle" reported that at last there was some positive news concerning marine matters. It appears that Northern Right Whales had a record birth rate that year. Fourteen Northern Right Whale calves were spotted in the waters off Georgia and Florida. This is not exactly a whale "baby boom," but 14 births are already quite a sensation as far as Northern Right Whales are concerned, particularly if one considers that less than 14 calves were born worldwide the previous year. Whether these 14 calves will suffice to preserve the species, however, is more than questionable.

In order to mate, give birth and nurture their young, Northern Right Whales migrate to the eastern coastal waters of the United States. Due to the intensive maritime traffic in this region, however, the slower calves are severely threatened. According to whale expert and environmental scientist Justin Cooke, collisions with vessels are the primary cause of death among Northern Right Whale calves. Injuries inflicted on the nursing whale cows can also severely impair the tending of the calves. Cooke considers fishing nets to be the second greatest threat to them.

Thanks to a method recently developed by a team of scientists affiliated with the New York Wildlife Conservation Society, it is now possible analyse the genes of whales that were killed more than 100 years ago. This makes it possible to take samples from endangered species like the Northern Right Whale without having to injure or kill the animal. Samples of baleen plates taken from scientific collections, for instance, already suffice as test material. Due to this revolutionary method it was also possible to identify a hitherto unknown species that differs from the Northern Right Whale. Today there are two separate populations of Northern Right Whales, one in the Pacific and one in the Atlantic. According to the new molecular-biological investigations these populations are so different from each other that some scientists feel they should be considered as distinct species. This would mean that, other than Bowhead Whales, there are three different species of right whale. The scientific name of the "new" species, which lives in isolation in the Northern Pacific, would then be *Eubalaena japonica*. Interestingly, the Pacific Northern Right Whale is more closely related to its fellow family member living thousands of kilometres away, namely the Southern Right Whale, than to the Atlantic Northern Right Whale *(E. glacialis)*.

For differences between Southern and Northern Right Whales and their origins see the previous section on Southern Right Whales.

Where & When

Due to excessive whaling and the drastic reduction of populations, the currently limited distribution of Northern Right Whales in no way mirrors their original range.

Today the species is generally found in the subpolar and temperate-cold waters of the Northern Hemisphere. Even though the species is often encountered in coastal waters, especially during calving season, they prefer the open water. Their primary feeding grounds in the western North Atlantic are Fundy Bay, Grand Maman Island and Brown's Bank, as well as the southern tip of Nova Scotia (Canada) and Cape Cod (USA).

The mating grounds of the Northern Right Whales have only recently been detected off the coast of Florida and Georgia (USA). An additional population (presumably a third species, *Eubalena japonica*) can occasionally be sighted in the Northern Pacific.

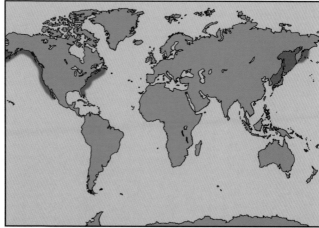

Northern Right Whale, distribution: Temperate-cold and cold offshore waters, only in the Northern Hemisphere.

Bowhead Whale, *Balaena mysticetus*

Bowhead Whale off Igloolik, Nunavut, Canada.   Saul Gonor/Seapics.com

Distinguishing Characteristics

Bowhead Whales have conspicuously large, massive and dusky bodies, as well as huge heads with highly-arched jawlines. They have no callosities or barnacle growths on their heads, and also lack a dorsal fin. A conspicuous notch behind the blowholes gives them a unique appearance in the water. It appears as if Bowhead Whales had two humps in a row. These "humps" are actually formed by the heads and bodies of the whales. Their widely separated and angularly placed blowholes produce a V-shaped blow that can be up to 7 m high. The left blow is usually somewhat higher than the right one.

Description

The body of a Bowhead Whale is large and very stocky. The species averages 15-16 m in length, occasionally up to 20 m. Accurate figures for their average weight are still lacking. However, their massive bodies with layers of blubber up to 70 cm thick lead to the assumption that they weigh around 60-80 t or more. In terms of their length, Bowhead Whales certainly rank among the largest whales. Like all other right whales, the female Bowhead Whale attains a larger siye (about 60 cm) and heavier weight than the male.

The size of a Bowhead Whale's domed head is immense, making up approximately 30-40% of its total body size. The long jawlines are also highly arched, giving the head its characteristic domed appearance. The lower jaw is wider than the upper jaw. A few bristles grow on its lower jaw. Like all members of this family, Bowhead Whales have no throat groves or dorsal fins.

Viewed in profile, there is a noticeable indentation behind the blowholes of a Bowhead Whale that separates the head from the rest of its body. This marked indentation gives all Bowhead Whales a typical surface appearance, which becomes particularly obvious when the water is calm: They appear to have two humps in a row. The smaller, triangular "hump" is formed by the head; the larger, round "hump" is made up of the rest of the body. The "neck" of the whale is usually covered by water. This indentation behind the blowholes becomes more pronounced as the whales grow older.

Their bodies are uniformly black or dark-brown with a few dark-brown or dark-grey spots. An irregular, large and individually varying white spot on the chin stands out from the overall dusky colouration. Several dark spots of varying shapes and sizes are in turn found on this white part of the chin, which are referred to as a "necklace." The area around the genitals and the anus of some animals are pale-grey to white.

In the case of younger animals, the white spot on the chin can extend down to the top of the stomach. Newly-born calves are often pale in colour and gradually turn darker as they grow older. Albinos are only rarely born. The skin of a Bowhead whale is uniformly smooth and without any traces of lumps, callosities or barnacle growths like Southern and Northern Right Whales.

Their large, spade-like flippers are dark on either side. The bone structure of the flippers is visible through the skin. Bowhead Whales have no dorsal fins or humps.

Their broad and powerful flukes can attain a width of 7 m, or almost half the total body length.

A Bowhead Whale at the surface. NW-Territories, Canada.   John Ford

They are uniformly dark on both sides, with pointed ends and a conspicuous median notch.

Another earmark of Bowhead Whales is their tall, up to 7-m-high, V-shaped blow. The left blow is usually higher than the right. The paired blows are set apart and at an angle, which is why the blow has the appearance of a V-shaped fountain rather than a cloud.

With a length of 4-4.5 m, the 250-350 baleen plates on either side of a Bowhead Whale's upper jaw are the longest of all whales. The record length is 5.80 m. The total weight of the baleen plates of a single animal can amount to more than one ton.

Easily Mistaken For

Bowhead Whales are easily identifiable. Their range, which is limited to the Northern Hemisphere, and very massive bodies make any mix-up with other whales unlikely, with the possible exception of Northern Right Whales. However, Bowhead Whales do not have collusions or barnacle growths on their heads like Northern Right Whales do and their bodies are more voluminous. The typical dual "humps" formed by their heads and backs make the long-distance identification of Bowhead Whales fairly simple as long as the water remains calm.

Fluke of a Bowhead Whale in the Sea of Okhotsk off Russia.   Robert Pitman/Seapics.com

Other Names
Great Polar Whale, Greenland Right Whale, Arctic Right Whale, Bowhead Right Whale, Greenland Whale (English); Grönlandwal, Polarwal (German); Baleine Franche du Groenland (French); Balena Franca della Groenlandia (Italian); Ballena de Cabeza Arqueada (Spanish); Baleia Franca Boreal, Baleia Legítima (Portuguese); Groenlandse Walvis (Dutch); Grønlandshval (Norwegian); Grönlanninvalas (Finnish); Grönlandsval (Swedish); Grønlandshval (Danish); Kiralick (Alaska Inuit).

Meaning of the Scientific Nomenclature
Balaena mysticetus Linnaeus, 1758. The Latin generic name *Balaena* means "whale." The Latin species name *mysticetus* means something like "moustached sea monster" and refers to the short bristles on the lower jaw.

Behaviour
Bowhead Whales are the only species of whale that lives exclusively in the Arctic. Generally they migrate along the glacial boundary individually, in pairs or in groups of three. Occasionally they will form groups of up to 40 animals in bounteous feeding grounds. The ties between a whale cow and its calf are very strong and they frequently maintain physical contact with each other. It is not unusual to find Belugas and Narwhals in the proximity of Bowhead Whales.

The bulls are not known to be aggressive during courtship. Therefore it is assumed that reproduction among Bowhead Whales is based on "sperm competition" rather than "social competition." The whale cows will mate with several males because impregnation depends primarily on the quantity of semen implanted in them. This reproductive strategy is common among species with large testicles.

Bowhead Whales will often swim for long distances underneath the pack ice. It is known that they can break through a 20-cm-thick layer of ice when they are unable to find a breathing hole. It could well be that they can gauge the thickness of the ice by emitting certain sounds. In this way they are able to steer away from layers of ice that would be too thick for them to break through.

Bowhead Whales normally swim at an average speed of 3-6 km/h. If so required they can attain a max speed of 10 km/h. They often swim on the surface with their mouths wide open, even when they are obviously not feeding. Why they do this is still unknown, but it may well be a way for the whales to lower their body temperatures.

Occasionally Bowhead Whales perform activities like breaching, lob-tailing, flipper-slapping or spy-hopping. They rarely breach, but when they do it will be several times successively. Bowhead Whales are most active in spring. When they breach about half of their bodies will clear the water and then usually fall sideways. The posterior part of their bodies will remain under water throughout the entire procedure.

Bowhead Whales occasionally emit short, low-frequency (50-350 Hz) "grumbling" sounds that almost sound like a door creaking. They are repeated frequently and obviously serve as a means of communication. On rare occasions they emit high-frequency tones over 3.5 kHz. These apparently serve as long-distance signals as they have been recorded at 156 decibels from distance of about 150 m.

In spite of the freezing cold water the photographer dives among blocks of ice down to the Bowhead Whale.   Doc White/Seapics.com

Diving

Normally Bowhead Whales breathe 4-6 times within 1-2 min, before they sound again. Thereby they often raise their flukes out of the water somewhat and let their tails bend to the right so that the tip of the fluke submerges last.

Bowhead Whales will generally not go deeper than 300 m. Their average dive time is 3-12 min, with 31 min being the longest ever recorded. They frequently resurface in the same place where they sounded.

Feeding Habits

Bowhead Whales generally feed by filtering tiny organisms out of the water. They usually take zooplankton like copepods, krill and amphipods. Occasionally they will also consume small fish, shrimps, crabs and snails. They ingest up to 600 kg daily.

Like most baleen whales, Bowhead Whales primarily feed during the summer in regions with a high volume of biomass. They are typical skimmers. Hereby they swim through the water with their mouths wide open to take in enormous quantities of nutrients, which they then filter through their baleen plates by closing their mouths again. This feeding technique is most effective with slow prey. Normally the whales will skim through concentrations of zooplankton at or just below the surface.

While feeding Bowhead Whales generally swim facing the sea bottom, but occasionally they turn up to 60° sideways. Aerial observations have shown that they are also benthic feeders, as large quantities of muddy water came out of their mouths upon surfacing. Like Gray Whales, they also left a cloudy trail behind them, which is a clear indication for bottom feeding.

It has also been observed that Bowhead Whales will occasionally cooperate while feeding in particularly nutritious waters. Thereby they skim through the water in a tight V-formation like a flock of geese, which obviously increases intake efficiency. The flanking animals will catch the prey that managed to evade or was pushed aside by those swimming in advance of them. This technique is particularly efficient in the case of highly mobile zooplankton like the luminous crustaceans called euphausiids or krill, for instance.

General Information

When Linnaeus first classified the Bowhead Whale in 1758 nothing was known about the differences between it and the Northern Right Whale, and mix-ups were common for a long time thereafter. Differences in age and range also led early whalers, including Alaskan Inuits, to assume that there were two distinct kinds of Bowhead Whale. It wasn't until 1866, when Eschricht and Reinhardt produced their encompassing description of Bowhead Whales, that they were officially separated from Northern Right Whales as a species. At this time, however, Northern Right Whales were still categorised under the genus *Balaena*.

The proper positioning of right whales in a suborder of baleen whales was finally confirmed by DNA-tests in the 1990s. These tests showed a marked affinity between the Bowhead Whale and the Northern and Southern Right Whale, and brought to light many concrete differences between them and all other baleen whales.

The early whalers and the Inuit were able to distinguish different "types" of Bowhead Whale by virtue of their size, skeletal structure, colour, length and shades of the baleen plates. These distinctions were later confirmed by genetic analyses.

Whaling had already drastically reduced the Bowhead Whale population of the eastern Arctic by the 18th century. Their lethargy and very thick layers of blubber made them an ideal target for whalers. Today they are one of the most vulnerable species of whale. They are still being hunted by Alaskan natives, who claim a traditional right to do so.

Due in great part to their limited numbers and remote range, Bowhead Whales are among the least studied whales. They range farther north than any other species of baleen whale.

At present there are probably 4-5 different populations of Bowhead Whales, but it is not known whether they intermix:

1. Davis Strait, Hudson Strait, Baffin Bay, Foxe Basin and the northern part of Hudson Bay. Due to the permanent formation of pack ice it is unlikely that this population has any contact with any of the others.
2. Bering Sea, Chukchi Sea and Beaufort Sea.
3. Sea of Okhotsk, could be part of the Beaufort Sea population.
4. North Atlantic, nearly extinct.
5. Barents Sea, with only a few surviving specimens.

Facts & Figures
Bowhead Whale

Size: 15-16 m, max 20 m
Weight: about 60-80 t
Longevity: about 40 years, possibly over 200
Sexual maturity: as of 12-14.5 m in length
Mating season: Spring
Gestation period: 12-13 months
Calving interval: every 3-6 years
Size at birth: 4-4.5 m
Weight at birth: about 2 t
Nursing period: 5-6 months, up to 6 m in length
Dive depth: 300 m
Dive time: max 30 min
Maximum speed: 10 km/h
Baleen plates: about 250-300 dark-grey baleen on each side
Blow: 7 m high, V-shaped, left blow somewhat higher
Group (Pod) size: usually 1-6, in bounteous feeding grounds more
Population: ca 50.000 at the beginning of the 19th century, only 5,000-8,000 today, extremely vulnerable!

Quick ID-Check
Bowhead Whale

Viewed in profile 2 humps (head and back) appear on surface

Dusky, very massive body

No dorsal fin

No barnacle growth on head

Large, spade-like flippers

White spot on chin with "necklace"

Very large, up to 7-m-wide fluke

V-shaped blow (7 m high)

Angularly placed blowholes

Fluke usually tips to the right while sounding

Lives exclusively in Arctic waters

If one can believe the scientists of the Scripps Institution of Oceanography, then Bowhead Whales are not only one of the heaviest living beings, but also live longer than most. Two flintstone harpoon points that were recently found by Alaskan Inuits in the blubber of a Bowhead Whale appear to have been made by Stone Age people. Other harpoon points were made of finely ground slate and ivory. The last time Alaskan Inuits hunted whales with such primitive points was in the 1870s! Since there could be no doubt about the genuineness of these finds, biologists saw themselves forced to add substantially to the longevity estimates available until then. The whales that were killed off the northern coast of Alaska had to be way over 100 years old.

Geochemist Jeffrey Bada of the Scripps Institution of Oceanography in California believes he has proof that these gentle giants can live longer than 200 years. The American scientist's new molecular-biological method to determine longevity is based on the analysis of a certain amino acid that is found in the bodies of the whales. Living organisms almost exclusively produce and use the so-called left-rotating form of this amino acid. Only after death has set in will the left-rotating amino acid be partially and gradually transformed into a right-rotating variant of this chief protein component.

Up until now this method, in which the ratio of the amount of the two variants of amino acid are used to determine the time of death, was only applied to fossils. In 2001 Jeffrey Bada discovered that the transformation of this amino acid will already take place in a living organism. He found out that the transformation takes place in those parts of the living organism that are cut off from continual renewal by metabolic processes, such as the teeth and the eye lenses.

When Bada's method was applied to the remains of a few male Bowhead Whales the results were astonishing: Four of the older bulls must have been 140-180 years old when they were killed. The oldest Bowhead Whale, according to the results of this method, roamed the icy sea for more than 200 years. Two independent teams of scientists are currently checking the spectacular findings of Bada and his colleagues.

Where & When

Bowhead Whales live exclusively in cold Arctic and Subarctic waters, never far from the pack ice. Usually they migrate along the glacial boundary of the Arctic, primarily around Alaska. In the winter the growing ice pack drives them south, in the summer they follow the receding glacial boundary back north.

Originally their range in the Northern Hemisphere was circumpolar. Due to intensive whaling, their current range is no longer the same. Skeletal remains near ancient Basque whaling stations show that Bowhead Whales once migrated at least as far south as the Strait of Belle Isle (Newfoundland). They can still be encountered in the Davis Strait, Hudson Strait, Baffin Bay, Foxe Basin and the northern part of Hudson Bay, as well as in the Bering Sea, Chukchen Sea, Beaufort Sea and the Sea of Okhotsk in Russia.

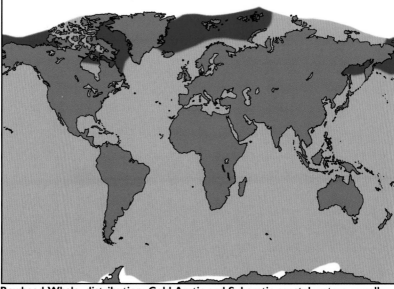

Bowhead Whale, distribution: Cold Arctic and Subarctic coastal waters, usually close to the pack ice

Distinguishing Characteristics of this Family
Pygmy Right Whales were once included in the family of right whales. On the basis of more recent findings, however, it seems more appropriate to place them in an independent family.

Pygmy Right Whales average 4-5 m in length and are thus the shortest of all baleen whales. They have a dorsal fin, short baleen plates and an arched rostrum. They live exclusively in the colder waters of the Southern Hemisphere.

Pygmy Right Whale, *Caperea marginata*

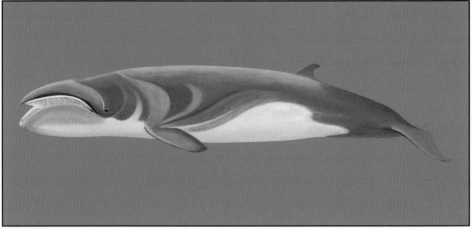

Pygmy Right Whale.   Pieter Arend Folkens

Distinguishing Characteristics
Pygmy Right Whales have a relatively slender and streamlined body. They are much slimmer than right whales, but not as slim as rorquals. A Pygmy Right Whale has a small, curved dorsal fin. Head and jawlines are arched. There are no lumps or barnacle growths on its head.

Description
The Pygmy Right Whale shows sexual dimorphism, females are larger than males. In contrast to right whales, it possesses a crescent-shaped dorsal fin. Its head is also much smaller in relation to the rest of the body, making up no more than 1/4 of the total body length. Head without callosities or barnacles, 210-230 ivory-coloured baleen plates with dark band. The narrow flippers are small and rounded at the ends. The fluke is dark on top and light with a dark border underneath. Its edge is concave with a conspicuous median notch. The dark-grey colouration on a the back extends down to its sides and is interspersed by a few lighter stripes. As the whale ages, its back will become darker. The pale-grey to white underside also turns darker with age.

Facts & Figures Pygmy Right Whale	Quick ID-Check Pygmy Right Whale
Size: 4-5 m, max 6.5 m	
Weight: 3-3.5 t	Small, slender, streamlined body
Longevity: about 90 years	
Gestation period: 10-11 months	Conspicuous, crescent-shaped dorsal fin
Calving interval: unknown	
Size at birth: 1.6-2 m	Domed head and arched jawlines
Weight at birth: unknown	
Dive time: max 5 min	Dark on top, light underside
Maximum speed: 9 km/h	
Baleen plates: 210-230 on each side, ivory-pale	White baleen plates, no throat grooves
Length of baleen plates: max 70 cm	
Group (Pod) size: usually single animals or in pairs, rarely more than 8 specimens	Inconspicuous behaviour
Population: Numbers unknown, but probably not as small as previously believed because the sp. has never been hunted; because of remote range and the likely confusion with Minke Whales, dependable estimates are difficult	Hardly visible on surface, slow swimmer, undulating motions
	Tip of snout emerges at sharp angle from the water

Easily Mistaken For
Accurate identification is difficult even from a close range. Even experienced whalers often mistook Minke Whales for Pygmy Right Whales in the past. The most conspicuous earmarks of the Pygmy Right Whale are the arched jawlines and slightly domed head. The jawlines of a Minke Whale are straight and, unlike Pygmy Right Whales, it does have throat grooves. Another distinguishing feature is the white spot or band on the flippers of most Minke Whales. The baleen plates of a Pygmy Right Whale are much longer than those of a Minke Whale, a difference that becomes immediately apparent in the case of stranded whales.

Other Names
Zwergglattwal (German); Baleine Pygmée, Baleine Franche Naine (French); Caperea (Italian); Ballena Franca Pigmea (Spanish); Baleia Pigmeia, Baleia Anã (Portuguese); Dwergwalvis (Dutch); Dverghval (Norwegian); Kääpiövalas (Finnish); Dvärgrätval (Swedish); Dværgrethval (Danish); Kosemi Kujira (Japanese); Gladkii Kit (Russian).

Meaning of the Scientific Nomenclature
Caperea marginata Gray, 1846. The Latin generic name *Caperea* refers to the shrivelled appearance of the tympanic membrane. The Latin species name *marginata* means "banded" and refers to the dark band on the lighter baleen plates.

Behaviour
Little is known about the behaviour of Pygmy Right Whales as they have seldom been sighted or observed. They are said to be shy animals that will only remain on the surface for a few seconds. Their blow is small and difficult to detect at sea. No special or conspicuous surface activities like breaching or lob-tailing have been observed so far. Occasionally Pygmy Right Whales are seen in the company of Pilot Whales, Sei Whales and eventually also Minke Whales, whereby the latter case could easily be based upon a mix-up because of the great similarity between the two species.

Diving
Similar to Minke Whales, Pygmy Right Whales surface at a sharp angle. The tip of the snout usually comes out of the water far enough so that the white under jaw (occasionally also the baleen plates) become visible. In contrast to Minke Whales, one will not always be able to see a Pygmy Right Whale's dorsal fin and back on the surface at the same time. It rarely raises its fluke while sounding. The whale's entire body appears to undulate as it swims. Pygmy Right Whales are slow swimmers, but they can sprint for short distances. Their dive time will not exceed 5 min.

Feeding Habits
Stomach contents analysis of stranded specimens has shown that they primarily feed on copepods.

General Information
This is not only the smallest of all baleen whales, but also the least known. Confirmed sightings are rare, probably because it can easily be confused with Minke Whales. Up until the 1960s this species was only known on the basis of stranded specimens. The first uw-photographs were taken in Plettenberg Bay, South Africa, in 1967.

Where & When
The few sightings recorded so far indicate that they spend most of their time in shallow coastal waters and protected bays of New Zealand, South Australia and South Africa. A confirmed sighting was made off the coast of Tierra del Fuego (Argentina) at 55° latitude south. Their distribution seems to depend upon surface temperatures of the water.

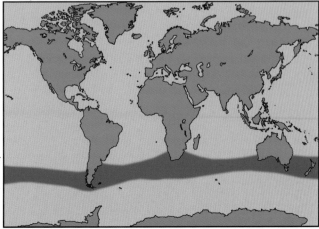

Pygmy Right Whale, distribution: All temperate, shallow coastal waters in the Southern Hemisphere

TÊTE-À-TÊTE

Only a few people have ever had the privilege of participating in one of the Sperm Whales' customary "social meetings." For a brief while they permitted Ralf Kiefner to join them as they held their "tête-à-tête" 20 km off the coast of Pico, an island in the Azores.

Eighteen Sperm Whales are drifting peacefully on the surface directly before us. I can make out their huge, box-like heads as they surface occasionally to take a breath of air. The sound of their heavy breathing is clearly audible. For fifteen years I waited in vain for the chance to participate in a "social meeting" of Sperm Whales. And now there they are, no farther away from us than 50 metres and not the least bit interested in our approaching boat.

Tense with excitement, I glide into the crystal-clear water of the Atlantic. Even though I can't make out the whales under water yet, I can clearly hear their clicking sounds. They are communicating with each other. The clicking sounds seem to be coming from all over in the water, and there is a crackling noise as if I were in the middle of room echoing with electrostatic charges. The sounds that Sperm Whales make are primarily composed of pulsating clicking noises in the range of 0.2-32 kHz. The whales emit the sounds for echolocation as well as communication. I keep on swimming in their direction as noiselessly as I possibly can.

Suddenly they loom in front of me, floating motionless on the surface in a star formation. Their heads are pressed together at the centre of the formation and their flukes form a mighty protective barrier on the periphery. A prospective attacker wouldn't stand a chance here. This characteristic configuration is referred to as a "lotus formation." The group is composed of several whale cows with a few calves. They are obviously so preoccupied with each other that they fail to take notice of me.

Scientists at Dalhousie University (Nova Scotia, Canada) believe that these "social meetings" not only serve the whales as a means of communicating with each other, but also play a role in their digestion. It is a well known fact that mammals have a highly inefficient digestive system as far as the absorption and consumption of oxygen is concerned. The metabolism of a mammal uses up a lot of oxygen. This obviously does not pose much of a problem for terrestrial mammals as they are surrounded by air. With marine mammals, however, the situation is somewhat more complicated. It is unlikely that the whales digest much while diving as this would be highly inefficient. Instead, whales tend to digest their food while resting on the surface, where there is sufficient oxygen available to them. This is why some scientists feel that the so-called "social meetings" are also taken advantage of by the whales for digestive purposes. However, an observation made in the Azores in 1998 refutes this theory. A team funded by National Geographic attached special cameras with satellite transmitters to Sperm Whales in order to film them while they hunted the giant squid of the deep. But every time the whales were about to dive, one of the whales would scrape away the cameras with its own body. The hoped-for shots of Sperm Whales chasing giant squid in deep water never

A solitary whale floating vertically in the water not far away from the others.

Eighteen Sperm Whales are drifting peacefully on the surface directly before us and accept our presence.

This characteristic configuration is referred to as a "lotus formation" which doesn't give prospective attackers a chance.

materialised. Nevertheless, the National Geographic team did manage to capture a unique scene on film that no one would have believed possible at the time. With their special equipment they were able to take sensational shots of a group of whales at a "social meeting" 400 metres below the surface.

It was only after I had almost circled "my" group of whales at a respectful distance, that I noticed a solitary whale floating vertically in the water not far away from the others. As I try to approach it cautiously a younger Sperm Whale suddenly breaks away from the "socialising" group, swims past me and the larger whale hanging vertically in the water and then disappears into the blue. While I am still gazing in wonderment at the spot where the whale calf vanished, the larger solitary animal starts to head in my direction. The Sperm Whale cow keeps coming closer. I can feel her echo sounding strike my body. It is as if numerous small shock waves were bouncing off me. I remain motionless on the surface. As the whale cow approaches me she tosses her head from side to side and opens her huge maw. There is no mistaking her threatening gestures and fear takes hold of me.

It would be very unwise not to take her threats seriously. I move away from the group and swim back to the boat. From the safety of its deck, I observe the eighteen whales for nearly an hour, up until they decide to break up their social meeting and leisurely move on.

As I watch the last whale swim away I suddenly recall Nathaniel Philbrick's book In the Heart of the Sea. It describes the final voyage of the "Essex," a whaling ship from Nantucket that sank somewhere out in the wide ocean in 1820. This authentic narrative inspired Herman Melville to write Moby Dick. Whereas Melville chose to end his novel with the destruction of the "Pequot" by Moby Dick, Philbrick's earlier account begins with the fatal encounter between the "Essex" and a Sperm Whale: ...It was on a beautiful spring morning (in the Southern Hemisphere, the ed.), on November 20, 1820, as the crew of the "Essex" was busy harpooning a few whales, that the boatswain happened to look over his shoulder. In utter amazement he watched as the mother ship capsized. "Look, look," he cried out in disbelief "What's happening to the ship?" What they didn't know was that about two miles away a mighty Sperm Whale bull had rammed the "Essex" with his enormous head while they were busy slaughtering Sperm Whale calves and their mothers. He had apparently taken revenge on them. It wasn't until 93 days later that the homeward-bound schooner "Dauphin" discovered the last survivors of the "Essex." They were floating on a few planks and had only managed to survive by drinking the blood and eating the flesh of their fellow seamen.

For a brief moment I was a guest at a Sperm Whales' "tête-à-tête." For me, it was a great and unexpected honour.

A female Sperm Whale opens her huge maw and approaches me head-on.

POISONOUS COCKTAIL

It happens again and again that male Sperm Whales lose their way while migrating as singles from their customary hunting grounds in the Arctic to their mating grounds in the North Sea and end up stranded on sandbars. Ralf Kiefner witnessed such a tragic event.

Sixteen young Sperm Whale bulls were washed up on the Danish island of Rømø on the night of March 27, 1996. The following year in December, fifteen Sperm Whale bulls lost their way in the North Sea and stranded along the coasts of Denmark, Holland and Germany. In January of 2002 another three Sperm Whale bulls stranded on the German North Sea coast near Friedrichskoog. The aforementioned sixteen Sperm Whale bulls had all perished at the same time and were already dead before their bodies washed up on the island of Rømø. "They died when they stranded on one of the sandbars out at sea," marine biologist Thyge Jensen explains. Two of the sixteen whale cadavers are accessible to the public; the remaining fourteen lie in a restricted military zone.

Back there, close to the water line, is where it must be. From afar I can already make out the huge body of a stranded Sperm Whale. It towers high above the crowd of onlookers surrounding it. It lies on its right side and faces the sea. Its left pectoral fin points straight up into the sky as if it were giving a parting salute. A gruesome sight awaits the curious multitude. In order to prevent plundering, the scientists have already removed the lower jaws of the whales. Depending on its size, a Sperm Whale tooth can net over US$ 1,000. Other than removing the lower jaws, the scientists also took a number of large tissue samples. They even extracted the eyes. All this was done in order to establish what caused the death of these animals.

The bodies of the whales have burst open and part of their entrails are hanging out. For a whale cadaver to "explode" like this is really nothing unusual as they are warm-blooded mammals just like humans. Due to an insulating layer of fat that is 10 or more centimetres thick, however, it takes longer for the inside of a whale"s body to cool down after rigor mortis has set in. This internal warmth causes the gases released by the process of decay to expand so much that the bodies literally "explode." Truly a gruesome sight.

Most of the onlookers have never seen a living whale. Now they are duly impressed by its size. And the whales stranded here are mere "rowdies," or young bulls with the relatively modest size of approximately 10 metres. Mature bulls can be18 metres long.

Something like an awed silence reigns over the beach in spite of the numerous onlookers. I can clearly read a mixture of respect, empathy and mourning in some of the faces around me. Deeply moved, they gaze upon the burst leviathan. A little boy next to me holds his nose and exclaims: "Phew, whales stink!" No wonder, considering he is looking at about 25 tonnes of rotting flesh.

The death of so many whales at once is indeed a very sad event. This holds true today as much as it did 400 years ago. On February 2 or 4, 1598, a Sperm Whale stranded between Katwijk and Scheveningen, in Holland. The unfortunate creature was an impressive testimonial of "the great variety of animals that God has placed on the land and in the

Mass strandings of Sperm Whales occur on many coasts, this one in June 1979 at Florence, Oregon.

water." Back then, around 4 o"clock in the afternoon, the first eye witnesses immediately fled over the dunes in panic. After a while, however, people came from all over to gape at this colossal creature that "had all the trappings of a miracle." "The posterior part of its tongue alone is as thick as a beer barrel... and its eye as large as a man can span between his thumb and index finger," a newsletter brought out by Henrick Haestens, an Amsterdam publisher, marvelled. German chronicler Hans Sibmacher reported "that its stately, almost two-metre-long penis clearly identifies it as a male animal. At first it thrashed about so much "that it could be heard for nearly a half a mile in every direction," he went on to say. At last it "died with a loud bursting or popping sound, as if a cannon were being fired..." At the same time, a torrent of water came pouring out of its throat "that stank so much that no one wanted to remain there."

To prevent looting, this stranded Sperm Whale's lower jaw including the valuable teeth has been sawed off (North Sea coast of Germany).

Why did this group of 16 "rowdy" young Sperm Whale bulls end up in the North Sea? As might be expected, the fairer sex is to blame. Sperm Whale bulls would certainly have it much easier if the capricious "ladies" would deign to meet their prospective suitors half way along their long journey from their solo hunting grounds in the Arctic Circle to the equator. Whereas "he" sees fit to seek his nourishment alone in the colder regions, "she" prefers to romp around in cosy warm waters and demands "his" timely appearance at her "doorstep" whenever it is mating time again.

Rather than bypassing the British Isles to the west as usual, these 16 bulls somehow got lost on their way from the Atlantic waters off Norway and found themselves stranded in the North Sea. "It is almost impossible for Sperm Whales to find a way out of this dead end," says the chief biologist of the Schutzstation Wattenmeer, a conservationist organisation in Sylt, Germany. "Rather than heading in a westerly direction towards the channel that leads back to the Atlantic, the whales instinctively turn south... and there they run into the shoreline."

Young Sperm Whale bulls are gregarious and roam far and wide in the course of their migrations across the open sea from the equator to the Arctic Circle. During their long wanderings they will sound to depths of 1,000 to 3,000 metres in order to hunt for deep-sea squid, their main source of nourishment. The shallow North Sea waters are definitely not their customary hunting grounds. It may well be that their phenomenal echolocation system, which is geared for the open sea, fails to operate accurately in the North Sea with its shallows of less than 20 metres and thus leads to their undoing. It takes sound several seconds to echo back from the deep ocean bottom, but in the shallow waters of the North Sea it comes ricocheting back in such short intervals that "Moby Dick" becomes confused, if not altogether "blind."

There really is no concrete answer to the question why some of the whales come to such a pitiful end in spite of their exceptional capabilities. Do these whales suffer from migraines? Are they moonstruck? Could it be that they are committing suicide as a form of protest against the whaling industry? Or is it some unknown defect in their navigation system? Were they led astray by a storm or some other disturbing sound wave caused by ships or ocean-bed blasting and drilling?

If one is to believe the renowned whale book author Richard Ellis, then "Sperm Whales have always had a certain predilection for the Dutch coast." Reports of stranded Sperm Whales are also common elsewhere in the world: 56 Sperm Whales stranded in California and 41 met the same fate near Florence, Oregon, in 1979. The gloomy record is currently being held by the coast of New Zealand, where 59 Sperm Whales died simultaneously in 1970 and no less than 72 stranded just four years later, in 1974. "Many of the going theories about the stranding of whales are primarily characterised by the fact that they can be neither refuted nor proven," Richard Ellis writes in his whale book under myths, fables and facts.

All attempts to date to find a plausible explanation seem to fit in remarkably well with the personal interests of those who propagate them. Dutch biologist Kees Camphuijsen, for instance, believes that there are geomagnetic lines running along the ocean floor by which the whales orient themselves. Iron oxide crystals have in fact been detected in samples taken from the brains of whales. As in the case of carrier pigeons, this may indicate that the whales are capable of registering such geomagnetic waves.

Neuropathologist Erwin Dahme blames parasites. He stipulates that parasites infesting the sensitive ears of the whales can disturb their sense of equilibrium. Greenpeace, on the other hand, makes oil rigs, ships" noises and pollution responsible for the mishap. But reports of stranded whales date back to the days when the seas were still relatively unaffected by pollution and industrial noises.

Substantial amounts of heavy metals were indeed found in the whale cadavers of Rømø. At first plans were made to process the cadavers of these 16 Sperm Whales as animal food, but then it was discovered that they were so highly contaminated with toxic substances that they had to be disposed of as hazardous waste! The costs for disposing the three Sperm Whales that stranded on the German North Sea coast in January of 2002 were estimated at 25.000 Euros.

The tonnes of intestines and intestinal contents that were analysed by the biologists contained so many toxic substances that the experts were absolutely dumbfounded. The bodies contained twenty times the amount of cadmium and twice the amount of quicksilver normally found in fish. "Strange and uncanny," concluded Leo Theander, the director of the local toxic waste dump. How true. Here is a colossal animal that journeys south from the cold Arctic region, far away from all industrial centres, and seeks its nourishment at inaccessible depths. And yet, the contents of its stomach are as

A horrible stench covers the coast until the cadavers are removed.

polluted as if it had been wallowing in the cooling basin of a metal-processing industry. Additional traces of industrial toxic wastes that could weaken the animals" immune system, such as polychlorinated biphenyl (PCBs as used in fire-control substances and capacitors) and pesticides (DDT), were found in the cadavers as well. In the meantime it has become known that tributyl tin (TBT as used in anti-fouling paints for ships) is also extremely hazardous for marine mammals. Scientists are now trying to figure out just how such large quantities of heavy metals ever found their way into the digestive system of Sperm Whales. Obviously they could only have been ingested by the whales through the natural food chain. They certainly did not imbibe them in undiluted form with a spoon. Nor is it likely that whales have amalgam fillings or that they now run on batteries!

In other words, these whales must have swum through waters that were highly contaminated with heavy metals and other industrial pollutants. This is supported by the results of recent tests that were conducted in the supposedly "pristine" Arctic region. Traces of heavy metals have been detected in areas that are far removed from any industrial compounds and this can hardly be the result of any natural processes. Evidently the ocean currents can carry toxic wastes for thousands of kilometres, from the industrial centres all the way to such remote and seemingly inaccessible regions. These wastes in turn cause massive harm to the fragile ecosystem of the Arctic which will be extremely difficult to repair in the future. For years scientists have warned us that rivers, rainfall and air currents transport toxic materials to the oceans where they will gradually accumulate. The smallest concentration of pollutants like phthalates (as found in PVC wraps), alkylphenole, PBCs and dioxine can already affect an animal"s hormone system and result in sterility. This is one of the main reasons why the belugas of the Saint Laurence Stream, which runs along the eastern coast of Canada and the United States, are currently in danger of extinction.

Like humans, Sperm Whales are situated at the end of the food chain. Could our own bodies eventually become as contaminated with toxic materials as theirs are now? I recall a bleak statement that I read recently: "First we poison the animals, then we poison ourselves."

The Killer Whale clearly demonstrates what distinguishes toothed from baleen whales.   H. Voigtmann

SPERM WHALES   PHYSETERIDAE

3 species: Pygmy Sperm Whale, *Kogia breviceps*
Dwarf Sperm Whale, *Kogia sima*
Sperm Whale, *Physeter catodon*

Distinguishing Characteristics of this Family

The common earmark of the species in this family is a bulbous head with a protruding upper jaw that lacks any functional teeth. All three species have blowholes that are offset to the left side of the head rather than in the middle as usual. Otherwise, these species differ markedly from each other. The variations in size are great: A Dwarf Sperm Whale attains a maximum size of 2.1 m and weighs up to 135 kg; a male Sperm Whale can grow to a length of 20 m and weigh 50 t. The proportions of the head also vary considerably: A Dwarf Sperm Whale's head comprises about 15% of its total length; that of a male Sperm Whale no more than 35%. Whereas the two smaller species have well developed dorsal fins, Sperm Whales only have small triangular or rounded humps. All three species are seldom encountered in coastal waters. They prefer deep offshore waters where they can hunt for squid.

Pygmy Sperm Whale, *Kogia breviceps*

A Pygmy Sperm Whale baby recovers in a tank after stranding in Florida.   Doug Perrine/Seapics.com

Distinguishing Characteristics

Other than its relatively small size, the principal earmark of a Pygmy Sperm Whale is its large, bulbous head. There is a half-moon-shaped pattern behind its eyes (see also the section on Dwarf Sperm Whales).

Description

Pygmy Sperm Whales are a robust species of whale averaging 2.8-3.5 m in length, which makes them smaller than some species of dolphin. Other than its characteristic head form, a Pygmy Sperm Whale more closely resembles a dolphin in appearance than a sperm whale. Its maximum weight is 400 kg.

The small and slightly-falcate dorsal fin is positioned just behind the middle of the back. The fluke has a wide, concave edge with a median notch. The blowhole is positioned fairly far down the back and, like all members of this family, somewhat offset to the left. The distance between the tip of the snout and the blowhole comprises about 10% of the total body length, whilst the blowhole is about 5 cm long and U-shaped. There is a conspicuous half-moon-shaped and alternating dark-light pattern behind the eyes. This characteristic feature somewhat resembles the gill cover (operculum) of a fish and has been appropriately designated as "false gills." The curious pattern is already evident in the whale embryo.

Younger whales have a row of hair bristles growing between the eyes and the jawlines, most of which will disappear with age. The body colour is usually dark-grey, while the back can range from blue to dark-grey. The colouration fades laterally and is off-white underneath. The frequent mention in reference literature of a "slightly pinkish" hue on the underside may be the result of postmortem discolouration. The skins of living Pygmy Sperm Whales have been described as "prune-like" in texture. Younger specimens will occasionally have a pale, circular spot in front of each eye and a somewhat more pointed snout, which makes their heads look rounder than the typical rectangular head shape of the mature animals. They take on this characteristic shape when they attain a length of 2.7 m, which is also when they reach maturity. This transformation may be connected to the development of echolocation.

Easily Mistaken For
It is very difficult to keep Pygmy Sperm Whales and Dwarf Sperm Whales apart. Both have a receding lower jaw and a half-moon pattern behind the eyes, which give them a shark-like appearance. Pygmy Sperm Whales are slightly larger, but they have markedly smaller dorsal fins located farther down the back.

Other Names:
Lesser Sperm Whale, Short-Headed Sperm Whale, Lesser Cachalot (English); Zwergpottwal (German); Cachalot Pygmée (French); Cogia di de Blainville (Italian); Cachalote Pigmeo (Spanish); Cachalote Pigmeu, Cachalote Anão (Portuguese); Dwergpotvis (Dutch); Dvergspermhval (Norwegian); Kääpiökaskelotti (Finnish); Dvärgkaskelot (Swedish); Almindelig Dværgkaskelot (Danish); Komakko Kujira (Japanese).

Meaning of the Scientific Nomenclature
Kogia breviceps (de Blainville, 1838). *Kogia* is the Latinised form of the Old English word "codger." The Latin species name *breviceps* means "short-headed." The generic name *Kogia* has also been associated with Cogia Effendi, a Turk who studied Mediterranean whales.

Behaviour
Knowledge about Pygmy Sperm Whales is primarily based on the stomach contents of stranded specimens (usually females with their calves). Very few observations have been made on the high seas. As they are extremely shy and have an inconspicuous blow, they are rarely sighted. Consequently, little is known about their behaviour. According to the analyses of their stomach contents, they are oceanic animals that seldom visit coastal waters. Whereas sightings of live specimens are few and far between, Pygmy Sperm Whales frequently strand along the eastern coast of the United States. Studies based on these stranded specimens suggest that they probably live in groups of 4-6 individuals. In 1993 a total of 51 animals were caught in drift nets cast out by Japanese and Taiwanese fishing fleets in the Northern Pacific. Nothing is known about their annual migration patterns.

Pygmy Sperm Whales are slow swimmers, whereby they keep their flippers pressed close to the body. The best chance to observe them is when they are resting on the surface. Hereby the head and back will be visible, while the fluke remains submerged. This posture makes it look as if they were propping up their flippers on the water's surface. It was in this resting state that a few vessels actually managed to get close to them.

All previous theories about the calving intervals of Pygmy Sperm Whales were thrown overboard by scientists following the discovery of a pregnant cow that was still nursing a 2-m-long calf.

Diving
Contrary to dolphins, Pygmy Sperm Whales will normally sound as soon as a vessel or diver approaches them. They do not roll forwards like a dolphin when sounding, but simply sink like a

Facts & Figures Pygmy Sperm Whale	Quick ID-Check Pygmy Sperm Whale
Size: 2.7-3.5 m	Small, robust body
Weight: max 400 kg	
Longevity: unknown	Small, inconspicuous, hooked dorsal fin
Sexual maturity: as of 2.7 m in length	
Mating season: Fall-Spring	Bulbous head
Gestation period: 11 months	
Calving interval: unknown	Blowhole offset to the left
Size at birth: 1-1.2 m	
Weight at birth: about 50 kg	Low and inconspicuous blow
Nursing period: around 12 months, perhaps up to 24 months	"False gills" behind the eyes
Dive depth: 200 m	
Dive time: unknown	Slow swimmer
Teeth: 24-32 narrow, curved, conical teeth in lower jaw; upper jaw toothless	Occasionally rests motionless on the surface
Group (Pod) size: probably 4-6, occasionally up to 10 animals	Usually sounds when approached
Population: unknown, but probably more numerous than expected	Sinks rather than dives

stone. If they are startled, they will expel a cloud of excrements, something that many other whales are also known to do. Perhaps, as in the case of cephalopods, this is a tactic to disorient predators. The surface activities of Pygmy Sperm Whales are much more inconspicuous than those of dolphins. Their maximum dive depth is approximately 200 m.

Feeding Habits
The analysis of the stomach contents of stranded animals has shown that they primarily feed on pelagic cephalopods. There were very few traces of inshore organisms. This means that Pygmy Sperm Whales hunt for prey on the bottom of offshore waters. Occasionally the remains of crabs, shrimp and small fish were found in the whales' stomachs.

People try to keep a stranded Pygmy Sperm Whale at the surface until professional help arrives. The species is clearly identifiable by its hooked dorsal fin. Hawaii.
Helmut Debelius

Pieter Arend Folkens

General Information
This species was first classified by the Compte de Blainville in 1838 on the basis of a skull that was found at the Cape of Good Hope. He named it *Physeter breviceps* because he thought it was a smaller variant of the Sperm Whale. In 1846 naturalist John E. Gray established the new genus *Kogia* for the species. In 1954 Pygmy Sperm Whales and Dwarf Sperm Whales were finally recognised as distinct species. Both species are alternatively placed in a family of its own (Kogiidae).

Where & When
Due to their inconspicuous way of life very little is known about the distribution of Pygmy Sperm Whales. Most of the information available was gleaned from the cadavers of stranded animals and probably present an incomplete picture. Pygmy Sperm Whales apparently prefer to live in the warmer waters of the tropical to temperate latitudes of the Atlantic, Pacific and Indian oceans. They are oceanic animals that occasionally also cross the continental shelf. The evidence collected so far originates from different regions so there may be separate populations. The species appears relatively frequently along the SE coast of the United States, especially in Florida. Specimens are also encountered quite frequently in southeastern Australia and around New Zealand. It is not yet known whether these "populations" are isolated from each other.

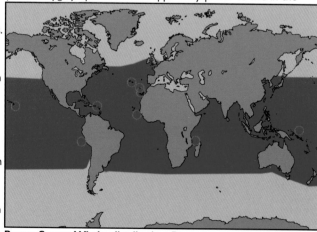

Pygmy Sperm Whale, distribution: Deep, temperate, subtropical & tropical offshore waters and continental shelf. Circles: Strandings.

Dwarf Sperm Whale, *Kogia sima*

Dwarf Sperm Whale.   Pieter Arend Folkens

Distinguishing Characteristics
Other than its small size, the most distinguishing characteristic of a Dwarf Sperm Whale is its blunt and square head. There is a conspicuous, half-moon-shaped, alternating light-dark pattern behind the eyes known as "false gills" (see section on Pygmy Sperm Whales).

Description
With its average length of 2.1-2.7 m, the Dwarf Sperm Whale is the smallest of all whales, smaller even than many species of dolphin. Other than its blunt and square head, this species actually more closely resembles a dolphin than a sperm whale. It is robust in appearance and weighs up to 275 kg.

There are a number of irregular grooves on its throat. The blowhole is situated relatively far down the back (almost level with the eyes) and, like Pygmy Sperm Whales, offset to the left. The distance between the tip of the snout and the blowhole makes up approximately 10% of its total body length. The blowhole is about 5 cm long and U-shaped. The dorsal fin sits in the middle of the back and is falcated like those of a Bottlenose Dolphin. The flippers are short, but wide. The fluke has a broad, concave edge with a well developed median notch.

The snout of a young Dwarf Sperm Whale is pointed but becomes increasingly rectangular with age. There are 14-24 small, conical and curved teeth on the lower jaw that grow to a maximum length of 3 cm. Normally the upper jaw is toothless, but specimens with up to 6 tiny teeth have been found.

The body is usually dark-grey, while the back can vary from blue-grey to almost black. This colouration pales laterally and turns white underneath. Mention in reference literature of an "occasionally slightly pinkish" hue on the underside may be the result of postmortem discolouration.

Easily Mistaken For
It is very difficult to keep Dwarf Sperm Whales and Pygmy Sperm Whales apart. The former is somewhat smaller and has a much larger dorsal fin that sits in the middle of the back. Both species have a receding lower jaw and a half-moon pattern behind the eyes, which give them a

shark-like appearance. The head of a Dwarf Sperm Whale is more square than that of a Pygmy Sperm Whale.

Because of their similar dorsal fins, Bottlenose Dolphins may be mistaken for Dwarf Sperm Whales. When the latter rest on the surface, their protruding fins can make them look like Bottlenose Dolphins from a distance. Once one gets a closer look, however, the different shape of the body and head, the offset position of the blowhole and the "false gills" behind the eyes immediately become apparent. Dolphins do not have a receding lower jaw, are not nearly as slow and usually somewhat larger.

Other Names:
Owen's Pygmy Sperm Whale (English); Kleine Pottwal, Kleinstpottwal, Kleinpottwal (German); Cachalot Nain (French); Cogia di Owen (Italian); Cachalote Enano (Spanish); Cachalote Anão, Cachalote Miúdo (Portuguese); Kleinste Potvis

Breaching Dwarf Sperm Whale. Caribbean.   Robert Pitman

(Dutch); Liten Dvergspermhval (Norwegian); Tyynenmerenkääpiökaskelotti (Finnish); Småkaskelot (Swedish); Lille Dværgkaskelot (Danish); Ogawa Kmakko Kujira (Japanese).

Meaning of the Scientific Nomenclature
Kogia sima (Owen 1866) - *Kogia* is the Latinised form for the Old English word "codger." The Latin species name *sima* means "short" and refers to the animal's small size. The generic name *Kogia* has also been associated with Cogia Effendi, a Turk who studied Mediterranean whales.

Behaviour
The sparse information available about this species is almost exclusively based on the study of dead specimens that were either stranded or caught in drift nets (e.g. in 1993 a total of 17 Dwarf Sperm Whales and 51 Pygmy Sperm Whales were caught in drift nets cast by Japanese and Taiwanese fishing fleets in the Northern Pacific).

Due to this specie's inconspicuous behaviour at sea, there is very little information available about its habits. Dwarf Sperm Whales normally live far from the coast and are very shy. Consequently, they are only rarely sighted. The only clues to their preferred habitat are based on

Facts & Figures Dwarf Sperm Whale	Quick ID-Check Dwarf Sperm Whale
Size: 2.1-2.7 m	Small body, conspicuous, falcated dorsal fin
Weight: max 275 kg	
Longevity: unknown	Conical, snub-nosed, almost square-shaped head
Sexual maturity: as of 2.1 m in length	
Mating season: Summer	
Gestation period: 9 months	Blowhole offset to the left, low, inconspicuous blow
Calving interval: unknown	
Size at birth: about 1 m	
Weight at birth: about 40-50 kg	"False Gills" behind the eyes
Nursing period: unknown	
Dive depth: 300 m	Very slow swimmer
Dive time: unknown	
Teeth: 14-24 small, curved, conical teeth in lower jaw; upper jaw normally toothless	Occasionally rests motionless on the surface
Group (Pod) size: 1-2	Usually sounds when approached
Population: unknown, but probably more numerous than expected	Sinks rather than dives

the analyses of the stomach contents of stranded animals. These suggest that the animals predominantly hunt in offshore waters with a max depth of 300 m.

Like Pygmy Sperm Whales, Dwarf Sperm Whales can best be observed while they are at rest on the surface. In this state their heads and backs become visible on the surface, but their flukes remain submerged. This position makes it look as if the whales were propping up their flippers on the water's surface, which is why the species is called "Uki Kujira" (Drifting Whale) in Japan. At times it is even possible to approach them by boat while they are resting in this fashion.

Dwarf Sperm Whales migrate at a slow pace as individuals or in pairs, rarely in groups of up to 10 animals. Observations of stranded animals suggest that the females live in groups with their own young.

The blow of a Dwarf Sperm Whale is inconspicuous and low. Breaching has seldom been observed. Bite-wounds found on the cadavers of stranded animals suggest that intra-species rivalries are not uncommon.

Diving See section of Pygmy Sperm Whales.

Feeding Habits
Analyses of the stomach contents of stranded animals have shown that Dwarf Sperm Whales primarily feed on cephalopods. But the remains of crabs, shrimp and small fish were also found in their intestines. The analyses showed as well that the proportional composition of the stomach contents can vary. More than 90% of the stomach contents of the females and their young consisted of the remains of cephalopods (usually small sepia) that live on the continental shelf. In the case of mature male animals about 70% of the contents were made up of the remains of oceanic cephalopods.

General Information
Dwarf Sperm Whales were first described by the English anatomist Owen in 1866. He based his observations on a skeleton that was found on a beach near Waltair, in Madras (India), and named the species *Euphyseter simus*. Even though Beddard listed two distinct species in the genus *Kogia* as early as 1902, Europeans continued to classify the Dwarf Sperm Whale together with *Kogia breviceps* for many years thereafter. It wasn't until Ogawa (1936) and Yamada (1954) completed their studies that *Kogia sima* was finally recognised as a separate species. Some systematists still feel that the Dwarf Sperm Whale is a coastal variant of the Pygmy Sperm Whale. More recent biological findings, however, support a separation.

Where & When
Due to their inconspicuous behaviour there is little accurate information available about the migration routes of Dwarf Sperm Whales. Presumably they live in the warm and temperate waters of both hemispheres. A few sightings suggest that they prefer deeper waters in the vicinity of the continental shelf.

A number of sightings made along the coast lead to the assumption that they frequent the southern tip of South Africa and the Sea of Cortez. Other inshore sightings were made off California, Hawaii, Guam, South Australia, Japan, Sri Lanka and the eastern coast of the United States. Three stranded animals were found along Europe's Atlantic coast (Portugal 1, France 2) and one specimen washed up along the Mediterranean coast of Italy.

No geographic variations or isolated populations are known to exist so far.

Dwarf Sperm Whale, distrib.: Deep, temperate to tropical waters in both hemispheres, both inshore & offshore. Circles: Strandings.

Sperm Whale, *Physeter catodon*

Because of its peculiar shape the Sperm Whale is an excellent diver. Caribbean.   Howard Hall

Distinguishing Characteristics

The earmark of a Sperm Whale is its huge, barrel-shaped head with an extraordinarily long and narrow lower jaw. Also typical are the tiny, hump-like dorsal fin and the wrinkled, prune-like skin. The characteristic S-shaped blowhole sits on the forward part of the head and is offset to the left. As a consequence, the bushy blow is always angled to the left and fore. This enables experienced whale watchers to identify the species from a distance and even tell in which direction it is headed.

Description

The powerful, massive body of a mature Sperm Whale weighs 35-57 tons. It is the largest of all toothed whales. Sexual dimorphism is quite evident in terms of size: Males average 15-18 m in length, the females 11-12 m. The largest Sperm Whale on record is a 20.7-m bull that was killed by a Soviet whaler off the Kurile Islands in the Northwest Pacific in 1950. The cross-section of a Sperm Whale's body is nearly round and grows largest at the base of the flippers. A male Sperm Whale is not fully grown until it is 35-60 years old. The large head with its flat front comprises about 25-30% of the whale's total body length. It holds the whale's name-giving spermaceti organ. This species has the largest brain in the entire animal kingdom. The brain of a male Sperm Whale is approximately 17 cm high, 25 cm long and 30 cm wide, and it weighs about 8 kg. Female Sperm Whales have smaller heads and brains (about 6 kg). Another typical characteristic of a Sperm Whale is the asymmetrical shape of the head. The right side is substantially larger than the left side, and the blowhole is offset to the left and fore. The blunt snout can be up to 1.5 m longer than the narrow lower jaw, which is hardly visible when the whale's mouth is shut. The long, Y-shaped jawbone has 30-60 (usually 46-48) large, conical teeth. These can attain a length of 20 cm and weigh more than 1 kg. The upper jaw has a series of small, rudimentary teeth that seldom break through the gums. Females have smaller and fewer teeth than the males. The mouth is frequently encircled by white spots. Many specimens have a few short throat grooves behind the corners of the mouth. The relatively small and inconspicuous eyes are located low on each side the head. The paddle-shaped flippers are very small, have irregular edges and sit relatively far back along the flanks.

The typical blow of a Sperm Whale. Azores.   Ralf Kiefner

The dorsal fin is actually a small, triangular or rounded hump. A series of smaller humps run all the way down to the tail stock. The fluke is triangular with slightly rounded tips. Its termination is straight and has a deep median notch, but it may also be highly irregular due to injuries.

The skin along the flanks is full of horizontal wrinkles. The skin itself is uniformly brown to dark-grey with occasional white spots along the belly. A Sperm Whale resting on the surface resembles a huge floating log. Light dots, spots or stripes can be found all over the whale's body.

The head and mouth are frequently covered with pale scars that were inflicted by the beaks and suckers of large cephalopods, a Sperm Whale's principal prey. Diatoms and whale lice often infest the scarred tissue and discolour it. Albino Sperm Whales, made famous by Herman Melville's *Moby Dick,* are very rare.

Easily Mistaken For

Sperm Whales are easily identifiable by their huge, barrel-shaped heads and offset blows. The way they sound, whereby they will almost always raise their flukes high out of the water, and their extremely long and deep dives are additional traits that make any confusions with other cetaceans highly unlikely.

Other Names:

Great Sperm Whale (English); Pottwal (German) Kaskelot, Cachalot, Cachalot Macrocéphale (French); Capodoglio (Italian); Cachalote (Spanish/Portuguese); Potvis (Dutch); Spermhval, Kaskelott, Hunshval (Norwegian); Kaskelotti (Finnish); Kaskelot (Swedish); Kaskelot (Danish); Makko Kujira(Japanese); Kashalot (Russian); Ballena Esperma (Latin American Spanish); *Physeter macrocephalus* (other scientific name).

Meaning of the Scientific Nomenclature

Physeter catodon Linnaeus 1758 - The Greek generic name *Physeter* means "blower," and the species name *catodon* means "teeth only in lower jaw." The other scientific name currently still in use, *Physeter macrocephalus,* has a different Greek species name meaning "big head."

Behaviour

Sperm Whales are oceanic creatures that seldom venture close to shore. They can also be encountered around submerged peaks or where the depth of the water increases rapidly away from the shore. Upwelling currents in such places carry many organic nutrients and thus provide the whales with an ample source of nourishment.

The migration behaviour of Sperm Whales differs from all other species of whale. The distribution of male and female specimens varies. Only the grown bulls are found in both tropical and polar waters in either hemisphere. Their seasonal migrations will take them to the remotest latitudes. During the summer months the bulls range from the Antarctic glaciers to the Arctic waters at 70° latitude north. During the winter months they wander to their respective mating grounds in warmer regions. The strain of such long migrations is obviously compensated by the abundance of nutrients in polar waters. The females, on the other hand, are bound to surface

temperatures that do not drop below 15° C. Consequently, they always remain between latitudes of 40° S and 45° N.

Although the various populations of Sperm Whales in the world are isolated from each other due to their respective seasonal wanderings, interbreeding does occur. The Atlantic and Indic populations intermingle at the Cape of Good Hope (35° latitude south); the Pacific and Indic populations come

Above: Powerfully breaching Sperm Whale off Galapagos.

Jim Watt

Left: The posterior margin of the fluke serves well in the identification of individuals. Azores.

Ralf Kiefner

together in the Sunda Strait and the region south of Tasmania (43° latitude south). Only the bulls will migrate past Cape Horn (57° latitude south). Only one case of contact between the northern and southern populations is known: A single marked specimen actually crossed the equator.

Social behaviour among Sperm Whales varies considerably. There are reports of Sperm Whales trying to help injured companions on the one hand, and accounts of them fleeing from harpooned relatives on the other. Occasionally they have been known to attack whaling ships. Hereby they either rammed the vessel with their enormous heads, struck it with their mighty flukes or actually bit into it with their large teeth. Such aggressive behaviour is common when the bulls rival for mates. In his book *In the Heart of the Sea*, Nathaniel Philbrick's relates the true story of the "Essex," a whaling ship from Nantucket that sank in 1820. It inspired Herman Melville to write *Moby Dick*. Whereas Melville chooses to end his novel with the whale's destruction of Captain Ahab's ship, Philbrick's account begins with the tragic fate of the "Essex." A mighty Sperm Whale bull rammed the "Essex" repeatedly until it sank. The few survivors were picked up by another whaling ship 93 days later. They had only managed to survive in one of the small whaling boats by drinking the blood and eating the flesh of their deceased companions. See also TÊTE-À-TÊTE on pages 116-118.

Although Sperm Whales are not nearly as famous for acrobatic breaching as grey or right whales, they still do so quite frequently (albeit rarely in succession). Most observations of breaching

The wrinkled skin of a Sperm Whale. Azores.   Ralf Kiefner

activities involve younger animals and occurred when the seas were rough. As long as they remain in their mating grounds, female Sperm Whales will normally only breach when males are also present. A breaching Sperm Whale breaks the surface at an angle and lands with a loud splash. It will seldom heave its entire body out of the water. Other surface activities such as lob-tailing can be observed quite frequently and may have a communicative function.

Sperm Whales live in four distinct social units:

1. Nursing or Breeding Schools

These groups are made up of females and their young, and usually number 20-40 animals. Calves of either sex maintain strong bonds with their mothers. Since they are still unable to dive to great depths, they will be watched over by older members of the group while their mothers search for food in the deep. Other females in the group will assume a mother's function as monitor and protector. "Aunts" and unrelated Sperm Whale cows "babysit" and fiercely protect the calves from predators like large sharks - a form of behaviour that is also common among terrestrial mammals like wolves.

When a whale cow is about to give birth, several mature females will assist during delivery and help the newborn calf swim to the surface so it can take its first breath. As soon as the male calves have been weaned and are able to fend for themselves, they will be expelled from the nursing and breeding schools. Then they form their own group, the so-called bachelor schools.

2. Bachelor Schools

Young, sexually immature male animals up to the age of about 25 form groups of 12-15 individuals. When they reach a length of about 9 m they become sexually mature and abandon the group.

3. Solitary Schools

Older, sexually mature bulls usually live and migrate as solitary individuals or in smaller groups of no more than 6 animals. Even when there are several bulls in the same area they will generally remain apart. They migrate all the way to polar latitudes and only join up with a nursing and breeding school during the mating season.

4. Mating Schools or "Harems"

During the mating season mature bulls join up with nursing and breeding schools and form so-called "harems." This will be preceded by frequent and fierce confrontations between the larger bulls vying for the attention of as many as 10 females at one time. Numerous traces of bite wounds are a testimonial to the violent nature of these clashes. The victorious bulls will impregnate several cows, for polygyny rules in a Sperm Whale's "harem."

Diving

When Sperm Whales sound without being disturbed, they raise their heads out of the water briefly as if they were taking a final deep breath and gathering momentum for the next dive. They will arch their backs prior to raising their huge flukes high above the surface.

Sperm Whales are lurking hunters. They descend to great depths, where they probably lie in wait for schools of unweary cephalopods. In order to conserve energy, they dive almost vertically at a speed of about 1-3 m/sec. They only cover short distances horizontally once they have reached their intended depth. This means that they do not cover great distances while diving and almost always surface in proximity of where they sounded. The average dive depth of a Sperm Whale ranges around 600-1,000 m. In 1955, for instance, a Sperm entangled itself in a transoceanic cable lying 1,113 metres below the surface of the ocean somewhere between Chile and Ecuador. After diving for 50-60 minutes, a Sperm Whale will surface again and breathe deeply about 50 times. Following a short pause of approximately 10 minutes, the whale will be ready for its next dive. The older bulls make the deepest and longest dives, sometimes lasting up to 1 hour and 52 minutes. On November 11, 1983, biologists recorded the clicking sounds five Sperm Whales made while diving in Caribbean waters. One of the recorded whales remained under water for 2 hours and 18 minutes. Younger Sperm Whales usually do not stay under longer than 20 minutes, and calves barely manage 7 minutes. By way of contrast, experienced pearl divers average a mere 2-2.5 minutes.

In 1970, American scientists using triangulation were able to prove that Sperm Whales can reach a depth of up to 2,500 m. From three different locations on the surface, they recorded the sounds made by diving whales. Their depth was then calculated from the difference in the time it took

Sounding Sperm Whale. Caribbean.   Howard Hall

for these sounds to reach each one of the submerged microphones. In 1969, two Sperm Whales were caught off the coast of Durban (South Africa) that had fresh, bottom-feeding sharks (*Scymnodon* sp.) in their stomachs. The seabed in that region lies at a depth of 3,193 m (Clarke, 1979).

How can a Sperm Whale dive so deep even though its lungs are not much larger proportionately than those of a human? How are they able to withstand the tremendous pressure that exists at such depths? How do they orient themselves while hunting in total darkness? The explanations are very complex.

With the aid of video cameras, American scientists have come much closer to solving the puzzle. In a remarkable technical effort, cameras were attached to the backs of dolphins, Sperm Whales and Blue Whales. These provided evidence that a 150 kg dolphin and a 150 t Blue Whale revert to the same ingenious techniques in order to conserve energy while diving. They barely move under water and let themselves drop down to the deep. According to Terrie Williams, a zoologist at the University of California in Santa Cruz, the whales go about diving in very relaxed manner. Instead of paddling while they descend, as has been assumed so far, they practically drop down to the deep like an immobile rock. In a sense, the animals simply shut off their engines to conserve 10-50% of their energy. On the surface they pump their bodies full of oxygen and then exhale just before sounding. The vital oxygen is not stored in their lungs, but in the muscles. As of a depth of about 80 m the residual air in the lungs is pressed so far up into the respiratory tract that the lungs eventually collapse. By storing the oxygen in their muscles the animals gain a double advantage. In the first place, no nitrogen can diffuse from the lungs into the circulatory system and form dangerous bubbles when they surface. Secondly, they become less buoyant. If one compares the breathing efficiency of whales with that of humans, a marked difference immediately becomes apparent. Whereas humans only exchange about 10-15% of the air in their lungs with every breath, Sperm Whales manage a whopping 90%. A Sperm Whale breathes much more efficiently than any terrestrial mammal, and this in spite of the fact that proportionately its lungs are by no means large. On the contrary, they are comparatively small - which is an additional advantage when diving to extreme depths. The pressure buildup while diving has less effect upon the solid parts of the body than it does on hollow spaces that are filled with air or some other gas. Whereas only the windpipe and the bronchial tube are reinforced in the case of terrestrial mammals, a Sperm Whale's entire respiratory system, from the beak-like larynx down to the tiniest branches of the bronchi, has been stiffened. According to E. J. Slijper (1958), professor for vertebral anatomy at the University of Amsterdam, even the internal and external lung tissues of a Sperm Whale are reinforced with elastic fibres. These fibrous reinforcements, which resemble the hose of a vacuum cleaner in structure, prevent the greater part of the whale's respiratory system from collapsing while it dives to great depths. Slijper also lists a peculiar system of valves as an additional physical adaptation to deep diving among Sperm Whales. It entails a system of up to 40 successive mucous membranes that are reinforced with rings of muscle fibre and extend into the bronchi. These can close off the entire bronchial cavity by contracting. They thus function as a sort of stop valve that prevents the air in the alveoli from being pressed into the rigid bronchial system while diving. This system of ring-like muscular fibres not only enables Sperm Whales to shut off every alveolar passage, but also the alveoli themselves. Countless flap valves and rings of muscle fibre prevent the Sperm Whale's ribs from caving in under great pressure. At a dive depth of 100 m, for instance, where the surrounding pressure is 11 atm (1+10), the volume of a gas will be reduced to 1/11 of what it was on the surface. The air inside the lungs is compressed so far at this point that the rib cage is in imminent danger of collapsing.

Another remarkable physiological adaptation these whales have made is that, unlike humans, their breathing reflex is not triggered by a certain concentration of carbon dioxide in the blood. Their respiratory system actually reacts to the onset of oxygen starvation. Consequently, they can make much more effective use of the available oxygen supply than terrestrial mammals, which will feel the urge to breathe long before the oxygen in their systems has been used up. In comparison to terrestrial mammals, the haemoglobin in a whale's red blood cells does not have a higher capacity to bind oxygen, but it can absorb greater quantities of the gas at a much faster rate. The saturation rate among whales is 40-45%, while that of terrestrial mammals ranges around 30-33%. The concentration of haemoglobin in a whale's blood is also higher. In the case of a Sperm Whale the ratio is 15.8 g in 100 cc. By way of contrast, a cow has 12.4 g. The amount of blood in a whale's body, on the other hand, is relatively small. It makes up a mere 3.9% of a Sperm Whale's total body weight, whereas the average for terrestrial mammals lies around 13%. A whale's blood actually fulfills the function of transporting oxygen rather than storing it, as it does not have a high binding capacity. It transports the oxygen directly to a special reservoir in the muscles, namely the myoglobin in the muscle fibres, where it will be needed later for the production of energy. Myoglobin is a protein pigment similar to haemoglobin, but its capacity to bind oxygen is nine times higher among marine mammals than terrestrial mammals. According to Slijper, a whale stores about 41% oxygen in its myoglobin, the same amount in the blood and 8% in other organs. Only 9% is stored in the whale's lungs. Humans, on the other hand, store 34% of their oxygen supply in the lungs and 13% in the myoglobin. All in all, when a Sperm Whale dives it has 40% more oxygen available to it than a human. This bounteous oxygen supply can be mobilised and transported to whichever organ requires it via the whale's circulatory system.

An additional organ seems to play an equally important role in a whale's capacity to store oxygen and compensate pressure, namely the so-called "miracle net" rete mirabilis. This is an extremely dense maze of fine interconnected and intertwined blood vessels. The most remarkable characteristic of the miracle net, which is bedded in connective tissues together with lymph vessels and adipose cells, is that it is saturated with blood. It covers the walls of the rib cage, where it is squeezed in between a few ribs, and extends along the backbone to the throat and parts of the brain. The walls of the arteries in this network, which reminds one of a blood-soaked sponge, are made up of muscle tissue. The veins leading to the miracle net, however, are very elastic. This makes it very likely that the miracle net can sustain substantial and rapid changes in volume, which would in turn compensate any strong fluctuations in blood pressure - much like a shock absorber.

Tomilin, a researcher in the field, assumes that the miracle net also maintains a constant flow of oxygen to the brain as well as a reserve supply for other principal organs. The capacity of this reservoir may possibly increase at the expense of the blubber surrounding the miracle net. Oxygen goes into solution in a Sperm Whale's blubber and spermaceti (fatty substance in the head) seven times faster than in water. One can, therefore, assume that there are still some unknown mechanisms promoting the rapid diffusion of

Even in a museum the mighty lower jaw of a Sperm Whale is most impressive.

oxygen from the blood to the blubber surrounding the miracle net. The miracle net thus clearly fulfills several functions at once: It stores oxygen, compensates fluctuations in the blood pressure and, in all likelihood, acts as a filler for hollow spaces under great pressure.

Nagel, an American scientist, was able to demonstrate the miracle net's function as a regulator of blood pressure with a certain experiment. The x-ray examination of an anaesthetised dolphin showed that its miracle net, which supplies the brain, rapidly absorbed large quantities of blood through the venous system and balanced out the irregular swells of blood being pumped by the heart. The brain continued to be supplied with a regular stream of blood under constant pressure.

Another important adaptation among that enhances a whale's ability to dive deep is a series of sophisticated energy-conservation measures. All marine mammals reduce their metabolism considerably as soon as they submerge. An elephant seal, for instance, can reduce its heartbeat to six beats per minute (120 are normal on the surface). In order to conserve even more energy, several of the whale's organs will function at a much slower rate under water than on the surface. The oxygen supply to less vital internal organs, such as the kidneys and the stomach, is nearly interrupted altogether. The flow of blood is slowed down, regulated and redirected by a series of sphincter muscles in the veins that resemble a network of one-way canals. Only vital organs like the brain, spinal cord and heart are continually supplied with oxygen during a dive.

When a whale dives deep its muscles have to function with an inadequate supply of oxygen, in which case there will be a buildup of lactic acid. With humans this occurs after excessive activity and invariably lead to painful cramps. By means of their venal sphincter muscles, which temporarily divert the flow of blood into a network of one-directional blood vessels, Sperm Whales are able to prevent the lactic acid in the muscles from entering the bloodstream. Once they begin to surface again, the one-directional flow of blood is reversed and the lactic acid allowed to enter the bloodstream where it will be broken down by a fresh supply of oxygen before the muscle cramps.

In 1970, American whale researcher Malcolm Clarke discovered the energy-conserving function of the spermaceti organ, to which Sperm Whales owe their name. The Latin meaning of the word spermaceti is "sperm of the whale." Of course, this substance has absolutely nothing in common with semen, as was erroneously though in the early days of whaling, but forms part of a highly sophisticated hydrostatic organ. About 90% of the large, barrel-shaped head of a Sperm Whale consists of an oily, wax-like substance with which it is able to regulate its buoyancy. Up until recently this substance was used as a high-grade elastic lubricant for high-performance engines and implemented by NASA in space travel technology. Spermaceti turns into a liquid at 30° C and, like all oils, becomes lighter than water. If the temperature drops below 30° C, however, spermaceti will solidify again. Solid spermaceti is heavier than water and produces a negative buoyancy quotient of no less than 2.5 t. For a neutrally buoyant whale, this is a substantial increase in negative buoyancy and enables it to descend from 200 to 1,000 m in just 3 minutes without expending any energy.

In Asia Sperm Whales are still being hunted.   Howard Hall

But just how does a Sperm Whale with a constant body temperature of 37° C regulate the temperature of the spermaceti? Malcolm Clarke was able to find the answer to this mystery - by no means an easy task considering the size of a Sperm Whale's head. Whereas the whale's left nasal passage leads directly to the blowhole, the right one branches off in various directions. It has numerous arms and diverticula, and can be up to 5 m long. Its branches spread throughout the spermaceti organ, up to the point where it terminates just before the blowhole. Water is probably pumped through the right nasal passage and into the spermaceti organ by means of muscular activity. Since a submerged whale is not able to breathe, it has to pump water into the right nasal passage during the surface interval. The light, fluid oil is transformed into a denser solid as soon as it comes into contact with the cold water. This cooling process enables the whale to regulate its buoyancy.

The oil is probably cooled in part through the skin as well, as the whale's head lacks an isolating layer of blubber. In addition, a complex network of arteries and veins enable a Sperm Whale to lower the temperature in its head under 30° C. These closely-packed blood vessels run throughout the head and function as a heat exchanger. Venous blood cools down the warmer arterial blood coming from the body. The whale is thus able to create a different temperature in its head than in the rest of its body.

When the whale ascends to the surface the solidified spermaceti liquefies again. This occurs when warm blood is pumped through a fine network of blood vessels in the spermaceti organ. In this way the whale establishes positive buoyancy again with the aid of its spermaceti organ and floats to the surface without exerting itself. In a sense, the animal's head functions like a diver's buoyancy compensating device (BCD). High pressure apparently poses no problems for a Sperm Whale. Its lungs collapse at a depth of 100 m and then he exchange of gas in the bronchi is no longer possible. But by then it is no longer necessary either, thanks to the complex process outlined above.

From Archimedes we have learned that an object placed in the water is buoyed up by the weight of the water it displaces. A whale has approximately the same density as water because 2/3 of its body is composed of the same incompressible substance. Consequently, it has little weight to carry around in the ocean.

Scuba divers are well aware of the fact that oxygen and nitrogen breathed under pressure will diffuse more rapidly into the various body tissues. Oxygen can be highly toxic at a certain depth. Depending upon the maximum depth and bottom time of a dive, nitrogen can also have a toxic effect (nitrogen narcosis). In addition, the nitrogen accumulated in the body tissues during a deep dive has to be breathed out again during specific decompression stages. How long this process takes depends upon just how saturated each tissue is. If the ascent is premature or too fast the gas will form bubbles in the bloodstream, which can lead to serious injuries like paralysis or pulmonary embolism and may even result in death. The physical symptoms for an excessive diffusion of gas into the bloodstream are referred to as the "bends." The bends, nitrogen narcosis and oxygen toxicity will not affect whales because they do not breathe compressed air.

Feeding Habits
Depending upon the season and availability, Sperm Whales primarily feed on cephalopods like octopus and squid, including giant squid (kraken) of the genus *Architeuthis*. A Sperm Whale captured off the Azores in 1955 had a giant squid in its stomach with 10.49-m tentacles and weighing 184 kg.

Most of the cephalopods found in the stomachs of Sperm Whales turned out to be bottom-dwellers. Bottom-dwelling fish and crabs were also found along with tin cans, all of which indicates that Sperm Whales hunt along the seabed. Curiously, surface-dwelling cephalopods are not consumed by Sperm Whales even though they abound in some of their feeding grounds.

Off the coasts of Island, Greenland, New Zealand and in the Northern Pacific Sperm Whales also feed on various larger (white tuna, barracuda, dusky sharks) and smaller fish (lantern fish, redfish). A 2.5-m deep-sea sand shark was found in the stomach of a large Sperm Whale bull caught off the Azores. A mature Sperm Whale bull takes up about 3-3.5% of its total body weight in nourishment daily. At an average weight of 50 t this amounts to a stately 1.5 t each day. According to observations made by Martin (1992), Sperm Whales hunt cooperatively by swimming parallel to each other. Particularly rich feeding grounds are visited regularly.

General Information

In the tenth edition of Linnaeus's *Systema Naturae* (1758) he describes four separate species of the genus *Physeter,* namely *P. catodon, P. macrocephalus, P. microps* and *P. tursio.* Some of his colleagues, however, expressed their doubts about this classification, as they felt that the latter two were in fact Pilot Whales or White Whales. In 1823, French naturalist Baron Georges Cuvier described Sperm Whales, albeit without giving them a scientific designation. Later whale researchers took over the name *P. macrocephalus* from the 1836 study by naturalist F. Cuvier. Nevertheless, a heated discussion over the correct designation for this species has been going on to the present day. In 1938, Boschma determined that the designation *P. catodon* really applied to about 100 animals that had stranded along the Orkney Islands in 1693 and were smaller than 7.3 m. He had serious doubts about whether these animals were in fact Sperm Whales, and proposed the reintroduction of the designation *P. macrocephalus.* Hershkowitz challenged this proposal in 1966 and propagated the name *P. catodon* again. Eigh years later, Husson and Holthuis reviewed this nomenclative muddle and concluded that *P. macrocephalus* was the correct designation after all. When Schevill (1987) reworked the first description by Linnaeus, he became convinced that *P. catodon* was the proper name. The confusion led Shevill to wonder why taxonomists could not agree on a standard scientific name for a Sperm Whale when every layman all over the world knows that it is a unique species. In the book *Mammal Species of the World* (Wilson & Reeder, 1993), Mead and Brownwell reach the conclusion that the name *P. catodon* has priority over *P. macrocephalus.* To confuse matters even further, some contemporary researchers are seriously considering the removal of Sperm Whales from the suborder of toothed whales altogether and placing them in the suborder of baleen whales, with which they are obviously closely related. In 1995 anatomist Milinkovitch discovered that, other than molecular-genetic similarities, there are also remarkable anatomical affinities between sperm whales and baleen whales, in spite of the fact that the former do have teeth and only one blowhole like all other toothed whales. For instance, they are the only species of toothed whale with two nasal passages, which is a typical attribute of baleen whales. However, the two nasal passages of a sperm whale terminate in a single blowhole and not in two separate ones like baleen whales. This new systemic classification would mean that both suborders need to be reworked. In that case, the whales would have to be segmented into three new groups: Baleen whale-like (Balaenopteridea), sperm-whale-like (Physeteroidea) and dolphin-like (Delphinoidea).

Sperm whales are the only species of whale that have a very unusual and valuable substance in their intestines, namely ambergris. Fresh ambergris is a dark, frequently waxy substance with a foul smell in a highly concentrated dose. When ambergris dries out it becomes lighter in colour and density and gives off a strong musk-like odour. In the past it was used for various medicinal purposes. Today it is primarily used by the perfume industry. However, numerous countries have since prohibited its exploitation.

Ambergris is composed of undigested remains, primarily the beaks of cephalopods, and thus actually a form of excrement. Lumps of ambergris are either found in the intestines of dead Sperm Whales or as flotsam, and usually weigh around 0.5-10 kg. The largest lump of ambergris on record was found in the Antarctic in 1953 and weighed 450 kg. A 322 kg clump was discovered off the Azores in 1944. Ambergris is a very valuable substance that is worth as much as gold.

In his book *Navegaçao de Cabotagem,* Brazilian author Jorge Amado relates the true story of Karl Hansen, who was also known by the name of "Hansen Bahia." This impoverished German from Hamburg used to live in a tiny hut on Amaralina Beach in Bahia (Brazil). One day he found a strange lump that had washed up directly in front of his abode. In order to verify whether it was ambergris, he removed a small piece from it and then boarded a crowded trolley to town. A thorough examination of the probe confirmed that it was pure ambergris. Certain now that he was a rich man, Karl hailed a taxi in order to make it home as quickly as possible. Upon arrival the consternated man discovered that his donkey had eaten the entire lump of priceless ambergris.

The teeth of a Sperm Whale are also highly valued. During the early whaling days whalers used to pass the time engraving and carving the teeth of slaughtered Sperm Whales, an art form that became known as scrimshaw.

The echolocation of a Sperm Whale encompasses a great variety of soundwaves that serve it as a means of communication and orientation (acoustic sight). Sperm Whales swimming in a group will communicate with each other by making clicking sounds. Each individual sends out a steady barrage of pulsed clicks that somewhat resemble Morse code. Each animal can recognise and locate fellow group members on the basis of their distinctive signals. Sperm Whales can cover a sound spectrum of up to 15 octaves (humans only manage 3). The sounds themselves range from low (inaudible for humans) to high (both audible and inaudible for humans) frequencies. The sound repertoire of a Sperm Whale is limited to pulsed clicks. They do not produce musical tones like Humpback Whales. The pulsed clicks last about 2-30 mS each and range between 0.2-32 kHz in frequency. They are used for intraspecies communication, orientation and location of prey. Humans can only hear the lower frequency sounds ranging up to approximately 18 kHz. At rest, Sperm Whales emit about 6 clicks per second. Once a prey has been localised, the clicks are emitted at a faster rate. When the prey is caught and swallowed, the sounds will temporarily cease. It may well be that Sperm Whales also use their pulsed clicks to stun prey. The largest cephalopod ever found in the stomach of a Sperm Whale had tentacles 14 m long. It is assumed that larger animals such as these are either stunned or somehow immobilised by the clicking sounds.

Oelschläger, a German scientist, discovered that the pulsed clicks are vibrations produced in the soft parts of the head. Other than the nasal complex, this soft part is made up of a fatty mass known as the melon. This "acoustic lens" enables Sperm Whales to "see" their surroundings better than humans can with their eye lenses. A blindfolded dolphin, for example, has the ability to differentiate between two metal ball bearings that are almost identical in circumference - something a human would be incapable of. Sperm Whales have the largest melon of all whales. Besides serving as a buoyancy compensator, the melon (spermaceti organ) also functions as a focussing lens for the soundwaves of echolocation. Here the soundwaves are bundled and then transmitted in a fixed direction. The skull bones behind the melon act as a parabolic reflector that prevents emitted soundwaves from reaching the whale's ears and causing distracting disturbances.

Precise orientation requires more than just the exact transmission of sounds, however. An equally effective reception of reflected soundwaves is just as important. In the course of evolution the ears of a whale have adapted to this need. Sperm Whales have the most highly developed sense of hearing of all living beings. Their auditory nerve is made up of approximately 200,000 fibres (that of humans has about 50,000). For the sake of an optimised streamline flow, the outer ears of a whale have regressed considerably in the course of its evolution. In addition, the organ of hearing had to be properly isolated from the noises made by the whale itself so that the reception would not be impaired. The ear eventually separated itself from the skull bones and is now merely attached to the head by a connective tissue. This effectively isolates it from all other vibrations in the whale's head. The air-filled middle ear was retained, while the auditory canal has vanished right

Facts & Figures Sperm Whale	Quick ID-Check Sperm Whale
Size: bulls 15-18 m, max 20.7 m; cows 11-12 m	Huge, barrel-shaped head
Weight: about 35-57 t	
Longevity: approx 60-70 years	No dorsal fin, only a small hump
Sexual maturity: cows with 7-13 years; bulls with 18-20 years	Small flippers
Mating season: Late summer-early spring	
Gestation period: 15-16 months	Dark body with wrinkled skin
Calving interval: every 4-6 years	
Size at birth: approx 4 m	S-shaped blowhole offset to the front and left of the head
Weight at birth: approx 1 t	
Nursing period: at least 2, max 10 years	Raises fluke high when sounding
Dive depth: 600-1,000 m, max over 3,000 m	
Dive time: up to 60 min, max 2 hours 18 min	Straight termination of fluke
Maximum speed: 30 km/h	
Blow: 2-4 m high, offset to the front and left	Dives for a very long time, surface intervals short
Group (Pod) size: usually 1-40, rarely up to 100	
Population: approx 500.000-2,000,000; the exact number is unknown; although hunted intensively, they are not considered to be endangered	

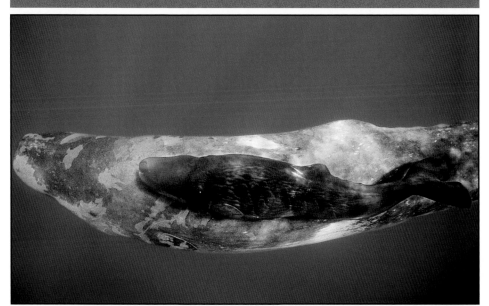

This dark-skinned calf stays close to its mother who is shedding her skin. Azores.   Doug Perrine

along with the outer ear. The outer ear became obsolete because soft tissues conduct soundwaves under water as well as the water itself. Air-filled cavities surrounding the ear form an additional barrier against disturbing noises.

The huge, toothed lower jaw of a Sperm Whale is definitely not crucial to its ability to hunt large cephalopods. Sperm Whales with deformed lower jaws are far from uncommon. The reason for this may be intraspecies confrontations, illness or even genetic defects. Such deformations apparently do not hinder the whale's hunting activities.

Where & When

The Sperm Whale is found worldwide in all oceans. They range from the polar ice edge to the equator in both hemispheres. They prefer deep waters and rarely come close to shore if the depth is less than 200 m. Their favourite haunts are deep submarine canyons in the vicinity of the continental shelf. During the summer the bulls migrate to the cold waters of the Arctic and Antarctic. At this time their range extends from the glaciers of the Antarctic to 75° latitude north in the Arctic. During the hemispherically respective winter months they migrate to their mating grounds in temperate and tropical waters. The cows always remain within 40° latitude south and 45° latitude north. A few populations are sedentary all year round, while others move about permanently in search of prey. Despite its wide distribution in the waters of the neighbouring Atlantic, this species is seldom encountered in the Mediterranean Sea.

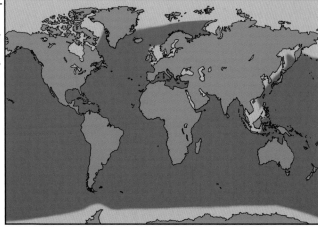

Sperm Whale, distribution: Worldwide in all deep offshore and inshore waters.

ENIGMATIC BELUGA

In Chedabucto Bay in the East Canadian Province of Nova Scotia, the underwater photographer Brian Skerry experienced some magical moments, sharing time and some amazing dives with "Wilma", a resident but enigmatic Beluga.

As I kneeled on the sloping gravel bottom, I leaned into the current, trying to steady myself. We were only ten metres deep, yet the particle-filtered sunlight had already reduced the visibility to that of a dimly-lit pub, and my eyes strained against the featureless green water, waiting for the shape to appear. An icy trickle of sea water was meandering down my back as I turned to see Jim, three metres away, rhythmically clicking two stones together in an attempt to telegraph some sort of benthic greeting into the deep.

When I turned back into the current, I saw her. She seemed to materialise from the green haze at the edge of my visibility as a pure-white apparition, moving slowly towards us, growing larger. She swam past me and gently approached Jim, inverting her body so that her 'melon' – the bulging forehead – rubbed the gravel bottom. I watched the two of them slowly bounce along the slope, twisting and pirouetting, kicking up small clouds of silt as they travelled in what appeared to be choreographed moves that only they knew.

PHOTOS: BRIAN SKERRY

Orphan Wilma craved company and delighted in playing with divers.

Thoroughly entranced, yet aware of why I was here, I brought my camera to bear and began firing. As we drifted into deeper water the current became swifter, the light grew dimmer and the dance between diver and whale dissolved as quickly as it had begun. Once again, Jim and I were alone in the cold sea. Not unlike Ahab, I too had travelled in search of the white whale. My journey, however, was not motivated by vengeance, but by intrigue. What drew me to a small bay in eastern Canada was a story that sounded much like a fable.

The story began in the autumn of 1993, when two Beluga whales were first seen swimming together at the mouth of Chedabucto Bay, Nova Scotia, near the open sea. The following spring, a female adult Beluga was found dead on a beach, her body riddled with bullet holes. Around the same time, various fishermen, who plied these waters on a daily basis, reported seeing the smaller whale in the region of a navigational buoy that marked a channel close to shore. Now orphaned, it seemed as though the young whale had settled upon the buoy – which was always in the same position, rattling and clanging – as a surrogate mother. What intrigued me most, however, were the rumours about the whale's interaction with humans.

It was during my quest to learn more about this legendary whale that I came into contact with Jim Johnson, a diver who resided near Chedabucto Bay. Like the story of the whale, Jim Johnson's life also seemed to have been torn from the pages of a storybook. Nearing his sixtieth year, Jim had experienced much in his life. He had sailed the world before the mast, lived in

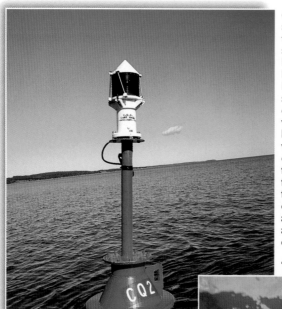

exotic locales, spent time on whaling ships as an observer, and worked throughout Canada's pack ice as a conservation officer with the sealing fleet. He worked on the production of MGM's 'Mutiny on the Bounty' in French Polynesia, initially as part of the support crew, ultimately becoming a cast member doing underwater stunt work, most notably the dangerous keelhauling scenes. In the 1960's, Jim was part of a documentary film expedition to Cocos Island, Costa Rica that focused on treasure hunting. Other film projects, mostly involving sharks, followed. Although he reflected fondly on these past adventures, Jim readily admitted to never having encountered anything quite like what was now occurring in Chedabucto Bay.

I was told that the whale's name was 'Wilma', though it was unclear as to who had actually named her. Jim explained how he had befriended Wilma by diving with her often and how this whale truly seemed to seek out human contact. In summer months, she could be found frolicking with kayakers and canoeists; in the winter months, she greeted sea urchin divers working at the bottom of the harbour. It seemed that Wilma had indeed found her home in Chedabucto Bay.

The morning of my first dive in Chedabucto Bay was picture-perfect. The July sun sparkled through the thick foliage surrounding the hills that sheltered the bay, and the sky was clear and crisp. As I stood in knee-deep water on the boat ramp, waiting for the trailer to back down, I inhaled the combined sweet fragrance of freshly cut grass and cool salt water. Although it was midsummer (with air temperatures of perhaps 24°C), the water was still quite cool. Having chosen greater mobility over guaranteed (albeit cumbersome)

After her mother died Wilma became attached to a mooring buoy sited in the mouth of Chedabucto Bay. The buoy appeared to act as a surrogate mother for the 5 or 6-year-old whale.

warmth, I had selected a full 7 mm wetsuit. However, I could already tell that a drysuit would have been more comfortable.

With the inflatable boat now free from the trailer, we hoisted ourselves over the pontoons and fired up the outboard. We navigated slowly through the array of moored lobster boats, and then altered course for the far side of the bay. Despite the fantastic stories that Jim told about Wilma, it was hard for me to believe that I, too, would actually confront this mythical (at least to my mind) creature.

Kneeling at a depth of about 17 m, a cloud of sand particles swirled around my head. It had happened. I had actually come face-to-face with Wilma. Within seconds of the encounter, it was already beginning to seem like a dream.

I needed something more to convince me that this was real. I looked at Jim, hoping for some form of sign language that would indicate she would soon return. Jim simply pointed towards the surface with his thumb. It was time to get out.

I fought the strong current holding my camera housing in one hand, as I kicked hard and pulled myself along the rocks with my free hand, trying to inch my way back to the point where I could exit. We ascended the slope and surfaced, wading towards the beach with a torrent of tide rippling around our bodies. We shed some gear and cast our attention towards the middle of the bay, looking for some sign of the animal we have seen underwater. "Over there", Jim said, and pointed to a large, red buoy 100 metres away.

The ivory back of a whale slowly porpoising was easily distinguishable against the dark water. We dragged

Wilma would cautiously swim up to visiting snorkellers, sizing up the intruder. She would also happily follow swimmers down to the sea bed and gradually move closer and closer, keeping eye contact.

One of Wilma's interactions with humans.

our Zodiac off the beach and motored across the bay towards the buoy. When we were within 30 metres of it, we cut the engine and slowed to a drift. The morning quiet was broken by the loud sound of exhalation and the gentle lapping of water. I looked out to the sound and saw a four-metres whale, directly off our port side and heading right for the boat.

She glided in smoothly and rolled upside down as she passed underneath the boat. I scrambled for my fins, grabbed my camera housing and slipped into the water. I snorkelled away from the boat and as I glanced back, I saw a white shape gaining fast in my wake. I stopped swimming and hung motionless, waiting to see what would happen. The Beluga swam within touching distance, turning its head as if to size me up. Taking three quick breaths, I held the last and did a jack-knife dive, heading for the bottom, hoping the whale would follow. As the muddy bottom came into view, I rolled on my back and was startled to see the whale's silhouette, just one and a half metre directly above me.

She moved in cautiously, inverting her body, and stared straight into my eyes. I could not believe what was happening: This wild animal was choosing to make contact! I felt as if I had been thrust into the midst of a mystical New Age poster! I extended my hand and lightly scratched her head. Her eyes closed slowly, as if to signal her fondness for touch. We slowly drifted across the field of sand dollars, skates and flounders carpeting the floor of this magical cove, like long-lost friends becoming reacquainted after a long spell apart. Losing track of time and having forgotten the need to breathe, the aching in my lungs jolted me back to reality, insisting I immediately return to the surface.

The hours of interaction passed quickly as I, too, learned the choreography of Beluga ballet. We swam circles around her 'mother', the buoy, raced along the surface and floated together in the emerald sea. Occasionally we would pause from our games and rest at the surface. She lay, sunlight rippling along her body, and she would lift my hand with her muzzle as if inviting me to stroke her back and scratch her head. I needed no encouragement. I removed my neoprene mitt and I ran my hand along Wilma's dorsal region. It felt smooth and soft and I watched her eyes close slowly as I stroked her body.

With the sun beginning to slip below the tree line and my body chilled to the bone, I had extended my stay as long as possible. Finally, I fell back into the Zodiac, drawing to a close my first encounter with this magnificent animal.

I made several more trips to Chedabucto Bay. Each journey renewed my faith in miracles, for I saw extraordinary things. I watched Wilma bring fish and lobsters to Jim, seated in his boat, in a way which could only be described as bearing gifts. I saw her invent games that seemed to amuse herself, including one in which she would play 'catch' with a frond of kelp plucked from the bottom. In addition, I watched her 'inspect' boat anchors, stand on her head, and swim with children. Whenever Jim or I would return to the Zodiac and she still wished to play, she would encourage us back into the water by gently tugging at the nearest hand. Mostly, though, I simply treasured the time spent in her company.

I also wondered about Wilma's life apart from people. Beluga whales are known to dive deeper than 1,000 metres and hold their breath for up to twenty-five minutes when searching for food. I was curious to know if she, too, was occasionally venturing out into deeper water. Chedabucto Bay appeared to have a plentiful supply of fish and invertebrates, which make up the major part of a Beluga's diet, so perhaps such hunting trips were unnecessary. The region of the bay in which Wilma was most often seen is an estuarine system, being fed by a freshwater river.

Beluga calves are dark- to brownish grey at birth and become pure white between the ages of 5 and 12.

Beluga whales are known to frequent rivers in certain areas of the world and have even been observed 500 miles up the Yukon River in Alaska. This prolonged contact with fresh water is often related to the moulting of the Beluga's skin. I had seen Wilma only perhaps one mile upriver, but wondered if she had made much further journeys as well, and mused on the notion that she had grown a little bit bigger with each return. I also knew that these polar whales were called 'sea canaries' due to their varied vocal abilities. Using the blowhole on the top of their head, Beluga whales create whistling birdcalls and noises made by boats. Although I never heard Wilma reproducing such sounds, I wondered if at times she too called out into the sea and whether or not there was ever a response.

In the winter of 1999, Wilma was seen for the last time in Chedabucto Bay. It was predicted that upon reaching sexual maturity, (around the age of seven), the Beluga might very well swim off in search of a mate. Many hoped that Wilma might attract a mate to her and begin a family in Chedabucto Bay and so become the southernmost population of Beluga whales. This hope was actually plausible, since at one time many, many years ago, such a population did exist. Unfortunately, due to the temper of the times, they were wiped out by hunting. But the hoped-for Chedabucto pod was not to be.

The bay has returned to the way it was in 1992, before Wilma, when a resident whale was but a dream. A beautiful, quaint harbour remains, with brightly-coloured lobster boats tied to moorings. Ospreys still dive for fish, seals continue to hunt here in winter and the river feeding into the bay still ebbs and flows. All that is missing is the white whale.

It is easy to wax anthropomorphic in the case of Wilma and to speculate on our 'inter-species communication', since the experiences I had with her were so unlikely anything I had ever known with other wild animals. Likewise, for those of an analytical bent, it is not especially difficult to theorise as to why this animal sought human contact: She was orphaned, she was young and she was lonely.

Either way, sharing time with her was amazing. One might even say, magical. Maybe, just maybe, she thinks so too.

Wilma would spend hours swimming with divers. She would play tag with you, and would even tug at your hand if you returned to the boat before she had finished playing.

The numerous species of the **DOLPHINS** (in a wider sense, Delphinoidea) are subdivided into 3 families: Family White Whales, Monodontidae
2 species: Beluga, *Delphinapterus leucas*
Narwhal, *Monodon monocerus*
Family Dolphins, Delphinidae (following the Monodontidae)
Family Porpoises, Phocoenidae (following the Delphinidae)

Distinguishing Characteristics of these Families

All members of these three families have streamlined bodies that range from 1.2 m (Vaquita, Finless Porpoise) to 10 m (Killer Whale) in length. Not all species have a snout that is markedly set off against the melon and the site of highly precise echolocation. But almost all of the species have a large number of small, conical teeth in both jaws. Exceptions are Risso's Dolphins and Narwhals (lower jaw toothless, upper jaw 0-2 teeth). Most species have a fluke with a conspicuous median notch and, with few exceptions, well developed dorsal fins. Another common characteristic is the pronounced social structure of the groups, which can number from a few hundred to a thousand or more specimens in especially rich feeding grounds.

Beluga, *Delphinapterus leucas*

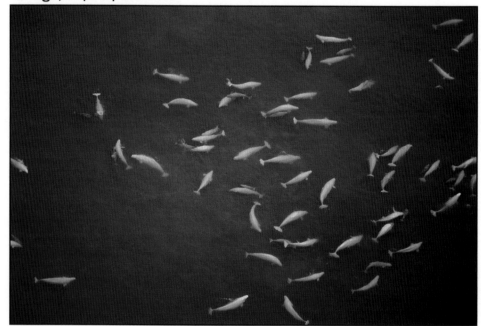

During the summer thousands of Belugas gather in river estuaries of the Arctic.   All Photos R. Kiefner

Distinguishing Characteristics

Mature Belugas are white, sometimes also yellowish in colour, and have a stocky body with a bulbous melon. They do not have a dorsal fin. Instead, some individuals have a small dorsal ridge that is darker than the rest of the body. Belugas are the only white whales found in the cold inshore waters of the Arctic and Subarctic.

Description

Belugas can attain a length of 4-6 m and weigh around 0.4-1.5 t. Their rounded bodies are quite stocky. In adaptation to the Arctic environment, they are protected by a relatively thick layer of blubber. Males only differ from females in size. Mature bulls are approximately 25% larger than the cows and have a more developed musculature. In contrast to many other species of whale, there are few recognisable differences between individual Belugas. The relatively small head of a Beluga has a very prominent melon that can vary in shape. Its snout is very small and its cervical vertebrae are not attached to each other. Its spade-like flippers are wide and highly movable. The flippers of an adult animal curl upwards like those of a Narwhal. The termination of the fluke is convex (increasingly so with age) with a well developed median notch and occasionally also a dark-brown border. The flukes of adult animals often curve upwards, while those of the young are almost always straight. Belugas have 10-22 conical teeth in their upper jaws and 6-22 of them in their lower jaws. Depending upon its eating habits and the quantity of substrate, the teeth of a Beluga will usually be worn down by the time it is 8 years old. The teeth are composed of alternating layers of transparent and opaque dentine from which it is possible to determine the animal's age. The transparent layers develop during the summer mating season when food is

Worn down teeth of a Beluga.

scarce, while the opaque layers grow when the Belugas are in their nutrient rich feeding grounds. An adult Beluga has a characteristic white to yellowish colouration. The colour of the younger whales varies from brown to blue-grey, which is why they are referred to as "Blues." This colour will gradually pale as the animals reach maturity.

Easily Mistaken For
Because of the great similarity between Beluga and Irrawaddi Dolphin, some systematists place the latter in the same family. Indeed, they look very much alike in colour and shape of the body. The Irrawaddi Dolphin also has an unfused neck as well as a few other anatomical parities in the structure of the head. In a sense it is the "tropical counterpart" of a Beluga, as each species lives in an entirely different region. Belugas live in Arctic and Subarctic waters, while Irrawaddi Dolphins prefer the shallow coastal and fluvial waters of the tropical Indo-Pacific. Consequently, it is practically impossible to mix them up. Furthermore, in contrast to Belugas, an Irrawaddi Dolphin has a small, quasi-triangular dorsal fin and a less prominent melon. In spite of their conspicuous colour, Belugas can be difficult to detect on the surface, especially when they are swimming close to ice floes.

Other Names
White Whale, Beluga Whale, Sea Canary (English); Weißwal, Weißer Delphin (German); Bélouga (French); Beluga (Spanish); Beluga, Golfinho Branco (Portuguese); Witte Dolfijn (Dutch); Hvithval, Hvidvisk (Norwegian); Maitovalas (Finnish); Vitval (Swedish); Hvidhval (Danish); Belukha (Russian).

Meaning of the Scientific Nomenclature
Delphinapterus leucas (Pallas 1776) - The generic name *Delphinapterus* is composed of the Greek word *delphinos* (dolphin), the prefix *a* (without) and *pteros* (wings). The species name stems from the Greek *leucos* (white). In translation the scientific name means "white dolphin without wings," with reference to the colour of the species and the missing dorsal fin.

Behaviour
Belugas are very social and curious animals. They often raise their heads out of the water while swimming and look around (spy-hopping). When they do so, they keep their bodies in a vertical position and often nod or turn their heads. Even though they are shortsighted on the surface, they spy-hop so often that dried out eyes is common affliction among them. It has been proven that they purposely squint in order to see better on the surface. Belugas normally swim slowly and spend most of their time near the surface. Surface activities like surfing, bow-riding, lob-tailing of flipper-slapping have seldom been observed in the wild.

Left: Belugas obviously enjoy rubbing off their old skin on the gravel bottom of shallow rivers where they literally "take a warm bath". The warm river water soaks the skin and makes it softer which facilitates the shedding process.

Below: When rubbing off their skin, Belugas often partly emerge from the water.

They will only breach when taught to do so in captivity. Their swimming motions are smooth and wave-like. Their normal velocity while migrating ranges from 8-18 km/h, but if threatened they can briefly speed up to more than 30 km/h. Belugas either sleep "hanging from the surface" or close to the bottom in shallow water where they will occasionally prop themselves up with their flippers. They surface to breathe in regular intervals of 3 min.

Belugas are well adapted to an inshore life between blocks of floating ice and manoeuvre around shallow waters with great agility. As long as they do not fall prey to some predator like a polar bear, Belugas stand a good chance of surviving if they should happen to strand. They simply wait out the low tide and then crawl like a seal to safety once the high tide moves in. It has been observed that the males frequently gather in a rosette formation, whereby they form a circle with their heads together in the middle and their flukes facing the periphery. They obviously communicate with each other quite intensively on such an occasion. They also frequently keep their mouths wide open, but not as a show of aggression. Instead, they appear to be testing their strength in a playful manner much like puppy dogs tend to do. Curiously, untrained captive Belugas like to drive away (unwelcome?) guests standing at the edge of the basin by spitting fountains of water in their direction. This remarkable behaviour has been observed in aquariums in New York, Vancouver and Duisburg. Irrawaddi Dolphins are known to behave in the same way. It could be that they use this technique to bring down small animals sitting on overhanging branches or to uncover prey hidden in the sand.

During the summer thousands of Belugas gather in the estuaries of their respective ranges, where the water is "warmer" than along the coast. Here they rub themselves along the gravel or sand on the river bottom in order to scrape off their moulting skin. The old layer of skin is yellowish rather than white and infested with parasites. The warmer water causes the old skin to well up and this makes it easier for the animals to scrape it off. In addition, the warmer water also activates certain hormones that speed up the moulting process and promote the growth of fresh skin and blubber. This kind of skin hygiene is not practised by Belugas in captivity because the water in their basins is kept at a constant temperature. The estuaries with their more temperate waters are also a perfect place for younger Belugas to grow up in until they can acquire an adequate layer of isolating blubber. This they will not only need in order to stay warm in the cold Arctic waters, but also as an energy reserve for their annual migrations.

Belugas are really at home in the shallow coastal waters, rivers and estuaries of the Arctic. Individual animals, however, will spend the entire year in the Gulf of St. Lawrence (North Atlantic) and the Cook and Yukatat inlets in Alaska (Northern Pacific). Belugas have a preference for ice-covered regions in which the wind and currents have opened up narrow passages where they can surface to breathe. Occasionally they will also swim along the polar ice edge or into permanently ice-free regions. Only when they are migrating will they venture out upon the open ocean. In spring, when the pack ice begins to melt and channels open up, the Belugas migrate in smaller groups to the more temperate waters of the estuaries. In the summer, when even more of the pack ice has melted, they gather in herds of hundreds and even thousands of animals and migrate far upriver. Belugas have been sighted more than 700 km inland in Alaska's Yukon River. They have even been known to swim almost 2,000 km upstream in the Argun River, in the former Soviet Union. In 1966 a disoriented Beluga named "Moby Dick" by the local media swam 400 km up the Rhine River. Another one was sighted before Hamburg's gangways on the Elbe River. A Beluga tagged west of Hudson Bay (Canada) in summer, was sighted 800 km farther north 7 weeks later.

In spite of their long migration routes, Belugas are slow swimmers. This makes them an easy prey for Killer Whales and polar bears. Polar bears lie in wait for them along fissures in the pack ice where they come up to breathe. As soon as a Beluga surfaces, the bear hooks the whale with its sharp claws and drags it out of the water. Once it was observed how a Beluga stranded in a shallow puddle at low tide was torn to pieces by a polar bear in less than half a minute.

During the summer migrations male and female Belugas remain together. Otherwise they live in groups of 5-20 animals that are separated by gender. "Nursing Groups" are made up of females with their young, while "Blues Groups" are composed of male rowdies 3-4 years old. The adult and sexually mature males living in "Bachelor Groups" will preside over a "harem" during the mating season. Rutting females are often pursued by several males. During copulation, which takes a relatively long time, both partners swim in circles close to the surface. Calves are born during the summer (usually in July) following a gestation period of 14.5 months. They average around 1.4-1.7 m in length and weigh about 45-75 kg. The calves are nursed for about 20 months with rich mother's milk containing 22-23% fat. They maintain close contact to their mothers, often riding on their backs in order to conserve energy. The calves will remain with their mothers until they become sexually mature at the age of about 6 years. This is why Beluga cows with two calves are a fairly common sight. While the younger calf is still being nursed, its older sibling will fend for itself but still remain with the "family."

There are 7 different Beluga populations and their various migration patterns have been carefully observed via satellite. The Belugas from **Somerset Island** (Canada) wander anti-clockwise in a northwesterly direction to Perl Sound, a channel running between Somerset Island and Prince of Wales Island. Here they spend the month of August consuming huge quantities of polar codfish. In the beginning of September they continue northwards into the Barrow Strait, where they gorge themselves with polar codfish again on their way along the southern coast of Devon Island. From here they will pass through Lancaster Sound and head for the open waters of northern Baffin Bay. On their way to Greenland they take advantage of the large ice-free zones created by the wind and ocean currents. Once they arrive, probably about 1/5 of the population will spend the winter there. The remainder keep going along the coast of Greenland until they reach 75° latitude north around mid-October. From there they swim along the deep fjords in a southerly direction until they are stopped by the pack ice edge around Disko Island. Here they patrol up and down the ice edge all winter long.

In May, when the ice begins to melt, the Belugas set off on their long journey back to Lancaster Sound. During this migration they occasionally join up with the "northern winter population" and together they head along the southern shores of Lancaster Sound to Prince Regent Inlet (west of Somerset Island) or Cunningham Inlet (north of Somerset Island). The highest concentration of Belugas around Somerset Island occurs in late July-early August, during the full-moon springtide. Then the Belugas will gather in the river estuaries in order to shed their moulting skins. At this time aerial photographs will be taken of them and their numbers counted. This regular monitoring has shown that these temporary gatherings involve the entire population.

Another population originating from the **western part of Hudson Bay** leaves its summer range and makes its way north to Hudson Strait, where it meets up with a smaller population from the eastern part of Hudson Bay. Together they head for their winter feeding grounds. The **Mackenzie** population migrates past the southern and northern coasts of Banks Island and reunites at the southern shore of Melville Island. Amazingly, the Mackenzie population does not interact with the Somerset Island population even though they are just a few kilometres apart at this time. The Mackenzie population spends the winter along the ice edge as far as the Bering Sea. Remnant populations of Belugas also exist in the polar regions of Russia and Norway, but little is known about their numbers and migration patterns.

For many years now, Dr. Thomas Smith, one of the leading experts on Belugas, has been studying the behaviour of groups of these whales in the coastal regions and estuaries of the Arctic with the help of satellite stations. Part of his work consists in capturing Belugas in the shallow estuaries and attaching transmitters to them. In a painlessly process, the transmitters are anchored in the blubber with long nails. After about three months the nails grow out of the blubber and the whales lose the transmitters, which cost around US$ 15,000 each. An incredible amount of data is transmitted during this short period. More than 60 Belugas have been captured and tagged in this way since 1987. The objectives of this expensive operation, which is being financed by the Canadian government, are to gather additional information about the whales' behaviour on the open sea, their migration routes and their dive depths as little is known about these activities. See also ENIGMATIC BELUGA on the pages 140-145.

Diving
Belugas manoeuvre expertly between ice floes and, thanks to their unfused necks, are able to catch their prey in narrow fissures along the sheet of ice. Their typical diving behaviour consists of several shallow and short dives followed by one deep dive. The shallow dives average around 20 m and last for 1-3 min; the deep dives can reach 600 m and last for 5-20 minutes.

More recent studies have shown that Belugas will venture far underneath the sheet of ice, where they always manage to find a breathing hole. It is likely that they scan the dark underside of the ice sheet for light spots indicating where the vital breathing holes are. From an aeroplane these breathing holes are also visible as dark round holes in the sheet of ice. When the melted ice mixes with the salt water, however, they appear as milky-white spots on the surface of the ice sheet.

Feeding Habits
Belugas have the most varied diet of all whales. They feed on various fish (capelin, sand eels, coalfish, diverse species of Arctic cod, herring, flounder, halibut, salmon, shellfish), crustaceans (shrimp) and cephalopods (octopus), as well as molluscs and other invertebrates. Sand, rubble and algae found in the stomach contents of Belugas indicate that they are primarily bottom-feeders, even though they also effectively hunt shoaling fish. Captive animals will even nibble at the sealing compound on the bottom of the basin.

In part, Belugas feed on the same prey as their near relatives, the Narwhals. However, the summer and winter feeding grounds of both species vary so that there is no competition between them for food. When they do meet up with each other they apparently avoid competition by searching for food at different depths. Perhaps this separation has something to do with the availability of food. Whereas the Narwhals prefer to gather and hunt in the deep and clear waters of the fjords, Belugas tend to remain in frequently turbid waters of the shallow bays. On rare occasions hundreds of representatives of both species come together.

Newly-developed intestinal sensors hidden inside of prey will soon round off our knowledge about the feeding habits of Belugas. These sensors transmit the intestinal temperature of the animal and its current depth. If the temperature suddenly drops during a dive, the whale has just ingested food at that depth. In this way it is also possible to gather information about the seasonal migration routes of the biomass in the Arctic Ocean. Very little is known about the migrations of the Belugas' principal prey, the Arctic cod. This up to 46 cm long shoaling fish is the most important link in the food chain of the entire Arctic Ocean. All

With a lot of luck and a warm diving suit one may succeed in photographing a Beluga in the wild.

marine mammals (whales, seals) and numerous species of bird and fish of the region primarily feed on Arctic cod. This fish tends to remain under the ice sheet where it can hide from predators in countless nooks and fissures. The numbers of Arctic cod that have been estimated to exist close to the surface do not suffice to provide nourishment for all marine mammals of the region. Belugas have a daily consumption of food that corresponds to about 3% of their total weight. During the ice-free Arctic summer huge schools of Arctic cod may well remain concealed 500 m below the surface in hollowed out spaces on the seabed. At this depth the Arctic cod may find some protection, but at the cost of a sinking body temperature which in turn impairs its mobility and makes it an easier prey for warm-blooded predators. The intestinal sensors have shown that Belugas do indeed descend to deep and wide hollows at the bottom of the Arctic Ocean, but little is known about the organisms living there. During the summer, when Belugas gather in the estuaries to rub off their moulting skins, their stomachs are almost empty and their layers of blubber are pretty much used up. During the mating season they have little interest in food.

General Information
In the years 1768-1774, German naturalist Peter Simon Pallas undertook several expeditions to Siberia. During one of these expeditions he witnessed the harpooning of a white whale where the Ob River empties into the Kara Sea (West Siberia), which he later described in his travelogue. In 1776 he named the newly-discovered white "dolphin" *Delphinus leucas*.

Its common name, Beluga, derives from the Russian word *belukha* (white one). It wasn't until 1804 that French naturalist Bernard Lacépède took note of the missing dorsal fin and established the order *Delphinapterus* for this species. A possible relationship with river dolphins (family Platanistidae) on the basis of the unfused neck could not be confirmed with a DNS analysis. The fused necks of most other cetaceans have a definite advantage in that their heads always retain an upstream position without the slightest muscular exertion. But since Belugas are slow swimmers, the unfused neck is not much of a disadvantage. On the contrary, it is very useful in searching for nourishment. In their outward appearance, Belugas are very similar to Irrawaddi Dolphins. Both species of whale are also able to affect their mimic by changing the form of their melons. Because of these anatomical similarities earlier systematists located both species in the family of Delphinapteridae. In 1984, Barnes placed them in the family of **Monodontidae** along with Narwhals. Many contemporary systematists reject this and it has not been adopted here either. On the basis of certain morphological similarities, the Irrawaddi Dolphin is classified under the family of **Delphinidae**.

Because of the extraordinary variety of sounds they make (whistles, cries, creaks, squeaks, roars, rasps, clicks) Belugas were referred to as "Sea Canaries" by the early seamen. The sounds (0.7-20 kHz), which can be clearly heard through a ship's hull as well as on the surface, are an important medium for intraspecies communication. The high squeaking sounds made by stranded or threatened Belugas probably express fear, while the panting rasps emitted by animals resting on the surface seem to convey pleasure. Resistance and aggression are communicated by snapping the jaws and bulging out the front part of the melon. A closed mouth and flattened melon signal friendliness. Other than communication, the high-frequency sounds are also used for orientation and localising prey.

Belugas can change the shape of their very prominent melons while making sounds. Thereby they vary the frequency of the emitted soundwaves and/or bundle them in various degrees of intensity. Thanks to the pliability of their melons Belugas are not only able to create a great variety of sounds, but also change their mimic. Perhaps this "cute" feature is why some of them are still being held captive in sea aquariums. Like all other toothed whales, a Beluga's melon houses its spermaceti organ. With it the whale is able to bundle and transmit soundwaves in a predetermined direction. The sounds are produced when the whale sets the vestibules in the nasal passage and the larynx vibrating by pressing air into them. Reflected soundwaves are collected by a very thin layer of bone in the lower jaw and then relayed over a fatty deposit to the middle ear.

Belugas probably have the most sophisticated echolocation system of all whales. Studies have shown that their echolocation is comparable to that of Bottlenose Dolphins. Both species have the ability to distinguish between objects that are 100 m away. Belugas, however, are less susceptible to irritation from background noises than Bottlenose Dolphins.

Belugas can even break through acoustic barriers. They are able to send and receive signals through a sheet of ice. This ability is undoubtedly crucial to their survival while swimming under the pack ice as it helps them to keep their orientation and to locate breathing holes. Like all toothed whales, Belugas will come to the aid of their relatives when they signal fear or danger. Belugas in Bristol Bay (Alaska) were lured away from salmon nets by the transmission of recorded sounds made by Killer Whales, their arch enemies.

Belugas are protected from the elements by a dense layer of blubber that, depending upon age, nutrition, anatomy and season, can attain a thickness of 2-22 cm. The skin of a Beluga, which is called *muktuk* in the language of the Inuit (Eskimo), is the richest source of vitamin C in the entire animal kingdom. It has the same vitamin C content as oranges. For this reason it is a vital component of the Inuit diet. During the fall its vitamin C content is much higher than in the summer, when the skins of the Belugas begin to moult. The outer skin (epidermis) of a Beluga is 5-12 mm thick, making it one of the densest in the animal kingdom. In comparison, the human epidermis averages 0.03-2.5 mm in thickness. In the cold Arctic waters the renewal of a Beluga's epidermis proceeds at a much lower rate than among humans and consequently it is much more likely to be befallen by parasites. These will eventually turn the skin yellow. Belugas prefer water temperatures ranging from −1.8° C in the

Facts & Figures Beluga	**Quick ID-Check Beluga**
Size: 4-6 m	
Weight: 0.4-1.5 t	Conspicuous white (at times yellowish) colour
Longevity: 30-40 years	
Sexual maturity: cows with 5 years; bulls with 8-10 years	No dorsal fin
Mating season: Spring-Summer	Compact body
Gestation period: 14.5 months	
Calving interval: every 3 years	Small, flexible head
Size at birth: 1.5 m	
Weight at birth: 45-75 kg	Prominent melon
Nursing period: 18-23 months	
Dive depth: max 600 m	Slow swimmer
Dive time: 15-20 min	
Maximum speed: bursts of 30 km/h	Frequent spy-hopping
Teeth: 10-22 conical teeth in upper jaw, 6-22 in lower jaw	Range in the high Arctic
Group (Pod) size: 5-20, up to several thousand in the summer	
Population: approx 10.000-20,000	

winter to 3° C in the summer, with a high of 9° C in the estuaries. Because Belugas live close to the ice edge, they occasionally become locked within ice holes, in which case they are an easy prey for polar bears or Inuit hunters. In the Inuit language these ice traps are called *sassat,* which means something like "filled up" and is an apt description of the situation.

The most spectacular attempt to free whales entrapped by ice took place in the Senjawin Strait, south of the Bering Strait, in December of 1984, when the Soviet administration organised the rescue of some 3,000 Belugas enclosed by thick pack ice. It took the huge icebreaker "Moskwa" almost a month to make its way through 19 km of pack ice and reach the trapped whales. In the meantime helpers worked round the clock to keep the breathing hole clear, which was far too small for so many whales to begin with. The real problems began when the icebreaker finally reached the site. No one could tell the captain just how he was supposed to make the whales understand that they had to follow the ship out of the ice hole. After four days of fruitless efforts, the attempt was made to lure the whales with music. Various melodies and styles of music were tried out, whereby it became apparent that Belugas seemed to have a predilection for classical music. At the end of February the "Moskwa" finally sailed out of the ice hole with music booming from numerous loudspeakers and successfully led about 2,000 Belugas back to freedom.

About 700 Belugas are still being killed by humans each season in the region of the former Nuuk (Godthåb) in southern Greenland alone. The population there has been reduced by 75% in the meantime. The seasonal appearance of large numbers of Belugas has led Greenlanders to the false assumption that there are multitudes of these white whales. At present the Canadian government is spending a lot of money to prove that the Canadian and Greenlander Belugas are one and the same group. The attempt is being made to ascertain the exact size of the population and whether it is already endangered or not. In the 1980s the population was estimated at approximately 20,000-23,000 animals. Today it is less than half that size and will take very long to recover, if at all.

Estimates of the total stock of Belugas vary considerably. Prior estimates are usually inflated as a result of the massive seasonal congregations of whales in the estuaries. Present-day estimates of the worldwide population of Belugas range from 10,000-20,000 individuals. The growth rate of a herd of Belugas is 8% per annum at the most. Females are sexually mature at the age of 5; males at the age of 8-10. A female Beluga can conceive until it is about 21 years old. With a calving interval of three years with only one offspring each time, this means a maximum of 6 births during the entire life span of a single Beluga cow.

Other than Killer Whales, the natural enemies of Belugas include Greenland sharks *(Somniosus microcephalus)* and polar bears *(Ursus maritimus).*

Where & When

Belugas mainly live in the shallow waters, rivers and estuaries of the Arctic and Subarctic. Groups of Belugas can also be sighted the year round in the Gulf of St. Lawrence and the Northern Pacific (as far north as Cook and Yakutat inlets in Alaska). Seasonal occurrence and migration routes depend on the extent of the ice edge. Their range can extend north to 80° and south to 46° latitude (mouth of the St. Lawrence River). In the winter they prefer to live in regions with loose pack ice. During the summer thousands of Belugas gather in the shallow and warmer bays and estuaries, e.g. in Somerset Island (Canada). Belugas can usually be sighted in the calm, shallow coastal waters with rocky or sandy bottoms off Scandinavia, Russia, Greenland and North America (Canada, Alaska). They tend to avoid the surf zone. Sightings on the open sea are only possible when they migrate.

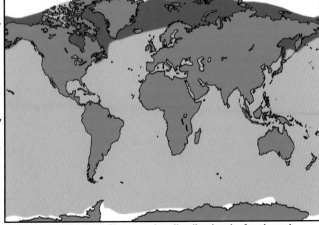

Beluga, distribution: Circumpolar distribution in Arctic and Subarctic waters as far as the ice edge.

WHALING WITH A CAMERA

The old fisherman Sigurbjörn Sörensson, who lives in the small fishing village of Husavik in northern Island, is a member of an unpopular minority. He and a handful of other Islanders have come to the conclusion that it is better to make whales a tourist attraction than to kill them. "Living whales," Sörenson argues, "will do a lot more for our country than dead whales." And the old man is absolutely right. The author was there to see for himself and came away convinced.

To promote whale watching in a country that has been in the news so often during the past few years for its whaling activities may seem paradoxical at first. But if some additional income could be generated by whale-watching tourism here then it would really be another important step towards the general protection of whales in Europe. Whale watching can replace whaling, and is certainly more a more humane and profitable activity.

Whaling was discontinued in Island in 1988 following the international boycott of its fishing industry. Since 2/3 of the island's exports are fish products, this boycott had a disastrous effect on its economy. In spite of this, more than 95% of the Islanders are in favour of resuming commercial whaling without being able to give a plausible reason for why it should be done. Even though it is practically impossible to market whale meat nowadays and the potential demand for it in the local restaurants can hardly be considered a lucrative venture, Island's whalers are busy refurbishing their whaling ships.

This attitude can only be understood as a public act of defiance against the international boycott, as well as a very personal expression of anxiety about having to adapt to economic changes. At any rate, the threat of another international boycott is the only thing that still keeps Island's whalers at bay. "Whaling is legitimate, important and necessary because there are far too many whales and they are eating up all of our fish," is frequently heard comment around here.

Fact of the matter is, that recently enforced fishing quota have led to a marked increase in the local fish population. However, this did not come to pass without drastic consequences for Island's inhabitants. The international boycott and the fishing quotas are what forced 65-year-old Sigurbjörn Sörensson to give up his profession. For many generations he and his family fished the waters around Island in their old cutter, the "Knörrinn." "We used to catch up to 900 tonnes of fish a year," he recalls proudly.

In those days there were still a lot seals, dolphins and whales in the bay, but no one paid much attention to them. It wasn't until much later, when they had some free time on their hands, that Sörensson and his family discovered just how fascinating these animals could be. Since they did not feel like scrapping their old cutter just because fishing was no longer profitable, they modified it into a comfortable whale-watching boat. The first such vessel on the island.

They hit upon the idea a few years ago when the first whales were sighted again in the bay of Husavik. Today various species of dolphin can be encountered here along with Minke Whales, Fin Whales and, more recently, even Humpback Whales. It should be noted, however, that the inhabitants of this sleepy little fishing village in the northwest of Island were actually never in the whaling business. The whalers came from the surroundings communities where it was well known that this bay was a habitual meeting place for whales.

Sigurbjörn, captain of the "Knörrinn" once more, and his sons Arni Sigurbjarnarson and Heimir

A son of the former fisherman Sigurbjörn Sörensson tells some whale enthusiast all about cetaceans.

PHOTOS: RALF KIEFNER

Hartarson could hardly wait for the new whale-watching season to open. In the summer of 1995, their very first year in the business, no less than 1,000 whale watchers signed up with them. Sigurbjörn is happy to be on board his old cutter again and he really enjoys taking tourists out to see the whales. "We spotted whales on 59 out of a total of 60 excursions last year," he assures us. Even though he is well aware that whaling might soon be legalised

Whale watchers take photos of whales which nowadays have become more abundant in Islandic waters.

again, he still expects that many more people will come to watch the whales in the bay of Husavik.

During the last few years many of the inhabitants of Husaviks have gradually come to view this new branch of tourism with less skepticism. Word has gotten around that the whales have finally come back to the land of whaling.

A group of Common Dolphins riding the wave in front of the "Knörrinn".

In the meantime some of the locals have even come to appreciate the whales - at least those who have been out to see them with Sigurbjörn. "Incomparable," was the elated response I got when I asked one of them how the trip out to the whales had been.

Heimir is just about convinced that the whales have grown fond of the "Knörrinn" and are able to recognise the sound of its engine. "It's like a dog that knows the sound of its owner's car. The whales have since become familiar with the sound of our boat's engine and propeller. They know that we do not mean to harm them." Indeed, the trusting whales often come within a few metres of his boat, swim alongside of it for a while and take a good look at the passengers on board.

More and more Islanders have learned to appreciate the benefits that this new branch of tourism brings to their nation. Whale watching could thus soon develop into an additional tourist attraction in Island and provide thousands with new job opportunities - far more than the whaling industry ever will with its paltry 300 prospective workplaces.

Narwhal, *Monodon monocerus*

Aerial view of Narwhals near Baffin Island, Canadian Arctic.   Doc White/Seapics.com

Distinguishing Characteristics
Narwhals have a stocky body with a white underside and a mottled back without a dorsal fin. The males have a unique spiralling tusk that can be several metres long. Their flukes are also unlike any other cetacean's, being semi-circular in appearance. Few marine mammals range as far north as Narwhals do.

Description
Adult Narwhals average 4-5.3 m in length and 1-1.5 t in weight. Since they live in Arctic waters they have a relatively thick layer of blubber. Some specimens have a flat hump in place of a dorsal fin. Their relatively small and rounded heads terminate in blunt snouts. Even though their heads are thickset, their necks are still very flexible. Like Belugas, Irrawaddi Dolphins and the various species of river dolphins, their cervical vertebrae are not fused.

The foetus of a Narwhal has 6 teeth in the upper jaw and 2 teeth in the lower jaw. Only the first two teeth in the upper jaw will develop further, however, while the others remain hidden under the gums and are reabsorbed as the animal ages. The left tooth will erupt through the upper lip of most one-year-old males and grow into a tusk. The average length of these hollow and rather fragile dental protrusions is 2 m, but they can attain a length of 3.15 m. Their circumference can be as wide as 10 cm at the base and their weight as much as 10-14 kg. The front part of the tusk is smooth and shines as if polished, while the remainder is usually covered with a red or greenish layer of algae *(Rhodochorton* sp.) and diatoms. In some rare cases both teeth will erupt to form a double tusk. Less than 3% of the females also have a tusk, but a smaller one that will not exceed 1.2 m in length. Broken tusks are quite common among older Narwhals.

A Narwhal's fluke has an unusual form that differs markedly from that of all other cetaceans and reminds one of a mermaid's tail. Whereas most whales and dolphins have flukes with concave or straight terminations, a Narwhal's fluke is conspicuously convex at the end. Its roundness increases as the animal ages until it eventually has the appearance of a "reversed" fluke. It also has a well developed median notch.

The short, dark-grey flippers of a Narwhal curl upwards slightly at the ends, a feature that becomes more pronounced with age. The flippers and flukes of adult animals have a dark, sometimes even black border. The blow is relatively weak and inconspicuous. The back and flanks of an adult Narwhal are mottled-grey in colour, while the underside is off-white. As the animal ages its skin becomes lighter, but never loses its mottled, marbled pattern. Newborn calves are uniformly grey, in some cases sprinkled with patches of dark-blue.

Easily Mistaken For
Because of their distribution, uncommonly shaped flukes and mottled skins, Narwhals are easily distinguishable from all other species of whale. Only older female specimens with their paler backs might be confused with Belugas in the more remote northern ranges. However, since older Narwhals rarely lose their mottled patterns entirely, this is also highly unlikely. The males, of course, are always easy to recognise because of their unique tusks. The uniformly grey calves could be mistaken for young Belugas as long as their mothers are not present.

Other Names
Narwal, Einhorn der Meere (German); Narval (French); Narvalo (Italian); Narval (Spanish); Narval (Portuguese); Narwal (Dutch); Hornhval, Lighval, Narhval (Norwegian); Sarvivalas (Finnish); Narval (Swedish); Narhval (Danish); Narhvalus (Icelandic); Narval (Russian); Tugalik (Inuit).

Meaning of the Scientific Nomenclature
Monodon monocerus Linnaeus 1758 - Swedish naturalist Linné named this species *Monodon monocerus* ("one tooth, one horn") with reference to its formidable tusk. The scientific name is composed of the Greek words *monos* (a single one), *odous* (tooth) and *ceros* (horn).

Behaviour
Observations of Narwhals are only possible during the very short Arctic summer. Due to the poor weather and light conditions, little is known about the activities and whereabouts of Narwhals during the long Arctic winter. Narwhals shy away from humans and vessels. Whenever a vessels approaches them they generally keep perfectly still and sink out of sight. The Inuit refer to this peculiar behaviour, during which the whales also refrain from making any noise, as *ardlingayuk* (rigidity and silence). This reaction, which occurs as soon as a vessel comes within 50-60 m of the animals, is a protective measure against their natural enemies, the Killer Whales. As soon as Narwhals hear the sounds of a Killer Whale, they will remain motionless and utterly silent. Other natural enemies include polar bears and sharks.

Narwhals are very active on the surface. Spy-hopping, flipper-slapping and lob-tailing can be observed quite frequently. When surfacing or spy-hopping they raise their tusks out of the water. Breaching, on the other hand, will rarely occur. When swimming fast they will occasionally leap out of the water (porpoising).

Narwhals are very gregarious and live in tight associations of 2-10 animals. Females with their calves form one group and weaned youngsters and adult males another. Male groups usually live farther offshore than the female groups. Segregation by sex is especially evident during the summer season and the fall migration. At this time the groups are much larger than during the feeding season and can be distributed over several square kilometres. During the summer large pods of several hundred, sometimes even thousands, of Narwhals will gather close to the shore.

Little is known about the mating habits of Narwhals. The tusks obviously play an important role when the males rival for the attention of females. It has often been observed that they cross their tusks like swords, which sounds like wood beating on wood. Occasionally a tusk will break off during such a contest. The bulls often have scars on their heads that were inflicted by a forward lunging rival. Broken tusks found among the cadavers of bulls also attest their use as a weapon. Like the horns of a mountain goat or the antlers of a deer, a Narwhal's tusk plays an important role in social ranking. Status and privileges depend upon the size of this secondary sex characteristic. The strongest males with the largest tusks will mate most often. When Narwhals are entrapped by the pack ice, they can break through an ice sheet up to 15 cm in thick in order to breathe. They do so with their well padded melons. Earlier contentions that they burst through the ice with their tusks have proven to be false, as the whales take great care not to break them. In spite of their close relationship with Belugas, Narwhals do not migrate to estuaries during summer to scrape off their moulting skins.

Diving
It is assumed that Narwhals can descend to depths of 500-1,000 m, even though they prefer to feed in shallow coastal waters. While searching for nourishment they make erratic movements and only remain briefly on the surface before diving again for 7-30 min. All members of a group will dive at about the same time. While migrating Narwhals spend 60% of their time just beneath the surface, where they move at a pace of about 9 km/h. On the surface they will normally average

around 4 km/h. When the seas are calm they like to rest on the surface, whereby a part of their backs and flippers remain visible for about 10 min. In rough seas they seek deeper waters.

Feeding Habits

Squid, Polar Cod and other fish like capelin, sand eels, coalfish, herring, flounder, halibut, shellfish, salmon and cod, as well as crabs and shrimp are their preferred prey. Deep-sea fish like Greenland Halibut and rosefish, which they also feed on, attest that Narwhals hunt in deep waters. Analyses of the stomach contents of Narwhals performed in 1978-79 in Pond Inlet (Baffin Island, Canada) showed that fish make up more than 90% of their diet. Shrimp are their mainstay during the summer. Their daily consumption ranges around 45-80 kg.

General Information

The name "Narwhal" probably stems from the Norwegian word *nar* (dead body), which may be a reference to this species' wan skin. Lehmann (1965), however, feels that the name is based on the Old German word *narwa* (narrow), which refers to the animals' slender tusks. The priceless tusk of a male Narwhal was worth more than gold and precious gems during the Middle Ages. Well up until the 17th century it was still commonly believed that this "horn," which travelling merchants occasionally imported from distant lands, belonged to one of the legendary unicorns. Scientists speculated over the possible function of the strange tusk for over a century, and there are numerous earlier accounts of duelling Narwhals. At first it was falsely assumed that the tusk played an important role in feeding (burrowing through sediment, spearing prey) or in breaking through thin sheets of ice. If this were the case, however, the tusk-less females of the species would have starved or drowned under the ice. Another wild theory stipulated that the tusk functioned as an antenna or a cooling mechanism! According to Kingsley and Ramsay (1988), the stability of the tusk is reinforced by its spiralled structure. In this sense it is similar to the twisted trunks of trees often encountered in particularly exposed places, which can withstand the wind better than a smooth trunk. Scientists feel that the reason why the tusk grows straight rather than curved has something to do with streamlining.

Killer Whales, walruses and polar bears prey on Narwhals. Greenland sharks are also known to feed on the cadavers of Narwhals that got entangled in fishing nets. As might be expected, however, their worst enemy is the human race. For centuries they were hunted down for the sake of their tusks and vitamin-rich skins. It wasn't until 1971 that they were finally protected by the Canadian government under the Fisheries Act. This act prohibits anyone from hunting this species with the exception of the Inuit, who are allowed to kill five whales each year for their own consumption. Unfortunately, the Inuit, who now hunt with guns and motorboats, are somewhat wasteful in their methods as many of the dispatched animals sink before they can be retrieved and others die as a result of gunshot wounds after they manage to flee. In addition, the great value of the tusks results in an disproportionate killing of adult bulls by Inuit hunters.

Since the 17th century, commercial whalers have also occasionally hunted Narwhals for their tusks. In China and Japan there is still a widespread belief that the tusks have medicinal healing properties, even though there is absolutely no scientific evidence for it. The trade in Narwhal

Facts & Figures Narwal	**Quick ID-Check Narwal**
Size: 4-5.3 m	
Weight: 1-1.5 t	Males have a long, spiralled tusk
Longevity: 40-50 years	
Sexual maturity: cows with 5-8 years; bulls with 11-13 years	Back edge of fluke convex
Mating season: March-May	Back and flanks dark and mottled
Gestation period: 14-15.3 months, births usually in Summer (end of May until August)	No dorsal fin, a flat hump instead
Calving interval: every 3 years	
Size at birth: 1.6 m	Short flippers with dark and upwards-curling tips
Weight at birth: 80 kg	
Nursing period: minimum 1 year, usually 2	
Dive depth: max 1,000 m	Blunt snout, rounded rostrum
Dive time: max 30 min	
Teeth: 0-2 in upper jaw, lower jaw toothless	Only found in Arctic waters
Weight of tusk: 10-14 kg	
Group (Pod) size: 2-25, on rare occasions hundreds and even thousands of animals in relatively small areas	
Population: 20,000-35,000	

ivory has been strictly prohibited by CITES since 1983. Occasionally Narwhals become entrapped in ice holes. This can happen when the pack ice freezes up so fast that the animals are unable to head for the open water in time. In such a situation a number of animals will often congregate around a small breathing hole and try to keep it open. The Inuit designate this phenomenon as *sassat* (overabundance), which is an apt description of what often happens in Disko Bay (West Greenland). Most of the Narwhals die of overexertion while trying to keep the breathing hole open, while the weakened animals are an easy prey for polar bears and Inuit hunters.

The total size of the Narwhal population is unknown. Contemporary estimates range between 20,000-35,000 animals. The population in the Canadian Arctic, where the species is relatively common, is estimated at 10,000 specimens. Narwhals are seldom encountered south of 67° latitude north. Individual animals have been sighted in England and Holland, but these were undoubtedly strays. Narwhals communicate with different whistling sounds and use a series of whistling and clicking noises for echolocation. Contrary to earlier beliefs that the sounds emitted by Narwhals are limited to the same spectrum as the human ear, it is now known that the clicks used in echolocation are ultrasonic waves ranging between 20 kHz and 100 kHz.

Inuit hunters have killed a male Narwhal.
Doc White/Seapics.com

Where & When

Narwhals range farther north than any other species of whale. They live exclusively in the higher latitudes of the Arctic seas, always close to the ice sheet barrier and often in between the pack ice. They prefer the deep waters between 67° and 80° latitude north and rarely wander farther south. During the spring and summer months they remain in circumpolar regions. Their migrations depend upon the extent of the ice sheet. They will only come close to shore if the water there is deep, such as in fjords. During the summer they occasionally wander into more shallow areas. At this time they can be sighted quite frequently in the eastern Canadian Arctic region (Admiral Bay, Pond Bay, Milne Bay, Eclipse Sound, Navy Bay) and in northwestern Greenland (Melville Bay in Inglefield Fjord). The largest gatherings of Narwhals during the winter occur in Davis Strait and Baffin Bay, situated west of Greenland, and in the archipelago of the eastern Canadian Arctic. Most animals spend the winter inside the pack ice north of 67° latitude north. They are only rarely sighted in the waters off central and western Canada, Alaska and Siberia.

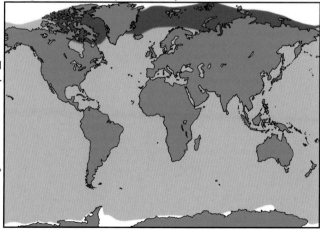

Narwhal, distribution: Circumpolar range in the high Arctic, always close to the ice sheet.

KILLER WHALES
LIVING UP TO THEIR NAME

Wildlife cameramen Douglas Allan, Tom Fitz and the English author Sue Flood had come to Monterey, California, hoping to film what seemed like the marine version of finding a needle in a haystack: Killer whales hunting down grey whales.

I felt somewhat nauseous as I desperately scanned the horizon for the distinctive heart-shaped blow of a grey whale. The white-caps were making spotting particularly difficult today (was the a blow I saw out of the corner of my eye, or simply spray?) and I felt sceptical about the likelihood of my spotting a whale blow in such conditions. I wondered if my nausea was the result of the choppy seas or nervousness at the prospect of returning home with nothing to show for three weeks of hard work?

Not only would we have to find the killer whales which could be several miles offshore, then witness them moving in for the kill... oh yes, and film it all! Each morning we were up at around 5am and spending a good 8 or 9 hours on the water searching in vain for signs of the whales. We knew that only a few people had ever been fortunate enough to observe at attack – if fortunate is the right word – and no one had ever managed to film such an event. I was beginning to think I knew why.

A killer whale (Orcinus orca) attacking a grey whale calf (Eschrichtius robustus) off the coast of California.

Suddenly the marine radio crackled into life as one of the local fishermen radioed in. "Richard, I think I see something – looks like a pod of killers and they're after something!" Richard noted down the co-ordinates of the sighting then cranked up the engines by a few knots and we were off! Was our luck about to change?

In June 1996 I started work on the forthcoming BBC Natural

The grey whale mother tries to lift her calf as killer whales attack again and again.

History Unit series "The Blue Planet", an eight part series on the natural history of the world's oceans. It will range from the smallest plankton to the blue whale,

No chance: As the grey whale mother fights against a killer whale with her head, two more orcas attack from behind.

journeying from coral reefs, to temperate waters and to the polar seas; from the coastlines out to the Open ocean and finally into the Deep. It is being filmed over three years using the latest digital technology, and will be transmitted in 2001.

Over the past two years the production team has been diligently searching for fascinating behavioural stories of marine life and of course, if this behaviour has not been previously filmed, so much the better! We had come across several accounts of killer whales attacking seals, sea lions, other whales and even great white sharks. However, as only a few people have ever witnessed such attacks it seemed wildly optimistic at best to hope to be able to film such a predation.

Then early last year whale biologist Nancy Black approached The Blue Planet team to see if we would be interested in trying to film an extraordinary piece of marine mammal behaviour. Nancy and her co-worker Richard Ternullo had witnessed killer whales hunting down and finally killing grey-whale calves off the Californian coast. The behaviour she described sounded extremely interesting... but once again, surely impossible?!

Mother Grey whale protects her calf with her own body.

I knew that to be able to capture such rare behaviour for the first time would be a real coup for the series but so would filming the Loch Ness Monster, and I thought that sounded about as likely! So when asked to look into the feasibility of a filming trip I was somewhat sceptical. And when Nancy told me that during ten years of working with whales in Monterey Bay she had only ever seen one attack from start to finish my heart sank! It did not exactly sound like a dead cert!

However, two weeks and several long phone calls with Nancy later, I decided that, although it was a long shot, it was worth the financial risk. So now several weeks later I found myself lurching around on a boat in the Pacific with Doug and Tom, some very expensive camera gear and, initially, a distinct absence of whales. But encouragingly, we were starting to hear the odd reports of grey whales from both fishing boats

The killer whales ram the calf which is soon injured.

The Californian Grey whale calf is heavily bleeding and will be killed soon.

and local cetacean biologists, so we knew the grey whales were well way on their way northwards on their annual migration.

The grey whale mothers give birth during January and February in sheltered lagoons in Baja California, then slowly begin to make their way north to Alaska to their summer feeding grounds. Their calf begins this incredible 18,000-mile round trip when it is just a few weeks old.

In April and May the mothers and the calves are seen off Monterey Bay on the Californian coast. Here, the more experienced mothers are thought to lead their calves close to the shore, a longer but safer route as the kelp beds in the shallows provide a place for them to hide and so afford some protection from attack. However some, thought to be the younger mothers, take a short cut across the bay, travelling over the Monterey Canyon. Out over the deep water there is no place to hide and the grey whales are vulnerable to attack by killer whales.

Tom, Doug and I started to quickly kit up, donning our waterproofs, checking and re-checking the camera gear, making sure everything was to hand on the off-chance that this was a real sighting.

As we approached we saw a flash of a black and white, and then another. We had found the killer whales. And there, just a few hundred yards ahead, was a grey whale mother and calf, and the gap between them was closing... and closing. Suddenly the water erupted with violent splashing, as whale flukes and fins broke the surface. It WAS an attack!

I had heard killer whales compared to a wolf pack and now I could see why. I watched as the pod of about 15 mostly female killer whales worked together to tire the grey whales, and to separate the mother from her calf.

The attack was sustained and violent. The killer whales would repeatedly ram into the side of the young grey whale with extraordinary force, no doubt inflicting serious internal injuries. At times, these attacks were so intense that the calf's body was thrust partly out of the water. The calf was around 20 foot long so the force needed must have been tremendous. The killer whales would also occasionally launch themselves out of the water and smash down on top of the calf, holding it under water in an attempt to drown it. The calf's wild, staring eye as the killer whales attacked over and over again was a haunting sight. It was extraordinary to watch such a concerted effort by the killer whales and one couldn't help but admire their co-operation and strength.

It was painful to watch the desperate calf literally fighting for its life and I wished that the killer whales would despatch the calf once and for all and bring its suffering to an end. Yet I was simultaneously mesmerised by this incredible behaviour, both from a biologist's and wildlife filmmaker's viewpoint.

But the most moving sight of all was to see the mother repeatedly try to protect her calf. She would attempt to re-position herself between the killer whales and her calf if they were separated, or more dramatically would try to physically support the calf, swimming underneath it and trying to push it out of the way of the killer whales – again, an incredible feat of strength.

As the calf began to roll in the water we could see its bleeding pectorals fins, with distinct teeth marks where the killer whales had been holding the calf to prevent it surfacing and so drown it. The water around the calf began to turn red.

Finally, after several hours of trying to protect her calf from sustained attacks, the grey whale mother slowly swam away toward shore, almost as though she realised that all hope of saving her calf was lost. As the weakened calf began to breath it's last the attack suddenly subsided as quickly as it had begun. We had the occasional glimpse of it's beautifully dappled flank as a small group of females killer whales dived and pushed it to the surface as they fed, but then the calf's body sank slowly beneath the surface, for the final time. An oily slick was the only remaining clue as to the violence of the last few hours.

Exhausted and subdued, we headed back to shore.

CHASED BY A FALSE KILLER WHALE

Whales and Dolphins are not only the always smiling and playful friends of humans. Sometimes they also can get angry and demand for more respect. In this case, they even can be dangerous for human beings. The marine underwater photographers Stephen Wong and his wife Takako Uno have been in extreme danger when they were most aggressively chased by a False Killer Whale.

A group of False Killer Whales including a baby appears in the open water.

In the summer of 2000, my wife Takako, and I were photographing in the Pacific Ocean. We came across a pod of 30-40 False Killer Whales, but they were widely spread out. Hence, the underwater encounters in the morning resulted in only 3 to 4 flyby animals. As the day progressed, the pod got together, and we again tried to be in the water to film these animals.

I had 2 or 3 drops from the boat with the pack, but the whales were kind of shy. They always took off and dove. Yet, I was able to see about 12-16 individuals together underwater.

Though the visibility had turned murky in the afternoon, these drops were still rewarding. However, I had noticed that a couple of the bigger animals began opening their mouths from a distance. I thought "Oh, well, just a small intimidation. No worry."

In the next drop, the pod came and again these Pseudorcas dived after they had echo-located me. Trying to capture a few more images, I also tried to duck-dive and follow them. When I was almost out of air and ready to head for the surface (I guess from about 10 m depth), I suddenly felt strange and turned my head to my right, and there it was ... a big and kind of roundish animal next to me.

I immediately knew that I was in big trouble. This False Killer Whale came to within 1.5 metres, and I had to push my camera at its head. It spun and came directly underneath me, so I kicked with my fins at its large snout. Of course, my fins could not touch the animal, since the False Killer was so agile. Though panicking, I could still see there was some weird spark in its eyes. I had never seen the angry eyes of a False Killer Whale - that was my first time and hopefully also my last time.

During this brief encounter, the whale must have charged at me at least 4 times, and I could only react in the same way by placing my camera between us. It would continue spinning to one side and turning towards me repeatedly. Both the animal and I were gradually heading towards the surface during all these commotions. Then, abruptly, the whale jumped above my head and out of the water. The only thing that I could do was holding the camera above my face and head, hoping that the whale could neither bite nor crash-land directly on my head.

When I was floating at the surface, I was very scared because the splash that the animal had created had caused a lot of bubbles to foam everywhere. It had to be one of the most frightening moments

"The trouble began when a False Killer Whale came swimming directly towards me..."

in my life. I could not see anything around or under me except for the bubbles. Screaming out for help was the only sane reaction and luckily our rubber boat had been following me and Takako.

Trying to distract the animal, the captain reversed the engine a few times and quickly moved the boat closer to us. Incidentally, the captain had seen the entire False Killer Whale leaping out of the water, and thought that I must be having a great photo opportunity until I was screaming my lungs out for help.

At the same time during this drop, my wife was also in the water. This is what Takako saw: "After noting the direction of the pod of False Killer Whales, Stephen got into the water first and I followed. Stephen can swim faster, hence he soon was some distance in front of me. Then I saw Stephen diving down, following the pod of animals. Suddenly and out of the blue a big animal came from behind, acting like a vanguard or some kind of protector of the pod.

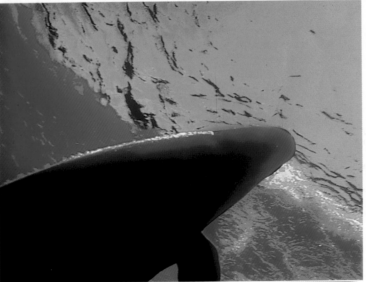

"Angrily the False Killer released bubbles of air when it banked away just in front of me."

I had never seen a False Killer Whale swimming so fast and fluidly. Maybe our previous drops into the ocean already had attracted its attention. This 5 to 6 metre long animal began to tailgate Stephen's fins. He never saw the whale coming, for he was quite focused on the main group. The big animal checked at Stephen's left and right leg, then again his black fins and, at times, even his hips. At the beginning, I thought this was a very curious whale, if only Stephen would turn around to get some nice photos.

"After I had returned to the boat the False Killer Whales raided a group of Bottlenose Dolphins."

However, from the movements and postures of the whale, I realised that something was not in order, and I started to scream into the water and tried to warn Stephen. Of course, nothing could get his attention right then…"

Now my part of the story continued: I was bobbing at the surface with white foamy bubbles all around me. About 10 metres from me and closer to the Zodiac, Takako had been floating at the surface during the whole time. She told me later that the False Killer had changed direction after it jumped above my head. The animal decided to charge at her. When Takako saw the whale coming, she started to kick her fins and tried to swim backwards. The animal gave up, and again decided to charge back at me. I was still floating among the bubbles and could see nothing. Then our captain had reversed the engine and the animal decided to bank away from me.

Trembling violently after this incident, Takako and I got back into the dinghy. We did not get into the water again for the rest of the day. Despite this we continued to follow the pod of whales, but our special friend always stayed next to our boat, crisscrossing the bow. Unbelievable! I think he was still angry and upset because of our presence.

Suddenly, another chance story emerged… A pod of large-sized oceanic Bottlenose Dolphins appeared. Presumably they wanted to play with the pod of False Killers. But somehow, something was going on underneath the surface (both pods came really close to our boat). We saw individuals of both species jumping out of the water, doing somersaults, and tumbling around. Actually, we believe 'our' False Killer was still angry and its family gang was also not in a playful state. We observed the False Killers start to bite the Bottlenose Dolphins. But the dolphins did not give up, and continued wanting to play with (or playfully harass) the False Killers. Again, members of both groups leaped and splashed. Then, one after the other, the animals took off. Wind came and we decided to leave the area.

Before this incident, I had another encounter with a pod of False Killers in Portugal in the summer of 1998. One of the bigger animals came next to my head (only once) and opened its mouth. I had also freaked out then. But it was only a brief incident and the animal soon continued to swim with its pod.

Today, I give these animals more respect when they start to open their mouths. I consider myself to have been extremely lucky, for I can not imagine what kind of damage I would have suffered through such a large animal. Of course, maybe the False Killer was only trying to prevent me from following his family.

However, looking back at the situation, I recognised that I could very well have been severely injured, particularly after I have seen other photographers' images of large tunas being attacked and literally vaporised by several False Killer Whales. By the way, Takako took some photos of me being chased by the large False Killer Whale. She had thought that since she could not help me anyway, she would better take a couple of photos for memory's sake. Interesting thought.

The family of **DELPHINIDAE** includes the greatest number of species of cetaceans and is divided into 5 subfamilies:

Subfamily Blackfish, Globicephalinae
Subfamily Dolphins, Delphininae
Subfamily Long Snouted Dolphins, Steninae
Subfamily Right Whale Dolphins, Lissodelphinae
Subfamily Black and White Dolphins, Cephalorhynchinae

Distinguishing Characteristics of this Family

All members of this family have streamlined bodies and prominent melons that they use for echolocation. With the exception of the northern and southern Right Whale Dolphins, all other species have more or less large dorsal fins. The number of conical teeth in their upper and lower jaws range from 28 to 250. The maximum length varies from 1.2 m (Hector's Dolphin) to 10 m (male Killer Whale). All species have a conspicuous median notch on the back edge of their flukes.

Dolphins live gregariously in tight family units and sometimes in association with other species of whale and dolphin. In bounteous feeding grounds they can number various thousand specimens.

BLACKFISH   GLOBICEPHALINAE

The **Subfamily Blackfish** comprises 6 species:
Pygmy Killer Whale, *Feresa attenuata*
Short-Finned Pilot Whale, *Globicephala macrorhynchus*
Long-Finned Pilot Whale, *Globicephala melas*
Killer Whale, *Orcinus orca*
Melon-Headed Whale, *Peponocephala electra*
False Killer Whale, *Pseudorca crassidens*

Distinguishing Characteristics of this Subfamily

Even though they differ markedly from most dolphins in outward appearance, the members of this subfamily are classified under the family of Delphinidae because they are more closely related to them than to other cetaceans. The term "whale" refers to their size only.

Their classification under the separate subfamily of Globicephalinae is based on the following criteria: Head with a rounded snout and no beak; at least three fused cervical vertebrae; no more than 15 teeth per jaw; and a minimum length of 2.1 m (adult animal). The largest adult members of this subfamily can grow up to 10 m and 9 t in weight (male Killer Whale), the smallest can grow up to 2,1 m and 110 kg in weight (Pygmy Killer Whale). In contrast to most dolphins, all species of Globicephalinae lack a prominent beak, but have a well developed dorsal fin that stabilises them while swimming at greater speeds. Killer Whales have the largest dorsal fin, which can extend as much as 1.8 m out of the water in the case of an adult male. The dorsal fin of a Long-Finned Pilot Whale, by way of contrast, is sharply hooked towards the tail. With the exception of the characteristic black-and-white colouration of a Killer Whale, all members of this subfamily have more or less dark bodies. All species are gregarious and occasionally associate with other species of whale and dolphin.

Pygmy Killer Whale, *Feresa attenuata*

Distinguishing Characteristics

Together with Melon-Headed Whales, Pygmy Killer Whales are the smallest species of the subfamily of Globicephalinae. Their slim and dark bodies have well developed, crescent-shaped dorsal fins that sit in midriff on the back. Their rounded heads lack a prominent beak. A white patch around the lips and occasionally also on the lower jaw reminds one of a goatee.

Description

The Pygmy Killer Whale ranks among the smallest members of its subfamily. Averaging 2.1-2.6 m in length and 110-170 kg in weight, it more closely resembles a dolphin than a Blackfish.

Its conspicuously large and hooked dorsal fin sits in the middle of its back. The flippers are relatively long with slightly rounded ends and irregular back edges. The back edge of its fluke is concave with a median notch. The uniformly dark, almost black skin of a Pygmy Killer Whale often bears numerous scratch marks. A conspicuous brown-grey patch extends all the way down its back. A large light-grey patch extends from its throat to the vent area and occasionally also covers both flanks.

On most occasions divers will encounter Pygmy Killer Whales in small groups. Hawaii.   Stephen Wong

Easily Mistaken For
Melon-Headed Whales, False Killer Whales, Short-Finned Pilot Whales and Long-Finned Pilot Whales may be mistaken for Pygmy Killer Whales. Because of their similar size and colouration, it is difficult to keep Pygmy Killer Whales and Melon-Headed Whales apart. The former have a slightly more rounded head and shorter, more rounded flippers than the latter. In addition, the patch on a Pygmy Killer Whale's back is somewhat larger and more conspicuous. Both species have white patches around the mouth, but these will occasionally extend to the chin of Pygmy Killer Whale as well. However, the most important distinguishing characteristic is the difference in group (pod) size: Whereas Melon-Headed Whales congregate in very large groups of 100-2,000 animals, Pygmy Killer Whales prefer to associate in much smaller groups of 15-50 (on rare occasions a few hundred) individuals. It is relatively easy to distinguish a Pygmy Killer Whale from a markedly larger False Killer Whale, Short-Finned Pilot Whale and Long-Finned Pilot Whale on the high seas. Furthermore, a Pygmy Killer Whale's melon is not nearly as bulbous as that of a Short-Finned Pilot Whale or a Long-Finned Pilot Whale.

Other Names
Blackfish, Slender Blackfish, Slender Pilot Whale (English); Zwerggrindwal, Zwergschwertwal (German); Orque Pygmée, Orque Nain (French); Feresa (Italian); Orca Pigmea (Spanish); Orca Anã (Portuguese); Dwerggriend (Dutch); Dvergspekkhogger (Norwegian); Kääpiömiekkavalas (Finnish); Dvärgspäckhuggare (Swedish); Almindelig Dværgspækhugger (Danish); Yume Gondo Kujira (Japanese).

Meaning of the Scientific Nomenclature
Feresa attenuata (Gray 1875) - The generic name *Feresa* stems from the common French designation for dolphins. The Latin species name *attenuata* is the female form of the Latin word *attenuatus* (slim, fine).

Facts & Figures Pygmy Killer Whale	Quick ID-Check Pygmy Killer Whale
Size: 2.1-2.6 m Weight: 110-170 kg Longevity: unknown Calving interval: unknown Size at birth: 0.8 m Weight at birth: unknown Dive time: unknown Teeth: 16-24 conical teeth in upper jaw, 20-26 in lower jaw Group (Pod) size: 15-30, sometimes 50, on rare occasions several hundred Population: Unknown	Small, slim body, dark back, flanks somewhat lighter, white patch on stomach Bulbous head without prominent snout Light patch around mouth, occasionally also chin Conspicuous crescent-shaped dorsal fin Relatively long, slightly rounded flippers Usually very shy

Behaviour

Since Pygmy Killer Whales shy away from vessels, little is known about their behaviour. Although they frequent all deeper tropical and subtropical waters, observations of the animals themselves or any of their surface activities like breaching, bow-riding and lob-tailing are few and far between. In a group, Pygmy Killer Whales will usually swim in a tight lateral formation. When threatened they form smaller groups that can scatter in all directions at the least sign of danger. With a bit of luck one may be able to observe them resting on the surface on a sunny day. On such rare occasions it might even be possible to approach them by boat. This species is often the victim of mass stranding. Captive Pygmy Killer Whales have reacted aggressively towards humans and other cetaceans. They are known to attack and even kill dolphins that share their basins. It appears that they are more deserving of the byname "killer" than their larger and more notorious cousins, the Killer Whales. According to some unconfirmed reports, they even chase after dolphins in the wild in order to kill and eat them. Other small species of whale will panic as soon as this species shows up.

Diving

Practically nothing is known about their diving behaviour. These animals are conspicuous swimmers that raise their heads high out of the water when they surface. In flight they leap clear out of the water. Under water they produce growling sounds that can also be heard on the surface.

Feeding Habits

Not much is known about the feeding habits of this species either. Analyses of their stomach contents have shown that they prey mainly on fish and squid. Occasionally they will hunt other dolphins, especially the younger animals.

Where & When

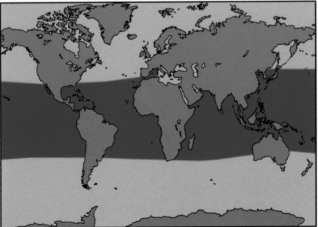

Pygmy Killer Whales prefer warm (tropical and subtropical), deep, offshore waters. Occasionally they have been sighted in temperate regions. Nothing is known about their migration routes. Because they shy away from vessels, their distribution could be much wider than is currently assumed. Most sightings take place in the tropical Pacific around Hawaii and Japan. There are sedentary populations along the Indic coast of Sri Lanka and the Caribbean coast of St. Vincent. On rare occasions they have been sighted in the Mediterranean.

Pygmy Killer Whale, distribution: All deep, warm (tropical to temperate) offshore waters.

Short-Finned Pilot Whale, *Globicephala macrorhynchus*

Short-Finned Pilot Whales are sought-after diving companions. Hawaii.   Jim Watt

Distinguishing Characteristics
The most conspicuous earmark of a Short-Finned Pilot Whale is its dark, slim and yet robust body. Other typical features include a noticeably hooked dorsal fin that sits midriff on the back and a chunky head with a bulbous melon.

Description
Short-Finned Pilot Whales range in size from 3.5-6.5 m and reach a maximum weight of 1.4 t. Males and females differ markedly from each other in size: The males are larger than the females, which rarely exceed 4.5 m in length. The head with its bulbous melon is a typical feature. Tests conducted with model ships having similarly shaped bows proved that this rounded form is perfectly streamlined. The melons of older males can extend beyond the snout. Younger animals have less prominent melons, giving their heads a more pointed appearance. A Short-Finned Pilot Whale's dorsal fin is relatively low and noticeably hooked towards the back. Its wide base sits slightly fore of the midriff. Like Long-Finned Pilot Whales, the dorsal fin of a Short-Finned Pilot Whale also becomes longer as the animal ages. The flippers sit near the head. Making up to 1/6 of its total body length, a Short-Finned Pilot Whale's flippers are markedly shorter, straighter and narrower than those of a Long-Finned Pilot Whale. Its body is almost uniformly dark-brown to jet-black with a grey patch in the shape of an anchor on the throat and chest. This patch, which extends down to the venting area, tapers down to a thin line between the flippers and then widens again. There will often be a grey or white streak running diagonally behind each eye. Occasionally the dorsal ridge will be of a lighter colouration. Its underside is usually lighter than its back or flanks, but not as pale as that of a Long-Finned Pilot Whale.

Easily Mistaken For
May be confused with Long-Finned Pilot Whales, Melon-Headed Whales and False Killer Whales. It is especially difficult to keep Short-Finned Pilot Whales and Long-Finned Pilot Whale apart on the open seas. They are best identified on the basis of their distribution, which will rarely overlap. Short-Finned Pilot Whales remain in the warm and temperate zones of the world's oceans. In the North Atlantic, where their respective ranges overlap, the two species can only be differentiated by their flippers: Those of a Long-Finned Pilot Whale measure about 1/5 of its total body length

Epimelitic behaviour of a Pilot Whale mother who carries her dead baby.   Doug Perrine/Seapics.com

and have a crook in the midsection; those of a Short-Finned Pilot Whale equal to about 1/6 of its total body length and do not have a crook in the midsection. Stranded Short-Finned Pilot Whales can be distinguished by the fact that they usually have fewer teeth and somewhat differently shaped heads than Long-Finned Pilot Whales. Short-Finned Pilot Whales are noticeably larger than Pygmy Killer Whales and Melon-Headed Whales. The False Killer Whale, on the other hand, is noticeably slimmer and has a pointed head. Furthermore, a Short-Finned Pilot Whale's dorsal fin is sharply hooked towards the back, while that of a False Killer Whale is only slightly curved at the most.

Other Names
Pothead Whale, Blackfish, Shortfin Pilot Whale, Pacific Pilot Whale, Caaing Whale (English); Kurzflossen-Grindwal, Indischer Grindwal, Nordamerikanischer Grindwal, Schwarzwal, Pilotwal (German); Globicéphale Tropical, Chaudron (French); Globicefalo di Gray (Italian); Calderón de Aletas Cortas (Spanish); Caldeirão, Boca de Panela Tropical (Portuguese); Indische Griend (Dutch); Kortfinnegrindhval (Norwegian); Isokuonopallopää (Finnish); Kortfenad Grindval (Swedish); Kortluffet Grindehval (Danish); Kobire Gondo Kujira (Japanese); Calderón, Ballena Piloto (Latin American Spanish).

Meaning of the Scientific Nomenclature
Globicephala macrorhynchus Gray 1846 - The generic name is made up of the Latin word *globus* (globe) and the Greek word *kephalos* (head). The species name is composed of the Greek words *makros* (large) and *rhynchos* (snout).

Behaviour
Even though Short-Finned Pilot Whales are very gregarious, they live in somewhat smaller groups (10-15 animals) than Long-Finned Pilot Whales. When they are hunting or migrating the groups of Short-Finned Pilot Whales can still encompass several hundred animals. The members of a group keep in close contact with each other and will usually act in unison. They practically feed, rest, wander and breathe synchronically. Short-Finned Pilot Whales are polygynous. The bulls will court several females and fiercely defend their harems against all rivals. Numerous scars on their bodies

attest this. In contrast to Sperm Whales, dominant Short-Finned Pilot Whales will remain with the group after the mating season is over. They function as group leaders and maintain its cohesiveness. During their migrations large groups of Short-Finned Pilot Whales will follow a single leader (hence the designation "pilot" whale). They are frequently sighted in the company of Bottlenose Dolphins and other small cetaceans, even though they will occasionally attack them as well. Short-Finned Pilot Whales usually hunt at night and rest or wander during the day. The animals occasionally venture inshore if there is an abundance of prey there. They are indifferent about vessels and, in contrast to Long-Finned Pilot Whales, have seldom been observed bow-riding. At times Short-Finned Pilot Whales will float lazily on the surface as if taking a nap or sunbath.

The tight social bonds between Short-Finned Pilot Whales are also evident in their propensity for mass stranding. Second only to False Killer Whales, there are more recorded instances of mass stranding among Short-Finned Pilot Whales than any other species of cetacean. It is still unknown why they do this, but many different theories have been presented. A plausible explanation would be some sort of illness or external irritation that causes the guiding animal to lose its orientation and lead its fellow group members to a certain death. Irritations could be induced by fluctuations in the magnetic field as a result of earthquakes, volcanic eruptions or blasting. Most of the mass stranding occurred in places where the magnetic fields, which the animals use for orientation, run almost perpendicular to the coastline or there are anomalies in the magnetic fields themselves. The racket made by ships and other forms of noise pollution could also be a source of irritation along with diseases or parasites that befall the inner ear of the lead animal. Once Short-Finned Pilot Whales have strayed into the shallows, they seldom find their way back to safer depths. They are oceanic animals and thus incapable of orienting themselves in shallow waters. The tight social bonds within a group of Short-Finned Pilot Whales also play a role when they are driven to shore by fishermen. Then the panicked animals will swim in very tight formations at speeds of up to 46 km/h. The fishermen herd the whales into a confined bay by shouting, throwing stones or striking the surface of the water with an object. As soon as the lead animal strands, the fishermen will have little trouble driving the remaining animals onto the shore and finishing them off. The last mass killings of Short-Finned Pilot Whales took place during the last few decades in the Caribbean, where several thousand animals were slaughtered in this fashion. Their natural enemies are Killer Whales and large sharks. See also CAPTAIN HOOK on pages 189-190.

Diving

Whether they are migrating or hunting, Short-Finned Pilot Whales swim and dive together, often in a long lateral line. Perhaps this habit of forming an up to 4-km-long line of parallel swimming individuals, the so-called "chorus line," has something to do with special hunting techniques. The animals take several short breaths before sounding. While hunting they will generally stay under water for about 10 min at depths ranging from 30-60 m. The longest dive on record lasted for 15 min, the deepest reached 610 m. When adult animals surface they normally only poke the tips of their heads out of the water. When moving at a faster pace, however, the anterior half of their bodies will clear the surface. Younger animals usually raise their heads a little higher out of the water. This whale's blow is only about 1 m high, but clearly visible and audible on a calm day.

Facts & Figures Short-Finned Pilot Whale	Quick ID-Check Short-Finned Pilot Whale
Size: 3.5-6.5 m	Black, slim but robust body
Weight: max 1-1.4 t	Paler, anchor-shaped pattern on underside
Longevity: females 60, males 45 years	
Gestation period: 15 months	Chunky head with bulbous melon
Calving interval: one calf every 3-4 years	
Size at birth: 1.4-2 m	Dorsal fin noticeably hooked towards the tail, sits midriff on the back
Weight at birth: 60 kg	
Nursing period: min 24 months	Relatively short flippers (1/6 of total body length), without crooks
Dive depth: max 610 m	
Dive time: 10-15 min	Prefers deep waters
Teeth: 14-18 relatively large teeth in each jaw	
Group (Pod) size: 6-50, on rare occasions several hundred	Indifferent about vessels
Population: Unknown, presumably endangered	

A distinguishing characteristic of the Short-Finned Pilot Whale are the straight flippers.   Ralf Kiefner

Feeding Habits
Short-Finned Pilot Whales mainly take squid and octopuses, but they will also feed on deep-sea fish when these are not available in sufficient quantities.

General Information
Lesson established the genus *Globicephala* in 1828, or 18 years before Short-Finned Pilot Whales were known to exist. In 1846 John E. Gray provided the first description of the species on the basis of a skeleton found in the South Seas and named it *Globicephala macrorhynchus*. Gray came to the erroneous conclusion that the living animal must have had a large *(macro-)* snout *(-rhynchus)*.

A few of the populations living in separation from one another could belong to different subspecies. Two populations off the coast of Japan, for instance, appear to be genetically distinct even though they have not been recognised as a separate subspecies so far.

It is not uncommon to find the remains of giant squid *(Architeuthis* spp.) after a group of Short-Finned Pilot Whales has passed by. It may well be that adult animals regurgitate part of their prey in order to feed younger animals that have been weaned but are still unable to hunt at greater depths.

Where & When
Short-Finned Pilot Whales prefer the deep and open tropical to temperate-warm waters of both hemispheres. Their range lies approximately between 45° latitude north and 35° latitude south, and includes the three great oceans.

Their distribution in the North Atlantic can't be determined precisely as this species is often confused with Long-Finned Pilot Whales. The outer limits of their range in the eastern North

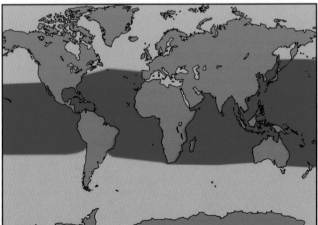

Atlantic probably extend to the Azores and Madeira.

Although Short-Finned Pilot Whales prefer deep waters along the edges of the continental shelf or above submarine canyons, they are often sighted near the coast. The most sedentary populations are found off Hawaii and Teneriffe (Canary Islands). Their migration routes are probably influenced by the availability of prey and direction of warm ocean currents.

Short-Finned Pilot Whale, distribution: In all deep tropical, subtropical and temperate-warm waters of the world's oceans.

Long-Finned Pilot Whale, *Globicephala melas*

Distinguishing Characteristics

The most conspicuous earmark of a Long-Finned Pilot Whale is its dark, slim and yet robust body. Other typical features include a noticeably hooked dorsal fin that sits midriff on the back and a thickset head with a bulbous melon. They often live in large groups.

Description

Long-Finned Pilot Whales range from 4-6 m in length and 1.8-3.5 t in weight. There is considerable variation in size between the males and females. The males can be up to 0.5 m longer than the females. In addition, the males' dorsal fins are fleshier, longer at the base and more curved towards the back. The dorsal fins of the females stand straighter. There is also a marked difference in the individual size of the populations living in the Northern and Southern hemispheres: The animals of the Northern Hemisphere grow approximately one metre longer.

The recurving flippers are a diagnostic characteristic of the Long-Finned Pilot Whale.   Ralf Kiefner

The bulbous melon is a typical feature of this species. Tests conducted with model ships having similarly shaped bows showed that this rounded form is perfectly streamlined. The melons of older males can extend beyond the snout. Younger animals have less prominent melons, giving their heads a more pointed appearance. A Long-Finned Pilot Whale's dorsal fin is relatively low and noticeably hooked towards the back. Its wide base sits on the anterior third of the body. The dorsal fin grows longer with age. The flippers sit near the head. Making up about 20-25% of the total body length, they are noticeably small and narrow. Each flipper is conspicuously angled backwards, much like the reversed crook of an elbow. This becomes more pronounced as the animal ages and helps to distinguish this species from Short-Finned Pilot Whales. Its body is almost uniformly dark-brown to black with a white patch in the shape of an anchor on the throat and chest.

Other Names

Pothead Whale, Blackfish, Atlantic Pilot Whale, Caaing Whale (English); Gewöhnlicher Grindwal, Langflossen-Grindwal, Schwarzwal, Pilotwal (German); Chaudron, Globicéphale Commun, Globicéphale Noir (French); Globicefalo (Italian); Calderón Común (Spanish); Boca de Panela, Baleia Piloto (Portuguese); Griend (Dutch); Grindhval (Norwegian); Grindvalas, Pallopää (Finnish); Grindval (Swedish); Langluffet Grindehval (Danish); Calderón, Ballena Piloto (Latin American Spanish).

Meaning of the Scientific Nomenclature

Globicephala melas (Traill 1809) - Generic name see previous species. The species name is based on the Greek word *melanos* (black). *G. melaena* (also used) is the feminine gender of the name.

Behaviour

Long-Finned Pilot Whales are very gregarious and live in groups of 10-200 animals. During the hunt or migration, a group may encompass as many as 500 individuals. In extraordinary cases several thousand animals will congregate. During their migrations large groups of Long-Finned Pilot Whales will follow a single leader (hence the designation "pilot" whale). They usually swim very close to each other and almost breathe simultaneously. While feeding, however, they will spread out over a large area. In between migrations or following the hunt, groups of Long-Finned Pilot Whales will often doze together on the surface. They occasionally venture inshore if there is an abundance of prey there. This is more likely to happen during summer and fall, as the animals head far out to sea in the winter and spring. Long-Finned Pilot Whales are polygynous. The bulls will court several females and fiercely defend their harems against all rivals. Numerous scars on their bodies attest this. In contrast to Sperm Whales, dominant Long-Finned Pilot Whales do not

Beached Long-Finned Pilot Whales near Northland, New Zealand.   Ingrid Visser/Seapics.com

leave the group after the mating season is over. Instead, they will lead the group and keep it together. Genetic analyses have shown that the males in a group are not always the fathers of all the calves in the group. Crossbreeding seems to take place quite regularly when different groups meet. In his study of summer congregations of the species off the coast of Newfoundland, Canadian biologist David E. Sergeant discovered that there were twice as many bulls in the larger groups as there were cows, and that these groups were under the control of the dominant males. Long-Finned Pilot Whales can frequently be seen in the company of Bottlenose Dolphins and other small cetaceans, even though they will occasionally attack them. They usually hunt at night and rest or wander during the day. They are not afraid of vessels and will often swim alongside or ride the bow wave. Lob-tailing and spy-hopping are also frequently observed. Younger animals breach more often than adults. Newborns average 1.8-1.9 m and grow about 0.5 m every six months.

Diving
Normally Long-Finned Pilot Whales will take several short breaths before diving for a few minutes. When they surface to breathe their snouts will barely come out of the water, which makes it difficult to see them. While hunting they will rarely stay under water longer than 5-10 min, but

Facts & Figures Long-Finned Pilot Whale	Quick ID-Check Long-Finned Pilot Whale

Size: 4-6 m
Weight: max 1.8-3.5 t
Longevity: 30-50 years
Sexual maturity: females at 6-10 years, males
  at 12
Mating season: April-July
Gestation period: 15.5-16 months
Calving interval: one calf every 3.5 years
Size at birth: 1.8-1.9 m
Weight at birth: 75 kg
Nursing period: 20.5-22 months
Dive depth: max 600 m
Dive time: 10 min
Teeth: 16-26 relatively small conical teeth in
  each jaw
Group (Pod) size: 10 to thousands
Population: Unknown, presumably endangered
	Slim but robust body
	
	Dark-brown or dark-grey to jet black in colour
	
	Lighter anchor-shaped patch on underside
	
	Thickset head with bulbous melon
	
	Dorsal fin hooked towards the back, sits fore
	  of the midriff
	
	Relatively long flippers (1/5-1/4 of total body
	  length), conspicuously bent backwards
	
	Active on the surface
	
	Prefers deep waters
	
	Does not shy away from vessels

they can descend to depths of 600 m. During their migrations, Long-Finned Pilot Whales usually dive just beneath the surface for periods of 1-2 min, and will rarely exceed 30-60 m in depth. Their blow is only about 1 m high, but clearly visible and audible on a calm day.

Feeding Habits
Short-Finned Pilot Whales mainly take shoaling cephalopods, especially the species *Todarodes sagittatus* and *Illex illecebrosus*. When these are not available in sufficient quantities they will occasionally feed on shoaling fish. Long-Finned Pilot Whales consume an equivalent of about 5% of their total body weight each day. This adds up to about 100 kg daily in the case of males and approximately 50 kg in the case of females.

General Information
In 1809 naturalist Thomas Traill provided the first description of a Long-Finned Pilot Whale based on a specimen that stranded on the Orkney Islands (Scotland) and named it *Delphinus melaena*. In 1828 this species was placed in Lesson's newly-created genus *Globicephala* and was known henceforth under the scientific name of *Globicephala melas*. In those days the generic name was still being applied to a large number of dolphin species. A few authors prefer to use the feminine form *melaena* rather than the original species name *melas*.

There are two populations of Long-Finned Pilot Whales: one in the North Atlantic and the other in the Southern Hemisphere. They are separated from each other by the tropical belt and may well represent two distinct subspecies even though they have not been recognised as such so far. In that case the northern population would become *G. melas melas* and the southern population *G. m. edwardii* in reference to a description of an animal found off the coast of South Africa by Smith in 1894. A number of authors support such a division primarily on the basis of minor differences in colouration and the geographic separation.

The hunt for Long-Finned Pilot Whales has a very long tradition and is still going on in some places today. When Long-Finned Pilot Whales pass by close to the shore, fishermen will either drive them into shallow bays and slaughter them there or head out to sea in order to harpoon the larger males. The oldest documented hunt for Long-Finned Pilot Whales in European waters dates back to 1584 and took place off the Färöer Islands (Denmark). In all likelihood, however, this tradition is much older. Long-Finned Pilot Whales are still being hunted today for "traditional purposes" in the Orkney, Shetland and Färöer Islands as well as in Norway, Greenland and Newfoundland.

An average of 1,000-1,500 Long-Finned Pilot Whales are caught off the Färöer Islands every year. Since the animals have become highly contaminated with pollutants in the meantime, however, the islanders have been warned not to consume their flesh. There is an average of 42-189 mg/kg of PCB in the blubber of a Long-Finned Pilot Whale. DDT averages around 42-94.2 mg/kg and its derivative DDE about 7.5-69.9 mg/kg.

Where & When
Long-Finned Pilot Whales are primarily pelagic and prefer deep, temperate to subpolar waters with temperatures ranging between 0-25° C. They tend to stay away from warmer waters. They will only come close to shore where the depth increases rapidly. They are frequently encountered along the rim of the continental shelf and off islands surrounded by deep waters. In the Atlantic the populations are separated from each other by the tropical belt, which is populated by their closely related cousins, the Short-Finned Pilot Whales. The ranges of both species overlap in the waters off Madeira and the Azores. Long-Finned Pilot Whales are occasionally sighted in the Mediterranean.

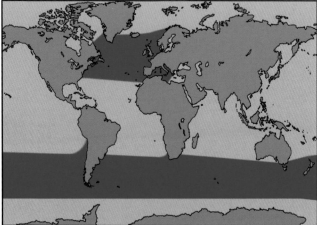

Long-Finned Pilot Whale, distribution: In all deep, temperate-cold and subpolar waters of the world's oceans with the exception of the Northern Pacific.

Killer Whale, *Orcinus orca*

Killer Whales often jump out of the water and roll in mid-air before falling back. Alaska. Francois Gohier

Distinguishing Characteristics

The characteristic black-and-white pattern and a vertical dorsal fin that can reach up to 1.8 m in height (males) make it easy to identify this species. Other typical features include an elliptical white patch over each eye, an individually distinct grey-white "saddle" behind the dorsal fin and a white patch on the underside. The latter extends from the lower jaw to the venting area, where it terminates in a three-pronged pattern. The two lateral prongs run up the flanks and aft of the dorsal fin, while the middle one encloses the genitals. The white patch itself becomes narrower between the flippers, much like an hourglass.

Description

With a maximum length of 10 m and weight of 9 t, the Killer Whale is the largest representative of the Delphinoidea. Its stocky body is very robust and its small, round head is slightly pointed. A well developed melon bulges markedly from its forehead. It does not have a prominent snout. Sexual dimorphism is manifested in both size and weight, as well as in the shape of the dorsal fin. Averaging 7-9 m in length, the males are longer and stronger than the females, which attain a length of 7-8 m. The average weight of the males is 4.5 t, that of the females 2-3 t. A Killer Whale bull weighing 9 t was found on Newport Beach (Rhode Island, USA) in 1961. Size and form of the sword-like dorsal fin vary with age and gender. Those of the males range around 1.67 m in length, those of the females 90 cm. It functions as a stabiliser while the animals swim. In profile it is shaped like an isosceles triangle with a slight forward pitch. As the animal ages, its dorsal fin will increase in size. It can attain a max of 1.8 m in height in the case of an older bull and develop a wavy form. Its overall shape, however, varies greatly. There will often be scars or nicks on the leading edge, which make it possible to identify individual whales. Regardless of gender, the dorsal fins of the calves are similar to those of the females in size and shape. The flippers are relatively large, paddle-shaped and black on both sides. They grow larger with age and can equal 20% of the total body length in the case of an older bull. The upper side of the fluke is black, the underside white. Its back edge is slightly convex and has a conspicuous median notch. The 20-28 large, conical teeth in each jaw interlock and turn inwards slightly. The blow of a Killer Whale is relatively low, bushy and easy to spot when the air is cold. Newborn calves average 1.5-2 m in length and weigh about 160 kg. The colour of their skin is light-grey with dark-blue patches. Thanks to the

A matriarchal group (headed by a female) off the coast of New Zealand.   Ingrid Visser/Seapics.com

high fat content of their mother's milk, they double their weight in the first month of their lives. Their mortality rate is still quite high, however, as only about 60% of the calves survive their first year. The varying patterns of the "saddle" patch and shapes of the dorsal fin have made it possible to photographically identify numerous individuals during the past 25 years.

Easily Mistaken For
Due to their size, high dorsal fins and characteristic black-and-white patterns Killer Whales are practically unmistakable.

Other Names
Orca, Orca Dolphin, Great Killer Whale, Grampus (English); Schwertwal, Orka, Mörderwal, Butzkopf (German); Orque (French); Orca (Spanish/Portuguese); Épaulard (Canadian French); Zwaardwalvis (Dutch); Spekkhogger (Norwegian); Miekkavalas (Finnish); Späckhuggare (Swedish); Spækhugger (Danish); Hahyrna (Islandic); Kosatka (Russian); Sakamata (Japanese).

Meaning of the Scientific Nomenclature
Orcinus orca (Linnaeus 1758) - The scientific name stems from the Latin *orca* and denotes "a species of whale." The Latin final syllable *-inus* means something like "similar, belonging to." According to some sources *orca* translates as "wild animal with a barrel-shaped body."

In this context it should also be mentioned that the Latin word *orc* means "terrible sea monster" and that *Orcus* is the name of the "Lord of the Underworld" (Hoyt). The tuna genus *Grammatorcynus* also bears the Latin designation *orcinus*.

Behaviour
Killer Whales are very inquisitive and playful. Breaching, lob-tailing, flipper-slapping and spy-hopping are frequently observed surface activities. Calves and adult animals breach very often. They usually come clear out of the water, turn slightly and land on their stomachs, backs or sides. The younger animals will often perform acrobatic gyrations when they leap.

Killer Whales are not as keen about bow-riding as other species of dolphin. Nevertheless, they are also fast swimmers that can reach speeds of up to 55 km/h, whereby they heave the

Keiko, the most famous of all Killer Whales. Oregon Coast Aquarium.   Marilyn Kazmers/Seapics.com

A Killer Whale mother with her calf off the Norwegian coast.   Amos Nachoum/Seapics.com

greater part of their bodies out of the water in order to breathe. Their average speed ranges around 15-20 km/h.

When Killer Whales spy-hop they raise their bodies vertically out of the water until the upper half of their flippers become visible on the surface, and then slowly sink out of sight again. It is not uncommon for several animals to spy-hop at the same time. Killer Whales can obviously see quite well on the surface, as they have no trouble spotting prey like seals or penguins on shore.

DNA analyses prepared in connection with research conducted in the Northeastern Pacific waters off the northwestern coast of the United States and Vancouver, Canada, have proven that there are three genetically distinct populations there which also differ from each other in behaviour. These populations have been designated as residents, transients and offshores.

The residents can be subdivided into a northern and a southern reproductive association, both of which remain within a 300-mile-wide coastal range all year round. These two have been studied most thoroughly.

The residents tend to follow set routes during their short forays into the surroundings. They usually live in groups of 5-25 animals. They vocalise more often than the members of the other populations, feed primarily on fish (especially salmon) and rarely dive longer than 4 min. Members of different groups of residents will interbreed during the annual mating gatherings, which ensures a genetic variation among their young.

The transients live in loose groups of 1-7 animals. They roam much farther than the two resident populations, whose home range they also occupy. They mostly prey on marine mammals and do not communicate with each other as frequently. In addition, they usually dive longer (15 min) and frequently change course under water.

Members of the resident and transient populations also differ in appearance: The dorsal fins of the transients are somewhat more pointed and sit closer to the middle of the back than those of the residents.

Due to the great extent of their territory, the offshore population is difficult to keep under observation. Less is known about them and their behaviour than the two previously mentioned populations. Its members prefer fish over marine mammals, but will occasionally prey on the latter as well.

Research conducted off the coast of Vancouver showed that the resident population has a particularly close matriarchal social structure and a common language (dialect). This dialect remains stable for several years, making it possible to identify the origin of widely scattered animals. Every group uses a certain dialect that each member is intimately familiar with. The number of calls and the accent of each vocalisation are characteristic for the group and taught to the calves by their mothers. Groups with similar dialects form so-called language schools.

According to John Ford, the scientist who discovered these dialects, this phenomenon is very rare among mammals. The dialects used by the Killer Whales appear to be different from that of any other non-human species ever studied.

The vocalisations of the Killer Whales can be divided into different categories: clicks, whistles and isolated calls. The clicks differ from those produced by other dolphins and are used for echolocation. They are narrow-banded and low-frequency (250-500 Hz). The whistles are used for short-distance communication between members of a group. When individual animals are farther apart, e.g when they are hunting, they resort to isolated calls.

Normally marine animals will only develop distinct dialects if the individual populations are geographically separated, as in the case of Humpback Whales. The Humpback Whale population of the Northern Pacific, for instance, vocalises different mating sounds than its relatives in the North Atlantic or the Southern Hemisphere. The existence of different dialects in close proximity to each other, as it occurs among the Killer Whale populations off the coast of Vancouver, implies that the vocalisations are not genetically preprogrammed, but passed on from generation to generation in a learning process.

The social ties within the group (or pod) are very close and durable. Intraspecies aggression is rare. A pod is the designation for a durable association of 3-20 individuals with their own vocalising dialect. Interrelated pods form a clan. Occasionally several clans will come together and form associations of 80-100 or more animals. The largest gathering of Killer Whales ever, estimated at 2,500 specimens, was spotted off the coast of Alaska a few years ago.

Today one differentiates between 5 different stages of social interaction among Killer Whales:
1) A **matriarchal group** is headed by a female. It is made up of 3-9 animals and can last up to 4 generations.
2) A **subpod** is made up of 1-11 matriarchal groups that almost always live together.
3) A **pod** is composed of 1-4 subpods that usually migrate together. Each pod can be identified by its distinct dialect.

Left: Makos are the fastest of all sharks. In spite of that fact this Killer Whale finally succeeded in hunting down a Mako shark as the photographer was able to document in New Zealand waters.

Ingrid Visser/ Seapics.com

Below: Killer Whales also eat other dolphins. The photographer witnessed how a Killer Whale catapulted a Dall's Harbour Porpoise into the air and consequently devoured it.

Robin Baird/ Seapics.com

4) A **clan** encompasses several pods. Depending upon the origin of each pod, there can be slightly different dialects within a clan.

5) An **association** encompasses several clans and can include hundreds or thousands of animals. The internal social structures within an association are subject to constant change. New groups are continually formed (always under the leadership of a female) and existing ones disbanded.

Just how strong the social bonds between Killer Whales are is evident from observations of animals coming to the aid of injured members of the group. When a calf ventures within reach of a fishing net, its mother will intervene and show it the way out again. Social bonds even play an important role in mass stranding. If one manages to lead a few of the stranded animals back to deeper waters, they will immediately return to their less fortunate relatives on the beach.

Migration routes and temporary regional gatherings of large numbers of Killer Whales, such as regularly occurs off the coast of Norway, are connected to the migration habits of their preferred prey (in this case herring). It has been verified that the Killer Whales sighted in the winter habitats of the herring around the Lofoten Islands in Norway turned up several hundred kilometres further south later that year in the spawning grounds of the herring situated off the coast of Møre (Norway).

More so than any other marine mammal, Killer Whales have the ability to adapt to changing environmental conditions. In 1970, for example, they left their habitual hunting grounds off Island because their preferred prey, the Atlantic Herring, had disappeared as a result of overfishing. Since then the Killer Whales spend the winter to the northwest of Norway. They simply followed the

Right: The Killer Whales off Norway have specialised on catching herring, which are concentrated into a "bait ball", stunned with the flukes, and then eaten. This particular hunting technique is referred to as a "carousel."

Amos Nachoum/ Seapics.com

Below: A rare photographic document: A Killer Whale eats a stingray off the coast of New Zealand.

Ingrid Visser/ Seapics.com

shoaling herring and are now regarded as unwelcome competitors by the local fishermen. In the short period between 1971 and 1981, no less than 369 Killer Whales were slaughtered off the Lofoten and Vesteralen islands. The animals in this region have since been placed under legal protection.

With the exception of short, regional wanderings that are affected by the extent of the ice barrier and the availability of prey, Killer Whales are not known to migrate regularly or for long distances. It may be that the species is more numerous in the Southern Hemisphere than in the Northern Hemisphere.

Diving
Killer Whales usually dive for 1-6 min, or a max of 25 min. This knowledge came about as a result of the observations made by Canadian researcher Michael Brigg and his colleagues, who were able to identify individual animals on the basis of their size, the shape of their dorsal fins and scars on them, as well as the pigmentation of their dorsal "saddle" patches.

Killer Whales actually do not rank among the deeper diving cetaceans. However, a Killer Whale that got entangled in a transoceanic cable lying at a depth of 1,000 m shows that the species can also dive deep (Heezen & Johnson, 1969).

Groups of Killer Whales either migrate in tight formations or spread over a wide area (up to 1 km from each other). They dive and surface in nearly perfect unison. Resident groups usually dive in a set pattern: In intervals of 10-30 sec they dip under water 4-5 times before diving for 3-4 min. Transients, on the other hand, do not have a set diving pattern. Resting animals remain briefly on the surface, whereby their bodies generally face in the same direction. In this resting position

There is no confirmed case of a Killer Whale attack on humans on record in literature. Examples of the gentleness of this species are shown in these photographs from the Sea of Cortez, Mexico, and a public aquarium.

Photo at the right:
Tom Campbell

Photo below:
Helmut Debelius

they will breathe calmly for about a half a minute and then dive for 3-4 min. They usually surface in the same place.

Feeding Habits

Killer Whales are known for their voraciousness - hence the popular name. They have the most varied diet of all cetaceans, ranging from herring to large marine mammals. Besides fish like salmon, cod and herring, they also take squid, sea birds and leatherback turtles. In addition, they prey on marine mammals like seals, sea lions, walruses and sea cows, as well as at least 25 different species of whale and dolphin, including Fin, Minke, Gray, Right, Bowhead and Beluga. They will even kill and eat young Blue Whales. See also KILLER WHALES LIVING UP TO THEIR NAME on pages 160-164.

When Killer Whales hunt larger whales they will frequently form large groups with a predetermined division of tasks. Some Killer Whales prefer younger specimens of large whale, usually attacking their heads first. They will bite into their prey and twist off bits of its tongue and blubber. It was once observed how a group of Killer Whales attacked a Blue Whale: A few individuals first swam under the Blue Whale to prevent it from sounding, while others pressed in on both sides of the stricken animal. Two individuals swam in front of the Blue Whale and several others remained behind it, thus cutting off all venues of escape. Every time the Blue Whale tried to descend, a few of the Killer Whales would swim directly over it and try to keep it from breathing. Once the Blue Whale was surrounded in this fashion, the Killer Whales kept on attacking its fluke and flippers from behind, biting off piece by piece until the animal could no longer move and finally bled to death.

Another example illustrates the intelligence of Killer Whales and their comprehension of the principle of cause and effect: It was observed how Killer Whales kept on circling a rock on which a group of sea lions were resting. The circling whales seemed to be well aware of the fact that the rising tide would soon engulf the rock their prey was sitting on. And sure enough, their patience soon paid off as one sea lion after the other slipped back into the water to face a certain death.

When Killer Whales hunt shoaling fish like herring, several individuals will herd the panicked school together close to the surface. The resulting concentration of herring, known as a "baitball," is about 3-4 m in circumference. This particular hunting technique is referred to as a "carousel."

The Killer Whales keep circling the baitball, driving back any fish attempting to escape by vocalising and forming walls of bubbles. Again and again the whales expose their white bellies to frighten the fish and force them ever closer together. Once the school of herring is sufficiently concentrated, the Killer Whales begin to strike it at random with their flukes. The blows immediately kill or stun countless fish, which are then promptly consumed.

Killer Whale populations living along the coast of the Valdés peninsula in Argentina and around the French Crozet Islands in the southern Indic will even exit the water temporarily while hunting: They toss themselves onto the slightly sloping gravel beach in order to catch unweary young seals. See also PATAGONIA HUNTERS on pp. 290-296.

General Information
In 1758 Linnaeus classified the Killer Whale as *Delphinus orca*. Later, the animal's sword-like dorsal fin motivated Van Beneden and Gervais to rename the species *Orca gladiator*. This designation never gained acceptance, however. The contemporary scientific name of *Orcinus orca* was introduced by Fitzinger in 1860. Even though a number of scientists have suggested in the past that the differences in body size and shape of the dorsal fin called for a division into several distinct species (e.g. *Orcinus gladiator, O. minor* etc), the genus still includes only one species.

A Killer Whale takes its time to search an Alaskan shore for seals.   Francois Gohier

Facts & Figures Killer Whale
Size: males 7-9 m, max 10 m; females 6-8 m
Weight: males 4.5-9 t, females 2-3 t
Longevity: average 50-60 years; males max of 60, females max of 90
Sexual maturity: females at 6-10 years, males at 12-16 years
Mating season: Spring and early Summer
Gestation period: 12-17 months
Calving interval: varies considerably, usually one calf every 3.5 years
Size at birth: 1.5-2 m
Weight at birth: 160 kg
Nursing period: 15 months
Dive depth: max 1,000 m
Dive time: 20-25 min
Max speed: 55 km/h
Migration speed: average of 5.5-7.5 km/h
Teeth: 20-28 conical teeth in each jaw
Dorsal fin: upright, max of 1.8 m among males, 0.9 m among females
Group (Pod) size: 1-5, also more than 100 when several groups meet
Population: approximately 70,000 in the Southern Hemisphere, total population unknown, presumably not endangered

Quick ID-Check Killer Whale
Conspicuous black-and-white pattern

Upright, high dorsal fin

White patch on underside, ends in three-pronged pattern

Elliptical white patch behind each eye

Large, paddle-shaped flippers

Stocky and robust body

Conspicuous sexual dimorphism (size, shape of dorsal fin)

Very active on surface

Silhouette of a Killer Whale off California.   H. Debelius

In the first century AD, Pliny the Elder described a Killer Whale in his *Naturalis Historiae* as a huge mass of flesh armed with terrible teeth. Spanish whalers of the 18th century gave it the name "Whale Murderer." They had observed how Killer Whales dispatched larger baleen whales and then gorged themselves on their tongues and lips. Indeed, Killer Whales are the only species of marine mammal without natural enemies. In spite of their terrible reputation, there are no confirmed attacks on humans. According to a story about the old whaling days off the coast of South Australia, Killer Whales have even been known to cooperate with humans. It is said that a group of Killer Whales helped whalers from the whaling station in Eden, which is situated near the border between New South Whales and Victoria, to hunt down Southern Right Whales. The Killer Whales herded the Southern Right Whales together and then drove them before the harpooners. The grateful whalers disposed of the bones and blubber and left the remains of the slaughtered whales for the Killer Whales. This fruitful teamwork went on until the leader of this group of Killer Whales died. The cooperation with the whalers was not continued by the next generation. Other than their reputation as "killers of the seas," the main reason why Killer Whales rank among the most popular cetaceans in aquariums is because of their great learning ability and adaptability. They quickly learn diverse tricks to entertain the public. The ratio between the weight of the brain and the total body weight of a Killer Whale is much greater than among baleen whales and corresponds approximately with that of Bottlenose Dolphins. The large size of a Killer Whale's brains is an indication for a higher development than many other species of cetacean. Due to the wide distribution of this species, there are no accurate estimations of the current population size. It is quite probable, however, that there are fewer Killer Whales today than were estimated in previous years. In 1993, for instance, 305 residents, 170 transients and approximately 200 offshores were counted off the coast of British Columbia and Washington. This is far less than earlier estimates for the same region.

Where & When

Killer Whales rank among the most widely ranging mammals of the world. As true "cosmopolitans," they populate all of the oceans in both hemispheres, from the edges of the pack ice to the warmer subtropical and tropical seas. The species generally dwells within 800 km of the coastline, but is also often sighted on the open seas. Although they prefer deeper waters, they can occasionally be encountered in shallow bays and estuaries.

Many Killer Whales gather off the Norwegian islands of Lofoten and Vesteralen from October until January. Up to 500 specimens are regularly counted at this time in Tysfjord and Oftfjord alone. Vancouver Island (West Canada) also has a fairly large resident population.

Killer Whale, distribution: Worldwide in all oceans, especially cold inshore and offshore waters.

Melon-Headed Whale, *Peponocephala electra*

Melon-Headed Whales off Hawaii.   Doug Perrine/Seapics.com

Distinguishing Characteristics
The Melon-Headed Whale is the smallest member of the subfamily Globicephalinae, along with the Pygmy Killer Whale. Its uniformly dark body is very slim and has a markedly curved dorsal fin sitting in the middle of the back. The pointed head has an under-developed snout. Sometimes with a lip-like white or pale-grey patch around mouth.

Description
Melon-Headed Whales average about 2.2-2.7 m in length and weigh around 150 kg. Sexual dimorphism is hardly noticeable: The females remain somewhat smaller than the males. The dorsal fin of a Melon-Headed Whale can be up to 25 cm high. Its flippers are relatively long (50 cm) and pointed. The back edge of its fluke is 60 cm wide, concave and has a median notch. The whale's pointed head somewhat resembles a melon in shape, hence the popular name. Its body is uniformly black or dark-grey with a darker cape-like strip along its back that is hardly visible at sea. Usually there is a pale-grey or white strip on the underside that runs from the thorax to the genitals. Because of its dark colour and numerous small teeth (40-52 in each jaw), the species also bears the name Many-Toothed Blackfish. Newborn calves measure 0.8-1 m in length and weigh around 15 kg.

Easily Mistaken For
Can be confused with False Killer Whales, Short-Finned Pilot Whales and Long-Finned Pilot Whales but is considerably smaller. In addition Pilot Whales have a more bulbous melon.

Other Names
Electra Dolphin, Hawaiian Blackfish, Many-Toothed Blackfish, Little Killer Whale (English); Breitschnabel-Delphin, Melonenkopf (German); Dauphin d'Electre, Péponocéphale (French); Peponocefalo (Italian); Calderón Pequeño (Spanish); Roaz-Indiano, Cabeça de Melão (Portuguese); Witlipdolfijn (Dutch); Melonhodedelphin (Norwegian); Melonipäävalas (Finnish); Melonhuvad Delphin, Brednosdelphin (Swedish); Mangetandet Dværgspækhugger (Danish); Kazuha Gondo Kujira (Japan).

Meaning of the Scientific Nomenclature
Peponocephala electra (Gray 1846) - *Peponocephala* (melon-headed) is made up of the Greek words *peponis* (melon, pumpkin) and *kephalos* (head). The species designation *electra* refers to Elektra, a nymph in Greek mythology.

Behaviour
Little is know about the behaviour of this shy species. Melon-Headed Whales are considered to be fast-swimming oceanic animals with tight social bonds. They are frequently involved in mass stranding. They usually live in large groups of 100-500 individuals, but it is not uncommon to encounter as many as 1000-2000 animals at once. As a group, Melon-Headed Whales usually swim in close proximity to each other and change directions simultaneously. Occasionally they can be observed breaching, lob-tailing and spy-hopping. As long as they are swimming at a slow pace, they will raise their heads out of the water upon surfacing. The larger groups of Melon-Headed Whales

Facts & Figures Melon-Headed Whale	Quick ID-Check Melon-Headed Whale
Size: 2.2-2.5 m, max 2.8 m Weight: 160 kg, max 275 kg Longevity: 47 years Sexual maturity: at 14 years Mating season: July-August Gestation period: 12 months Calving interval: unknown Size at birth: 0.8-1 m Weight at birth: 15 kg Dive time: unknown Teeth: 40-52 small conical teeth in each jaw Group (Pod) size: 100-500, max 2,000 Population: unknown	Dark, slim body Tall, markedly curved dorsal fin White lip-like patch around mouth Long, very pointed flippers Bends tail sharply when sounding Live in large to very large groups Swim in close formation, often change course Shy away from vessels

usually hunt close to the surface at night. This is when squid will ascend from great depths to hunt for fish. Then the water will literally start to "boil" when the Whales close in on the squid.

Diving
Diving behaviour largely unknown. Melon-Headed Whales are conspicuous swimmers that curve their tails sharply when sounding. When they swim at a faster pace, their entire bodies will come out of the water briefly. The resulting splash makes it difficult to recognise any body details.

Feeding Habits
Remains of pelagic squid and smaller fish were found in stomachs of stranded animals.

General Information
In 1846, J. E. Gray first described this species on the basis of a skeleton and named it *Lagenorhynchus electra*. Up until 1963, when the first living specimen was discovered off the coast of Japan, all knowledge about the supposed extinct species was solely based on skeletal finds. Accordingly, the surprise was great when a group of 500 animals swam into Suruga Bay in Japan in 1965. About 250 of them were caught and examined by scientists before their meat was released for consumption. After zoologists Masaharu Nishiwarki and Kenneth Norris had made independent examinations of the first specimens, they both expressed doubts about the classification of the species under the genus *Lagenorhynchus* and established the new generic name of *Peponocephala* in 1966.

Where & When
Distribution identical to that of the Pygmy Killer Whale. Both species prefer the deep tropical and sub-

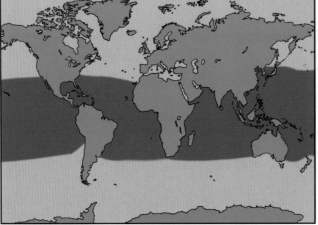

tropical seas on both sides of the globe. The extent to which they range north and south probably depends upon the flow of warm ocean currents. Both species are rarely encountered in warm-temperate waters or near the coast. Melon-Headed Whales are not found in the Mediterranean. Most sightings were made off the coasts of oceanic islands. Frequently encountered in the Pacific around Hawaii (all year), the eastern coast of Australia, Japan, French Polynesia, and Philippines (especially Cebu); Indian Ocean: Maldives; Atlantic: Antilles.

Melon-Headed Whale, distribution: Offshore in deep, tropical and subtropical waters of the world's seas.

CAPTAIN HOOK

As long as the inhabitants of the Spanish Canary Islands in the eastern Atlantic can remember, pilot whales have lived around Tenerife. Snorkelling with these animals is now only permitted with a license, every now and then granted to a dive centre. Underwater photographers Peter Verhoog and Georgina Wiersma were lucky enough to be on the right spot at the right time, and spent some unforgettable hours with these splendid toothed whales.

Like grey shadows the pilot whales approach, including a mother and her calf.

The total number of Short-finned Pilot Whales (Globicephala macrorhynchus) living around the island of Tenerife is estimated at about 180. Long term research of biologists has proven that around 40% of the whales are migrating to warmer waters during part of the year, the other 60% are resident.

Peter really wants to take shots of the leader of the pack, who has been nicknamed "Captain Hook". He had encountered this nearly 7 m long adult-male before, and is anxious to get more pictures. This famous pilot whale has taken an American female snorkeller down to a depth of 40 metres. Opinions about why this has happened vary and until today the reason for this event remains unclear. The woman touched the large male pilot whale several times and wanted to play with the giant. Maybe this triggered the behaviour of the whale. Luckily, Captain Hook brought her back to the surface. Except for some ear damage, she was unharmed. Shortly after this incident, snorkelling with the whales was no longer permitted, the large number of visitors disturbing the whales too much.

It is still very early in the morning when we go out, looking for the pilot whales, and the sun has only just started to colour the sky. When we leave the harbour with the Zodiac, our skipper Claude is already scanning the surface. All of a sudden everyone gets excited: The whales have been spotted! I don fins and mask, Peter checks his camera. Carefully, Claude steers the boat towards the dorsal fins that glide through the water. At his sign, we slowly slide into the water.

I hang in an immense azure aquarium, and wait for things to come. The depth here is about 2 kilometres. Then I see two grey shadows approach, a mother and her calf. The pilot whales are here! I swim slowly, not directly towards them, but trying to cross their path at an angle. They allow me to approach them quite closely, but the mother stays between me and her offspring. A large tail and another smaller one part the water in an extremely elegant manner. The female turns on her side, and looks at me. She probably doesn't like me, because with one swift movement she glides into deeper water, as if she knew that I cannot follow her.

The Zodiac picks me up, and we cruise the sea to find other pilot whales. Then we see more dorsal fins! Again, we glide cautiously into the water. The vast blue space is full of sounds: A faint song and lots of clicking sounds, used for echo-location and communication. These sounds are produced in the pilot whales' big, round heads, filled with a lens-shaped fatty deposit called "melon". I count 12 whales this time. The animals could easily swim away, but choose to stay with us. If we swim too slow, they slow down, too. They often break the surface to breathe, and when they submerge again, a trail of tiny bubbles emerges from each of their blowholes. Rays of sunlight dance on the whales' grey bodies which have a darker colour pattern. I swim and swim... Peter swims alongside me, hoping to catch me on film together with the pilot whales. A few seconds later, I am surrounded by giant shapes, I am in the middle of the pod! Peter dives down many times to take pictures. We snorkel hour after hour. After four hours, skipper Claude wants to

Hour after hour we snorkel with another pod of pilot whales off Tenerife...

return to the harbour because he sees the whale watching boats, filled with curious tourists, approaching in the distance. The other snorkellers are already exhausted, but we keep begging him for one more dive! For the last time, the two of us dive into the endless blue ocean. The pod of whales is about 10 metres away from us. All of a sudden a baby pilot whale approaches me. It is not shy, and clearly wants to investigate us. The small calf has a length of about one and a half metres, and must have been born only recently. When it is about five metres away from me, a giant shadow approaches. It's Captain Hook! The nearly 7-metre-long adult male, clearly the leader of the pack, swims towards me at very high speed, his tail making powerful, fast movements. He definitely does not want me to approach the calf, and positions himself between us. For one long, but too short, splendid, glorious minute, I swim with Captain Hook, secretly hoping he won't decide to 'play' with me. I see Peter taking photographs... I conquer the waves like a neoprene mermaid. The whale looks at me, I look at him. This is one of the most beautiful creatures I have ever seen. Then the illustrious leader decides that it is enough. He dives into the deep, taking his family with him. Peter and I stay behind on the surface, holding on to each other, gasping for breath. The coast of Tenerife is gone, the Zodiac is far away. We are so happy with this close encounter. Still, Peter looks a bit disappointed. I guess he just wanted to take pictures of me, going down with old Captain Hook. And being brought back to the surface again, of course!

..the illustrious leader of which is the notorious Captain Hook, a nearly 7-metre-long adult male.

False Killer Whale, *Pseudorca crassidens*

A False Killer Whale in a delphinarium shows its remarkable teeth.   Helmut Debelius

Distinguishing Characteristics
The body is very slim and has a markedly curved dorsal fin that sits far down the back. With the exception of a pale, anchor-shaped spot between the flippers, the body is uniformly black. This spot is not as noticeable as that on the body of a Long-Finned Pilot Whale, however. The very narrow head has a slightly receding brow and a snout that overhangs the lower jaw. The area around the blowhole is depressed, which can clearly be seen in profile and helps to identify the animal on the high seas. There is a noticeable bent ("elbow") in the middle of the leading edge of each flipper.

Description
False Killer Whales attain an average length of 4 m (max 6.1 m) and weigh around 1.1-1.4 t (males). With a max length of 5 m, the females are noticeably smaller and lighter.

The long melon extends slightly further than the lower jaw. The jawlines are straight and do not have a pale lip-like patch. The length of the slim and forward-placed flippers is equal to 1/8-1/10 of the total body length. The fluke is proportionately small and has a slightly concave back edge with a median notch. The large, conspicuously curved dorsal fin sits slightly lower than midriff. Its tip is rounded to pointed in form. No albinism has been registered so far for this predominantly black species.

Easily Mistaken For
Can be confused with Pygmy Killer Whales, Melon-Headed Whales, Long-Finned Pilot Whales and Short-Finned Pilot Whales. Its larger size, however, clearly differentiates a False Killer Whale from a Pygmy Killer Whale and a Melon-Headed Whale. It can be distinguished from both species of Pilot Whale by its noticeably slimmer head and body, markedly curved dolphin-like dorsal fin, more active surface behaviour and swimming style. A False Killer Whale's body will clear the surface of the water when it swims at a fast pace.

Other Names
False Pilot Whale, Pseudorca (English); Kleiner Schwertwal, Unechter Schwertwal, Falscher Schwertwal, Schwarzer Schwertwal, Mittlerer Schwertwal, Kleiner Mörder (German); Pseudorque,

Faux-Orque (French); Pseudorca (Italian); Orca Falsa (Spanish); Falsa Orca, Orca Bastarda (Portuguese); Zwarte Zwaardwalvis (Dutch); Falsk Spekkhogger (Norwegian); Pikkumiekkavalas (Finnish); Halvspäckhuggare (Swedish); Halvspækhugger (Danish); Oki Gondo Kujira (Japanese).

Meaning of the Scientific Nomenclature
Pseudorca crassidens (Owen 1846) - The generic name *Pseudorca* is made up of the Greek word *pseudes* (false) and the Latin word *orca* (designation for a whale). It refers to the species' similarity to Killer Whales. The species name *crassidens* means "thick-tooth"and is composed of the Latin words *crassus* (thick) and *dens* (tooth).

Behaviour
False Killer Whales are very gregarious animals that live in groups of 20-50 individuals (occasionally even several hundred specimens). One will rarely encounter smaller groups or pairs. The social structure of the group, which is composed of individuals of various ages, is not as well developed as it is among Killer Whales. Recently it has become known that False Killer Whales will occasionally hunt dolphins and other species of whale. In Hawaii it was observed how they attacked and killed a Humpback Whale calf. Nevertheless, they are frequently seen in the company of Bottlenose Dolphins and other species of dolphin. In spite of their predominantly pelagic way of life, mass stranding is common among False Killer Whales. The largest number of stranded cetaceans ever recorded involved 835 False Killer Whales that died in this fashion in Mar del Plata, Argentina, on October 10, 1946. Although the species ranges far and wide, it doesn't appear to be very numerous. Since calves are born throughout the year, there is evidently no set mating season. For their size, False Killer Whales are quite active and playful. They often approach vessels and like to bow-ride. They also breach frequently, twisting in the air and landing on their sides. False Killer Whales are fast swimmers, reaching speed of up to 22-26 km/h. Their heads and bodies will clear the surface of the water down to where the flippers sit. They frequently make unexpected stops while swimming fast, presumably to catch prey. They effectively implement echolocation to track down their prey. Other acoustic signals are used for interspecies communication. False Killer Whales often surface with their mouths open, thereby displaying their teeth. They tend to do this when approached by swimmers or divers, so that it may well be a threatening gesture. In spite of the aggressiveness they manifest in the wild, it is possible to maintain smaller False Killer Whales in an aquarium. They quickly get used to captivity and are very trainable. See also CHASED BY A FALSE KILLER WHALE (pp.165-167) and TROPHY HUNTER (pp.194-195).

Diving
False Killer Whales usually dive and hunt in groups, whereby they swim at a very fast pace and frequently alter their course.

Feeding Habits
False Killer Whales prey mainly on cephalopods. They also consume large fish like yellowtail tuna, bonito and mackerel. Occasionally they will attack marlin, tuna and other large fish that have been hooked by sports fishermen. In addition, they prey on different species of sea mammal. Large groups of False Killer Whales will sometimes attack dolphins as well as sick or wounded large whales.

Facts & Figures False Killer Whale	Quick ID-Check False Killer Whale
Size: males up to 6.1 m, females up to 5 m	
Weight: 1.1-1.4 t (males)	Uniformly dark, long, slim body
Longevity: 20 years	
Sexual maturity: females at about 2-4 years, males at 8-14 years	Slim head with rounded snout
Mating season: all year	Conspicuous, dolphin-like, curved dorsal fin
Gestation period: 11-12 months, perhaps up to 15.5 months	
Size at birth: 1.6-1.83 m	Flippers with hump on leading edge
Weight at birth: 80 kg	
Maximum speed: 22-26 km/h	Almost clears the water with its body when swimming fast
Teeth: 14-24 strong conical teeth in each of the jaws	Curious, approaches vessels
Group (Pod) size: 20-50, occasionally several hundred animals	
Population: unknown, presumably not endangered	Very active on surface

A False Killer Whale off the Azores in the Atlantic Ocean.   Stephen Wong

General Information

In 1846 Sir Richard Owen first described this species on the basis of skeletal remains that were found in Lincolnshire (England) and named it *Phocoena crassidens*. He thought back then that the species was extinct. Accordingly, the surprise was great when a group of False Killer Whales stranded in Kiel (Baltic Sea, Germany) in 1862. These animals were subsequently examined by Danish zoologist Johannes Reinhardt. He classified the species in a new genus and named it *Pseudorca* because of its similarity to Killer Whales. This classification is still accepted today.

False Killer Whales are hunted down in parts of the Caribbean and in Japan because the local fishermen hold them responsible for receding catches. In Japan the fishermen drive the animals onto the beach with their boats as soon as they appear. The meat of the stranded animals is then consumed.

Where & When

False Killer Whales are widely distributed, but do not appear very frequently. This is an oceanic species that lives in the deep tropical to temperate waters of all the world's oceans. They prefer warmer temperatures. The coldest regions in which they were ever sighted include the North Sea, the Scandinavian coast and 40° latitude south. Occasionally False Killer Whales will also approach islands that are surrounded by deep waters or the edge of the continental shelf. Also occurs in the Mediterranean and Red Sea.

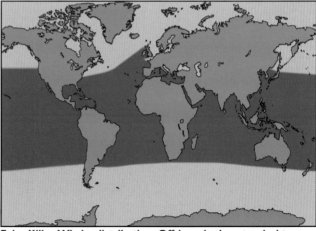

False Killer Whale, distribution: Offshore in deep tropical to temperate waters of all the world's oceans.

Almost nothing is known about the hunting behaviour of killerwhales - especially in tropical waters. Sometimes a little bit of it is revealed during a chance meeting. Photographer and eye-witness Mark Strickland recalls such a dramatic encounter.

ALL PHOTOS: MARK STRICKLAND

The beautiful sailfish *Istiophorus platypterus*, one of the fastest creatures in the sea, raises its high dorsal fin in threat display.

We are on our way to the Similan Islands off the coast of Thailand. As usual, everybody is watching the surface of the sea from the deck of the liveaboard. Suddenly Suzanne points at a peculiar black rectangle that is cruising in zig-zag fashion only a hundred metres from our vessel. Very close to it a dozen of large, dolphin-like dorsal fins appear. As we approach, we realise that the rectangle is the erected black dorsal fin of a sailfish. It is extremely difficult to approach this shy pelagic predator while diving. After the engines of our vessel have been shut down, we take the opportunity to snorkel towards the scene. Naturally, we also want to find out what is going on between the dolphins and the sailfish.

In the water, we are amazed by the size of the "dolphins" because they are three to five metres in length. Judging from their head shape, they have to be toothed whales. Obviously interested in us, they do not swim away, but circle beneath us, sometimes even belly-up. Our eyes meet. While we use all our fin-power trying to keep pace, it seems as if they wait for us to approach. How amusing it has to be for them to watch us humble creatures in the water. They swim in groups of three, but sometimes there are up to 15 individuals together. When one of the whales opens its mouth, I see its large teeth and realise that we are surrounded by a school of False killerwhales *Pseudorca crassidens*. They are predators, which - unlike dolphins - do not hunt for sardines and fusiliers, but utilise

their strong dentition to prey on large pelagic fish and marine mammals.

As if it were not fantastic enough to swim along with these whales that are hardly known from the Indian Ocean, we then approach the sailfish. With its fully erected dorsal fin, it obviously tries to impress the killerwhales. Although the whales are able to kill the fish any time, they seem to delight in terrorising it. A group of ten False killerwhales totally controls the sailfish: when it speeds up, it is immediately surrounded. A sailfish could certainly outswim a single killerwhale, but it cannot cope with their group strategy. The fish

Cornered by killerwhales, the sailfish clearly shows signs of stress: its normally brilliant blue coloration has become almost white on the body, and black on the dorsal fin.

shows strong signs of stress: while sailfish normally display wonderful shades of blue striped with bronze, it now is totally pale. It looks,   as if it is fighting for its life. Underwater photographs of sailfish are quite rare, but I succeed in shooting some of the terrified animal on its zig-zag course.

Breathless, one after the other of our snorkelling group gives in. Especially my legs are hurting, as I have to carry the additional weight of the heavy camera housing. Then the sailfish gets out of sight. I signal to Suzanne, who is swimming with me, to return to the liveaboard. Some of the False killerwhales are still swimming around us. Suddenly eight of

A group of False killerwhales *Pseudorca crassidens* pursues the sailfish. One of these toothed whales alone would have no chance to catch the speedy sailfish.

them come out of the blue and swim   towards us. I can clearly see that the largest of the group is holding something in its mouth. Suzanne and   I   dive towards   the marine   mammals to get a closer   look. Puzzled, we are watching from a distance   how the whale drops something and

After the meal: one of these False killerwhales holds a trophy of the hunt in its mouth. The object remains unidentified at this distance.

another individual immediately picks it up again. I have just reached the surface to get fresh air, when the killerwhale with the object in its mouth leaves the group in a depth of about six metres. It smoothly approaches Suzanne, who is diving in the same depth, and "spits out" the unknown object right in front of her. She instinctively grabs it, and brings it up with her. The object is the pectoral fin of a sailfish that has just been removed from the body! The whales must just have killed the surrounded sailfish. But what about this action? Was the fin a gift for Suzanne? Was it an invitation to play? Or was it just an unintentional move? I am, after all, happy not to have been a sailfish in the company of killerwhales!

Only after the whales have given the object as a "gift" to Suzanne, it can be identified: it is one of the pectoral fins of the sailfish!

The subfamily of **dolphins** has the largest number of species in the family of Delphinidae. In order to make identification easier, the Delphininae have been divided into two groups here:

Nine species with a long snout (beak):
    Common Dolphin, *Delphinus delphis*
    Long-Beaked Common Dolphin, *Delphinus capensis*
    Pantropical Spotted Dolphin, *Stenella attenuata*
    Atlantic Spotted Dolphin, Stenella frontalis
    Short-Snouted Spinner Dolphin, *Stenella clymene*
    Striped Dolphin, *Stenella coeruleoalba*
    Long-Snouted Spinner Dolphin, *Stenella longirostris*
    Bottlenose Dolphin, *Tursiops truncatus*
    Indo-Pacific Bottlenose Dolphin, *Tursiops aduncus*

Eight species with a short snout (beak):
    Atlantic White-Sided Dolphin, *Lagenorhynchus acutus*
    White-Beaked Dolphin, *Lagenorhynchus albirostris*
    Peale's Dolphin, *Lagenorhynchus australis*
    Hourglass Dolphin, *Lagenorhynchus cruciger*
    Dusky Dolphin, *Lagenorhynchus obscurus*
    Pacific White-Sided Dolphin, *Lagenorhynchus obliquidens*
    Fraser's Dolphin, *Lagenodelphis hosei*
    Irrawaddy Dolphin, *Orcaella brevirostris*

Distinguishing Characteristics of this Subfamily
All members of this subfamily have a rounded melon and a clearly demarcated snout (beak) that can be either long or short. With the exception of a few species (e.g. Irrawaddy Dolphin), two or more of their neck vertebrae will always be fused. They have 10-220 teeth in each jaw. Their dorsal fins are falcate and clearly demarcated. The length of the whole animal ranges from 1.6 to almost 4 m. They usually live in large groups with tight social bonds. They are generally considered to be inquisitive and will often perform acrobatic leaps.

Common Dolphin, *Delphinus delphis*

A Common Dolphin in the Mediterranean.   Ralf Kiefner

Even when photographed from the surface, this species is recognisable by its short snout.   Ralf Kiefner

Distinguishing Characteristics
The most conspicuous earmark is the lateral crisscross pattern that is yellowish-tan forward of the dorsal fin and grey behind it. Below the dorsal fin, where the crisscross lines intersect, a dark dorsal cape forms a noticeable V-shaped saddle that extends down to the flanks.

Description
This species attains a max length of 2.6 m, whereby the males grow slightly larger than the females. There is also a slight divergence in colouration between them (sexual dimorphism). The dark snout is separated from the flat forehead by a conspicuous fold and can vary somewhat in length and colour.

Easily Mistaken For
The Common Dolphin can easily be confused with the very similar Long-Beaked Common Dolphin. They were not recognised as two separate species until 1995. Common Dolphin: Stockier, shorter snout, more complex patterns, more rounded melon, narrower line running from the lower jaw to the flippers, brighter colouration, larger fluke and flippers. The Long-Beaked Common Dolphin lives inshore, while the Common Dolphin prefers offshore waters. The species is clearly distinguishable from all other dolphins on the basis of the yellowish-tan crisscross pattern forward of the dorsal fin.

Other Names
Short-Beaked Common Dolphin, Saddleback, White-Bellied Porpoise, Crisscross Dolphin, Hourglass Dolphin, (English); Gewöhnlicher Delphin (German); Dauphin Commun (French); Delphino Comune (Italian); Delphin Comun (Spanish); Golfinho Vulgar, Golfinho Comum (Portuguese); Gewone Dolfijn (Dutch); Delphin (Norwegian); Delfiini, Juoksiainen (Finnish); Springare (Swedish); Almindelig Delphin (Danish); Tobi Iruka (Japanese); Obyknovenny (Russian).

Meaning of the Scientific Nomenclature
Delphinus delphis Linnaeus 1758 - Latin *Delphinus* (dolphin) and Greek *delphis* (dolphin), meaning "dolphin-dolphin." The repetition indicates that this is one of the oldest known species of dolphin with which people of Antiquity were already well acquainted.

Behaviour
This species is very active and gregarious, living in groups of 10 to several thousand individuals, preferably in deep inshore waters. The size of the group varies according to the season, time of day (whether the animals hunt or rest) and the presence of prey. In areas with plentiful prey, the species will often join up with other dolphins (e.g. Long-Beaked Common Dolphin). Common Dolphins are very fast swimmers and agile acrobats. They frequently leap high out of the water and slap the surface with their heads, flippers or flukes. Their acrobatic leaps and somersaults can be readily recognised from afar. These animals are very inquisitive. In contrast to other species of dolphin, their attention can easily be diverted from their natural activities like hunting whenever a vessel approaches. Then they will approach the vessel in leaps and bounds in order to ride the bow wave. Their vocalising delights both swimmers and snorkellers. Their whistles and squeaks are clearly audible under water and can even be heard on the surface.

The groups are probably divided by gender: Mature males in one and pregnant and nursing females with adolescent animals of either gender in the other. These will intermix when hunting, migrating or mating. The largest groups form in the fall and winter. In the nutrient-rich regions of the Atlantic and Mediterranean they will also associate with Bottlenose Dolphins (*Tursiops truncatus*) and Striped Dolphins (*Stenella coeruleoalba*). In the Eastern Pacific they often remain close to schools of yellowfin tuna and thereby incur the danger of entanglement in fishing nets. The following behaviour has been observed in the Northern Pacific: Large groups rest together during the day and disband into smaller groups at night to hunt and feed. The next morning they once again gather into large groups to rest. The reason behind this nightly activity is that the deep scattering layer, which is primarily composed of zooplankton, shies away from the sunlight. At night the zooplankton moves close to the water's surface to feed on phytoplankton (usually one-celled algae). This attracts fish and cephalopods that feed on the zooplankton, which are in turn preyed on by dolphins.

Male whales and dolphins have recourse to two tactics in order to insure maximum reproduction: 1. The bulls prevent rivals from mating with "their" cows by fighting them off (polygynous mating behaviour); 2. The bulls try to mate with as many cows as often as possible without hindering each other (promiscuous mating behaviour).The latter entails sperm competition and the testicles of the bulls consequently attain an enormous size. The testicles of a male Common Dolphin weigh up to 4 kg each, which suggests an intensive sexual activity with relatively little rivalry (Kenagy & Trombulak, 1986). More recent investigations have confirmed this: Only 20% of the examined animals had fractured ribs or spinous processes (with the exception of Bottlenose Dolphins, other species of dolphin have fractured ribs in up to 70% of the cases). Furthermore, aggressive behaviour was directed more towards the cows (more fractures) than the rivals. According to one confirmed observation, the sexual activities of a pair of Common Dolphins lasted over two weeks and only ceased with the death of the male.

The literature of Antiquity already describes the sociable nature of Common Dolphins, reporting numerous cases in which shipwrecked mariners were kept afloat on the surface by them. This rescue instinct is apparently so strong that they will even bring up objects similar in size and shape to a member of the same species. This would also explain why they should bother to bring up a drowning human. Reports that the rescued mariners were also transported for days

Facts & Figures Common Dolphin	Quick ID-Check Common Dolphin
Size: 1.7-2.6 m	Hourglass pattern on flanks
Weight: 70-135 kg	
Longevity: 25-30 years	Anterior of flanks partially yellowish-tan
Sexual maturity: females at 6-7 years, males at 5-12 years	Dark back with V-shaped saddle under the dorsal fin
Mating season: Spring and Fall, possibly all year round in the tropics	
Gestation period: 10-11.5 months	Clearly demarcated, very long snout
Calving interval: 1 calf per year	
Size at birth: 0.8-1 m	Dark line running from snout to flippers
Weight at birth: 10 kg	
Dive depth: 70 m, max 300 m	Flippers and fluke usually dark
Dive time: 10 min	
Maximum speed: approx 60 km/h	Belly and lower flanks white
Teeth: 80-120 small conical teeth in each jaw	
Group size: 10-2,000 (Eastern Tropical Pacific)	Very active on surface
Population: unknown, presumably several million	

and brought safely to shore are highly questionable, however. Common Dolphins are apparently resident in some regions, while in others they will migrate back and forth seasonally (spring and summer) between deep offshore waters and the coast. These migrations probably have more to do with reproduction than the availability of prey.

Diving
Average dive time 5 m, max 10 min. Average dive depth rarely more than 70 m, max 300 m.

Feeding Habits
Like other oceanic dolphins, Common Dolphins also prefer pelagic fish. Depending upon the region and season, they primarily prey on shoaling fish (anchovies, mackerel, hake, sardines, herring, European hake) in the summer and cephalopods (sepia, squid) in the winter. They conserve energy by working together, whereby they dive under their shoaling prey and herd it together on the surface. See also DOLPHIN DANCE on pp. 241-243.

General Information
Common Dolphins were already well known among the Greeks and Romans of Antiquity and played an important role in their mythologies. Aristotle was the first to name this species "dolphin" and recognise it as a mammal. Linnaeus named it *Delphinus delphis* in 1758.

In spite of occasional attacks on Common Dolphins by False Killer Whales, the two species generally live side by side in harmony. Attacks by Killer Whales are also rare, but David H. Brown and Kenneth Norris did observe one such incident. The Killer Whales surrounded the dolphins as if they were a school of herring and herded them into a tight ball. Then one Killer Whale after another darted into the living mass and got its share of the prey while the others patrolled on the periphery to insure that no dolphins could escape. But it has also been reported by Brown and Caldwell (1966) that a captive False Killer Whale came to the aid of a female Common Dolphin when a Short-Finned Pilot Whale was about to devour its stillborn calf. Another incidence of mutual aid between the species was described by Logan and Robson (1971). In this case a female Dusky Dolphin helped a Common Dolphin to deliver.

Common Dolphins are considered to be the most numerous species of dolphin, even though their numbers are depleting rapidly in the Mediterranean, Black Sea and Eastern Tropical Pacific. The exact population status is unknown, but it is estimated that there are still several million animals alive today (including approx 900,000 specimens in the Eastern Tropical Pacific and 17,000 in the Western North Atlantic). Nevertheless, the species is considered to be endangered, primarily because of the tuna fisheries. Since they prey on shoaling fish, Common Dolphins are frequently caught in purse seine nets and other fishing gear. During the 1960s Soviet fishermen caught around 120,000 animals each year in the Black Sea. In 1988 the number of animals being caught annually was still as high as 100,000. Due to improved fishing methods and stricter regulations, these figures have since been markedly reduced. As the final link in the food chain, Common Dolphins (and all other dolphins) are highly susceptible to pollution. Particularly the animals living in the Mediterranean are highly contaminated with mercury, chlorofluorocarbons and heavy metals. As the species is not suited for life in captivity, usually dying within a few months, one will rarely encounter it in an aquarium.

Where & When
Widely distributed throughout all offshore tropical to warm-temperate waters of the world's seas. Atlantic: From the south of Newfoundland to Argentina and southern Scandinavia to South Africa. Pacific: From Japan to New Zealand and California to Chile. Also found in lesser bodies of water (Red Sea, Mediterranean, Black Sea). Prefers depths of 300 m and more. Often above the continental shelf as well as along steep coasts and islands.

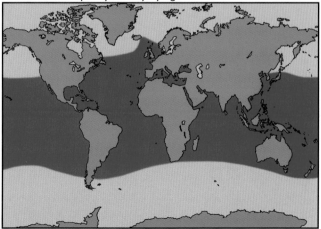

Common Dolphin, distribution: Deep, offshore, tropical to warm-temperate waters in all of the world's seas.

Long-Beaked Common Dolphin, *Delphinus capensis*

Lively Long-Beaked Common Dolphins off the coast of South Africa.   Rod Haestier

Distinguishing Characteristics see Common Dolphin.

Other Names

Cape Dolphin, Saddleback Dolphin, Criss-Cross Dolphin, Hourglass Dolphin (English); Küsten-delphin, Kap-Delphin, Gewöhnlicher Küstendelphin (German); Dauphin Commun (French); Delfin Común Costero (Spanish); Golfinho Comum Costeiro (Portuguese); Delphino (Italian); Tobi Iruka (Japanese).

Meaning of the Scientific Nomenclature

Delphinus capensis Gray 1828 - Latin *delphinus* (dolphin); capensis refers to the place of discovery, the Cape of Good Hope in South Africa.

Behaviour

Group size, surface activities, etc. are practically identical to the Common Dolphin. However, the species prefer inshore waters, especially steep coasts. See also TRAPPED, pp. 201-202.

Diving

Average dive time is 5-10 min. Average dive depth (during hunt) is 50 m, max 200 m.

Feeding Habits

Long-Beaked Common Dolphins prefer squid and inshore fish. Depending upon the season and region, they primarily feed on shoaling fish in the summer and sepia and squid in winter. They always hunt in groups and herd their prey into tight balls on the surface.

General Information

The first description was provided by Gray in 1828 on the basis of a specimen from the Cape of Good Hope (South Africa). Nevertheless, this species was long held to be a variant of the

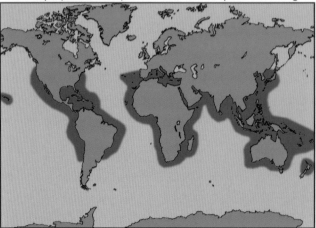

Common Dolphin *(D. delphis)*. It wasn't until 1995 that *D. capensis* was recognised as a distinct species on the basis of different DNA and morphology (size, length and width of the snout; more teeth and cervical vertebrae than *D. delphis)*. In addition, there are variances in distribution of the species. In spite of the existence of mixed groups, there has been no evidence of interbreeding between the two species so far. Since they prey on shoaling fish, these dolphins are often caught accidentally in fishing nets.

Long-Beaked Common Dolphin, distribution: Inshore, tropical and warm-temperate waters of all oceans.

Instead of going for a walk along the cliffs in the afternoons as usually, the photographer Rod Haestier found himself for some reason on an early walk on a nice day in January 2001 at De Kelders in Gansbaai (South Africa). He just wanted to take in the breath-taking views of South Africa's southern Cape coast, have a quick swim and then go to the office when he suddenly heard the "squeaking" of some dolphins.

Well, you can imagine my surprise and amazement when hearing dolphins "squeaking" and not being able to see them. A few steps later I found myself peering over the edge of the cliffs, and down below in a pool, a group of about 15 Long-beaked Common Dolphins (*Delphinus capensis*) swimming around and around in an anti-clockwise direction.

I watched for a while and then ran back home to collect my camera and cell phone. I phoned my brother, who was up in Durban, and he in turn contacted the scientists in Cape Town and doctors In Plettenberg Bay. During this time my friend Anton, swam out the channel in the hope that the dolphins may register that this is the way out and that they should change their swimming pattern, but to no avail.

Fred, a local diver from this area, also rushed to help, and he took control of the rescue operation. So, the three of us went in to see if we could somehow herd them into the channel. At this time the tide was coming in, so the surge and current of the sea rather strong. It was quite apparent that more people were needed, as the pool being about 15 m

Down below in a rock pool, a group of about 15 dolphins was swimming around and around without finding the way out.

We went into the water to form a barrier of arms and legs, trying to drive the dolphins back into the sea.

in diameter and approximately 5 m deep, the dolphins kept swimming below our feet, then around us and behind, keeping the same swimming pattern.

News soon travelled, so with all the extra divers we went back into the water to form a barrier of arms and legs. Slowly we closed in, and this is when some dolphins changed direction and headed out to sea. No sooner were half of them out of the pool, when three adults swam back in so as not to leave the "teenagers" behind. At this time the tide was high, so we decided to make one last attempt to prompt them out. We were unsuccessful, and felt it better to leave them alone for a while so as not to stress them out any further.

At 18.00 hrs the "rescue" group returned and then I decided to stay on the cliffs to witness and photograph the story. A difficult decision to make, as one does not always come across an opportunity like this. Well, how wonderful. Fred brought a net to help with the barrier, and this worked out well. On this first attempt two divers helped guide out two dolphins and they stayed at the mouth whilst the others re-grouped.

At one stage I thought they were going to sneak back in to join the others, but thankfully the remaining dolphins changed direction and headed out through the kelp and into the mouth. They all swam around a bit and the headed out to feed on a pocket of sardines. One dolphin was very excited and no doubt very happy, and gave a little aerial show, much to the delight of the crowd on the cliffs. More than likely they were met by the initial group who escaped, as several blows and fins could be seen in the bay during all of this time.

I must say that this was an awesome experience. Neither mammal nor man was injured, and no fear was felt whilst in the pool with the dolphins. During this time I seldom heard them calling out, so could it be that now that help was at hand their trust was in us?

It's difficult to say when and why they landed up in a little pool — more than likely they were chasing sardines for food, and then these little fish had been moving just too quick and so confused the echoes for the dolphins. And after 10 hours the cliffs were back to normal, and the rescue party and all visitors greatful that the dolphins were at last free again.

Now when I pass by this particular pool, I always see this one particular dolphin popping his head out above the others, having a look at the world outside the ocean.

Pantropical Spotted Dolphin, *Stenella attenuata*

Two Pantropical Spotted Dolphins are depicted here in all their elegance. Hawaii.   Chris Newbert

Distinguishing Characteristics
The adult animals are particularly easy to identify on the basis of their conspicuous and individualistic spotted pattern which, however, can vary considerably depending upon age and geographical distribution. The snout is long and narrow with a characteristic white tip and "lips."

Description
Stocky body, length 2-2.4 m, weight up to 120 kg, females somewhat smaller than males (sexual dimorphism). The snout is noticeably demarcated from the flat forehead by a fold. Flanks usually have grey stripes. Underside pale-grey with dark spots. As the animals age, the spots increase in size and number and almost completely cover up the primary colour in the case of older individuals. On the high seas the back can appear somewhat pale ("silverback") in the sunlight. No spots on the flippers. Conspicuous dark stripe running from the eyes to the flippers. Pigmentation in 5 stages: 1. Newborn calves are still spotless, with muted patterns. 2. Dorsal half darkens, ventral half stays pale. 3. As of 1.5 m in length the first spots begin to appear on the pale belly. 4. First light spots begin to appear on the dark back. Ventral spots increase in size and merge together. 5. Dorsal spots increase in size and number. A dark stirrup-like line joins the eyes, an additional dark

Facts & Figures Pantropical Spotted Dolphin	Quick ID-Check Pantropical Spotted Dolphin
Size: 1.6-2.4 m	
Weight: 90-120 kg	Slim body, dark-grey back
Longevity: approx 45 years	
Sexual maturity: females at 9-11 years, males at 12-15 years	Large falcate dorsal fin
Gestation period: 11.5 months	Mature animals markedly spotted, pattern of
Calving interval: every 2-3 years in Spring/Fall	spots varies individually
Size at birth: 0.8-0.9 m	
Dive depth: approx 200 m	Long, narrow snout with white "lips", white at
Maximum speed: 40 km/h	tip of snout
Teeth: 70-96 conical teeth in each jaw	
Group size: 50-1,000, occasionally up to 3,000	Dark stripe from eyes to flippers
Population: Eastern Tropical Pacific 2 million, total number unknown	Very active on surface

The white tip of the snout is clearly visible from afar when they leap.   Doug Perrine

line runs from the snout to the flippers. Individuals in some regional populations (Gulf of Mexico and Hawaii) are only sparsely spotted.

Easily Mistaken For
Might be confused with Bottlenose Dolphins, Indo-Pacific Hump-Backed Dolphins and Atlantic Spotted Dolphins. Confusion is most likely with the Atlantic Spotted Dolphin (especially in the NW-Atlantic, where the ranges of both species overlap), even though this species is somewhat more slender and has a darker stripe running between the eyes and flippers.

Other Names
Spotter, Spotted Porpoise, Pantropical White Spotted Dolphin, Bridled Dolphin, Slender-Beaked Dolphin (English); Pantropischer Fleckendelphin, Schlankdelphin, Gefleckter Delphin, Fleckendelphin (German); Dauphin Tacheté de Pantropical, Dauphin Tacheté du Pacifique, Dauphin Tropical (French); Stenella Maculata Pantropicale (Italian); Estenela Moteada (Spanish); Golfinho Malhado Pantropical (Portuguese); Slanke Dolfijn (Dutch); Hvitflekkdelphin (Norwegian); Trooppinentäplädelfiini (Finnish); Stilla Havets Fläckiga Delphin (Swedish); Pantropisk Plettet Delphin (Danish); Arari Iruka (Japanese); Delphin Manchado, Delphin Pintado (Latin American Spanish).

Meaning of the Scientific Nomenclature
Stenella attenuata (Gray 1846) - *Stenella* (J. E. Gray, 1866) is based on the Greek *stenos* (narrow, slim) and refers to the typical long, slim and clearly demarcated snout. Latin *attenuata* (tapering).

Behaviour
Very active species, leaps out of the water repeatedly (porpoising) when swimming at a fast pace. Also very gregarious. Group size ranges from approximately a few dozen (coastal variants, e.g. Central America) to several thousand (pelagic) individuals.

Diving
Inshore animals dive for shorter periods of time than their offshore relatives. Their dives are limited to the upper levels of water down to about 200 m.

Feeding Habits
The species hunts close to the surface on the open sea. Preferred prey is small shoaling fish, flying fish and squid. In coastal areas it also feeds on reef fish and benthic crustaceans.

General Information
First named *Delphinus attenuatus,* then *Steno attenuatus* and finally *Stenella attenuata* (all names by

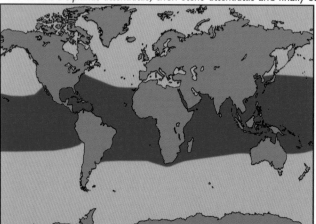

Gray). The reason for the diverse names is the lack of homogeneity in different populations and even within various groups. William F. Perrin (1987) separates *S. attenuata* from *S. frontalis* (Atlantic Spotted Dolphin).

Where & When
Worldwide inshore and offshore, in all tropical, subtropical and a few warm-temperate waters (25+° C) of the world's seas. Eastern Pacific: California to Peru; Western Pacific: Japan to Australia; Indian Ocean: Red Sea and west coast of Africa all the way to Australia.

Pantropical Spotted Dolphin, distribution: Worldwide inshore and offshore, in most tropical and warm-temperate waters.

Atlantic Spotted Dolphin, *Stenella frontalis*

Adults of this species have earmark spots, younger animals (back) still lack them. Azores.   Ralf Kiefner

Distinguishing Characteristics
Mature animals have clearly demarcated spots: Dark spots on a light background and in reverse as well. These can be large enough to partially cover up the animal's basic colour.

Description
Relatively robust body, up to 2.4 m in length and 140 kg in weight. Long, narrow snout with a fold where it demarcates itself from the prominent melon. Head form is similar to that of the Bottlenose Dolphin, but with straight rather than curved jawlines so that it lacks the typical "smile" of that species. Dorsal fin is clearly demarcated, with a broad base, falcate and usually uniformly dark without spots. Flippers are relatively long, slim, with pointed ends and no spots. The concave back edge of the fluke has a well developed median notch. Every adult animal has a unique pattern that remains unchanged throughout its life. This probably helps the animals identify each other in a group. There is considerable variation between the different populations in the patterns of spots and in general colouration, e.g. the pelagic variant in the East Atlantic and the Azores has almost no ventral spots. Newborn calves are still unspotted, but have a conspicuous dark-grey dorsal cape, light-grey flanks and a pale belly. After a year they get their first spots, first on the belly and flanks, later on the cape which then becomes increasingly noticeable. By the second year their bodies will be entirely covered with spots. As the animals age, the spots will increase in intensity, size and number.

Easily Mistaken For
Pantropical Spotted Dolphins, Bottlenose Dolphins, Indo-Pacific Bottlenose Dolphins (latter is similar, but range does not overlap). Atlantic Spotted Dolphins can be most easily confused with Pantropical Spotted Dolphins, but the former lives exclusively in the warmer regions of the Atlantic while the later are also found in the Pacific and Indian Ocean. Differences: Atlantic Spotted Dolphins are stockier, have a conspicuous pale-grey blaze on the flanks and distinct spots on the belly. The spots on a Pantropical Spotted Dolphin tend to blend in with the basic coloura- tion. Bottlenose Dolphin: Slimmer, body of adult animals completely covered with spots, snout longer and more narrow. Just a few Bottlenose Dolphins (North Atlantic) will have a similar diagonal pattern on the flanks.

Atlantic Spotted Dolphins searching for prey in the sandy bottom off the Bahamas.   Doug Perrine

Other Names
Long-Snouted Dolphin, Gulf Stream Dolphin, Bridled Dolphin (English); Atlantischer Fleckendelphin (German); Dauphin Tacheté de l'Atlantique (French); Stenella Maculata Atlantica (Italian); Delphin Pintado (Spanish); Golfinho Malhado do Atlântico, Golfinho Pintado (Portuguese); Gevlekte Dolfijn (Dutch); Flekkdelphin (Norwegian); Atlannintäplädelfiini (Finnish); Atlantens Fläckiga Delphin (Swedish); Atlantisk Plettet Delphin (Danish); Kasuri Iruka (Japanese).

Meaning of the Scientific Nomenclature
Stenella frontalis (G. Cuvier 1829) - *Stenella* - see *S. attenuata*. Latin *frontalis* (in front, forehead).

Behaviour
Very inquisitive, friendly, extremely active on surface. Especially the coastal variant frequently approaches swimmers and snorkellers. Fast swimmer, consecutive long leaps just above the surface (porpoising), especially when hunting. Very gregarious, lives in groups of 5-15 (coastal) and 25-50 (oceanic) individuals, max several hundred. Often in the company of Bottlenose Dolphins.

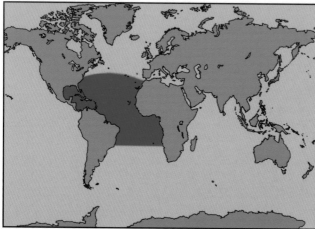

Diving
Usually surfaces perpendicularly: Tip of snout first, followed by head, back and dorsal fin. Coastal variant does not stay under as long as its oceanic relatives. Max depth approx 200 m.

Feeding Habits
Oceanic variant preys on small, pelagic shoaling fish and squid; coastal variant (larger teeth) also feeds on benthic and reef fish as well as crustaceans and other invertebrates living in the sandy bottom.

Atlantic Spotted Dolphin, distribution: Inshore and offshore in tropical to warm-temperate waters of the Atlantic.

General Information

First described as *Delphinus frontalis* by Baron Georges Cuvier in 1829. Due to great divergences in patterns and size (substantial variation depending upon distribution), there has been much confusion in the identification of this species, even among experts. Two species of Spotted Dolphin have been recognised since 1987: Atlantic and Pantropical (see section above). Fishermen in the Lesser Antilles (St. Vincent, Sat. Lucia, Dominica) still hunt this species with harpoons. Along the coast of West Africa, Brazil and Venezuela it is still occasionally caught with purse seine nets and other fishing gear. Its meat is either consumed or used as shark bait.

Where & When

Inshore and offshore in tropical to warm-temperate waters of the Atlantic between 48° N and 24° S. West Atlantic: USA to Brazil; East Atlantic: West Coast of Africa (rarely sighted). Sighted most often in

Top: Males competing with each other for group leadership.

Doug Perrine

Left: An Atlantic Spotted Dolphin hovering above branching corals off of Curacao, Netherlands Antilles.

Helmut Debelius

western North Atlantic along the eastern coast of the USA and the Gulf of Mexico. Most common dolphin in the Bahamas. Relatively frequent in the Canaries, Azores (especially in September) and St. Helena. Occasionally also in the Antilles and along the coast of Columbia and Venezuela.

Mating. The female's head (top) shows traces of "love bites." Steve Drogin

Aggressive social behaviour among Atlantic Spotted Dolphins off the Bahamas. Michele Hall

Short-Snouted Spinner Dolphin, *Stenella clymene*

This species has rarely been photographed, here in the Gulf of Mexico.   Robert Pitman/Seapics.com

Distinguishing Characteristics
Small tropical dolphin with a falcate dorsal fin (15 cm). Short snout, clearly demarcated, with a black tip. Forehead slightly rounded.

Description
Slender body, length 1.6-2 m, weight 60-90 kg. Back edge of fluke slightly concave with distinct median notch. Colouration very similar to Spinner Dolphin. Flippers, fluke and dorsal fin generally dark. Underside white. A pale-grey line runs from the snout to the flippers. There is a thin pale-grey stripe on the flanks that widens towards the back and completely encloses the base of the tail. A dark-grey dorsal cape extends from the melon to the pale-grey base of the tail. The lower jaw is various shades of white, while the tip of the snout and "lips" are always dark.

Facts & Figures Short-snouted Spinner Dolphin	Quick ID-Check Short-snouted Spinner Dolphin
Size: 1.6-2 m	Streamlined, tri-coloured body
Weight: 60-90 kg	
Longevity: unknown	Dark-grey dorsal cape extending from the high,
Calving interval: unknown	falcate dorsal fin to the white belly, pale-grey
Size at birth: 80 cm	stripe in-between
Weight at birth: unknown	
Dive time: unknown	Dark, narrow, pointed flippers, slim, pointed
Teeth: 78-98 conical teeth in each jaw	snout with dark tip
Group size: 5-50, occasionally up to 500	
Population: unknown	Twisting leaps

Easily Mistaken For
Spinner Dolphins, Bottlenose Dolphins and Indo-Pacific Bottlenose Dolphins. Up until 1981 this species was considered to be one of the many variants of Spinner Dolphin (see also "General Information"). Nevertheless, it differs as follows: Snout considerably shorter, head smaller, flippers shorter, dorsal fin falcate (rather than upright), head shorter and wider. In contrast to Spinner Dolphins, the dark dorsal cape of the species extends from the dorsal fin to just short of the white underside. The distribution of both species only overlaps in the tropical Atlantic. Bottlenose Dolphins are stockier and larger, and their range is located elsewhere.

Other Names
Clymene Dolphin, Helmet Dolphin, Senegal Dolphin (English); Clymene-Delphin (German); Dauphin du Clyméné (French); Stenella Clymene (Italian); Delphin Clymene (Spanish); Golfinho Fiandeiro de Bico Curto (Portuguese); Clymene Dolfijn (Dutch); Clymenedelphin (Norwegian); Clymenendelfiini (Finnish); Clymene Delphin (Swedish); Clymene-delphin (Danish).

Meaning of the Scientific Nomenclature
Stenella clymene (Gray 1850) - *Stenella* - see *S. attenuata*. *Clymene* is based on Klymene, daughter of Okeanos and Tethys in Greek mythology.

Behaviour
The only other species of dolphin besides Spinner Dolphins that twist around its own axis when it leaps. Rarely approaches vessels and does not ride the bow wave for very long. Occasionally associates with Spinner Dolphins, Common Dolphins and other species of dolphin. Group size 10-50, in nutrient-rich waters up to a few hundred. Stranded groups were separated by gender.

Diving
Like Spinner Dolphins, this species is a nocturnal hunter (down to depths of approx 200 m). It also tends to surface at a sharp angle: Snout first, followed by the head, back and dorsal fin.

Feeding Habits
Various species of fish and squid were found in the stomach contents of stranded animals.

General Information
According to Gray (1846), a skull found in the Natural History Museum (London) resembled that of a Spinner Dolphin but had fewer teeth. He named it *Delphinus metis,* but then realised that he had already applied the name to another skull that turned out to belong to a Bottlenose Dolphin. Gray thereupon chose the new species name *clymene.* Its classification as a distinct species was challenged by numerous taxonomists at first. Consequently, *S. clymene* was viewed as a regional variant of the Spinner Dolphin *S. longirostris* for quite a long time. It wasn't recognised as a distinct species until William Perrin completed his work in 1981.

Where & When
Distribution of the species is not well known, but it ranges exclusively in tropical and subtropical (also warm-temperate) waters of the Atlantic on both sides of the equator. Most often sighted in deep offshore regions of the Atlantic near the equator. Although it prefers deep waters, the species can still be regularly encountered in the Gulf of Mexico, Caribbean, the northwestern coast of Africa and along the northeastern shores of South America. The northernmost sightings occurred in the West Atlantic off Santa Catalina (Brazil) and in the East Atlantic off Angola.

Short-Snouted Spinner Dolphin, distribution: Tropical to subtropical Atlantic, in deep offshore waters.

Striped Dolphin, *Stenella coeruleoalba*

The typical pattern of this species is most readily recognizable on the surface. Azores.   Ralf Kiefner

Distinguishing Characteristics
Very slim body, large falcate dorsal fin. Two conspicuous black stripes on each side, one extending from the eyes to the flippers, the other from the eyes to the venting area. In-between these two stripes there will often be one or more short, dark lines above the flippers.

Description
Males up to 2.5 m in length and 150 kg in weight (regional variations), somewhat larger than females. Dark, relatively short snout clearly demarcated from the steep forehead by a fold. Back is dark-grey, blue-grey or tan from the snout to the base of the tail. Striped pattern (see above) varies depending on population, while the black face mask and two main lateral stripes remain constant. The pale-grey colouration along the flanks runs aft from the forehead and diverges into a blaze below the dorsal fin, but also encloses the entire base of the tail.

Easily Mistaken For
Long-Beaked Common Dolphin, Common Dolphin (similar in size, body shape and range). Although all three associate with each other, the species is easily distinguishable by its dark lateral stripes. It lacks the yellowish hourglass pattern on the flanks of the other two species.

Other Names
Streaker, Streaker Dolphin, Streaker Porpoise, Whitebelly, Euphrosyne Dolphin, Meyen's Dolphin, Gray's Dolphin, Blue-White Dolphin (English); Streifendelphin, Blau-Weißer Delphin, Gestreifter

Facts & Figures Striped Dolphin	Quick ID-Check Striped Dolphin
Size: 1.8-2.5 m	
Weight: 75-131 kg	Slim body
Longevity: 40-57 years	
Sexual maturity: females at 8.8 years, males at 9.8 years	Three dark blazes from eyes to anus, flippers, above flippers
Mating season: January-February, May-June, September-October	
Gestation period: 12 months	Dark back, white belly
Calving interval: 2-3 years	
Size at birth: 0.8- 1 m	Dark, markedly falcate dorsal fin, pale-grey blaze beneath it
Nursing period: 15-18 months	
Dive depth: max 200 m	
Dive time: up to 15 min	Usually occurs in large groups
Teeth: 72-98 small conical teeth in upper jaw, 78-110 in lower jaw	Very active on surface
Group size: 7-1,000, rarely up to 3,000	
Population: 2 million (estimate), endangered	

Delphin (German); Dauphin Bleu-et-Blanc (French); Stenella Striata (Italian); Estenella Listada (Spanish); Golfinho Riscado (Portuguese); Gestreepte Dolfijn (Dutch); Stripedelphin (Norwegian); Raitainendelfiini (Finnish); Strimmig Delphin (Swedish); Stribet Delphin (Danish); Megane Suji Iruka, Suji Iruka (Japanese); Polosatyy Del'fin (Russian); Delfín Listado (Latin American Spanish).

Meaning of the Scientific Nomenclature
Stenella coeruleoalba (Meyen 1833) - *Stenella* - see *S. attenuata; coeruleoalba* (blue-white) composed of Latin *coeruleus* (sky-blue) and *albus* (white).

Behaviour
Very inquisitive and playful, often leaps up to 7 m out of the water, enjoys bow-riding (especially in the Atlantic and Mediterranean). Swims at speeds of up to 30 km/h for more than 30 min and can even keep up with speedboats briefly as it leaps alongside. It also swims on its back and executes back somersaults. When swimming fast as a group, about 30% of the animals will come out of the water simultaneously. Although very active on the surface, it shies away from snorkellers more than other dolphins. Very gregarious, usually lives in groups of 100-400 individuals (up to 3,000 during seasonal migrations). Often in association with closely related species of dolphin (see above). In the Eastern Tropical Pacific it also swims along with yellowfin tuna and is often caught accidentally in the purse seine nets of the tuna fisheries. There are three mating seasons (January-February, May-June, September-October) during which the species forms "mating groups" (mature animals of both genders, very active) of about 200 individuals and "non-mating groups" (mothers with their young and adolescents) of up to 700 animals. Calves live together with their mothers in "kindergarten groups" for 1-2 years. After they have been weaned, they join a "juvenile group." At the age of about 16, sexually mature animals join a "mating group." Prefers the open sea, but there have been a few cases of mass stranding in recent years. Because these animals are so active, it is very difficult to keep them in captivity. Frequent reports of rivalry between Striped Dolphins and Common Dolphins in the Mediterranean have not been confirmed so far.

Diving
Dive time 5-10 min, max 15 min. Usually hunts at a depth of 200 m.

Feeding Habits
Analyses of stomach contents revealed 14 species of fish (e.g. cod), as well as crabs and squid.

General Information
First specimen caught off the eastern coast of South America, in the vicinity of the Rio de la Plata (Argentina). Named *Delphinus coeruleoalba* by German zoologist Franz Julius Meyen in 1833. Classified under *Stenella* after Gray (1866). Given several other names thereafter. The popular name "Spinner Dolphin" is a much more appropriate designation for the species than the scientific name "Blue-White Dolphin" as a blue-white colouration is not nearly as common as the brown-ochre striping. The species has been hunted for centuries in Japan, where more than 5,000-6,000 animals are still being killed each year for their meat. Population size is unknown, but it is considered an endangered species because of the yellowfin tuna fisheries.

Where & When
All tropical and subtropical waters, rarely in warm-temperate zones. Prefers deep high seas and seldom comes within 200 m of the shore (exception steep coastlines). In many regions it only occurs in limited numbers, but it is the most common species of dolphin found in the western Mediterranean. Often sighted in Japan, Hawaii, Papua New Guinea, Salomon Islands.

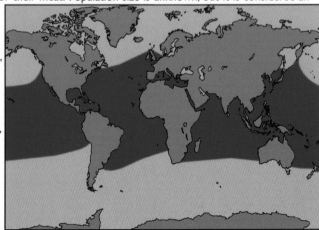

Striped Dolphin, distribution: Deep, offshore, tropical, subtropical and warm-temperate waters in all the world's seas.

Long-Snouted Spinner Dolphin, *Stenella longirostris*

A group of leaping Long-Snouted Spinner Dolphins in the Red Sea.   Helmut Debelius

Distinguishing Characteristics
This species is highly acrobatic. Its spinning leaps can be detected from afar. Divergences from other species of dolphin: Upright, triangular fin and a very slim, long and clearly demarcated snout with a black tip.

Description
Very slender, max 2.5 m in length and 75 kg in weight. Males somewhat larger than females (sexual dimorphism). Upright dorsal fin, not falcate, in the case of males it can even lean slightly forward. Flippers noticeably long and pointed. Back dark-grey. The extent of the pale-grey to white patch on underside varies greatly. Dark-grey diagonal blaze covers the top of the snout and runs back over the eyes to the flippers. Flippers, fluke and dorsal fin are dark. Size and colouration vary depending on the area of distribution, but all animals are slender and have a conspicuously long and thin snout. There are several geographically isolated variants in the Pacific alone: Costa Rican Spinner (max 2 m), Eastern Pacific Spinner (max 1.6 m, smallest variant), Hawaiian Spinner (max 2.5 m, largest variant). The latter is darker than the Costa Rican and Eastern Pacific spinners. Its body is dark-grey with several different paler patches around the throat, genitals and behind the flippers. The dorsal fins of the males are very upright, triangular and occasionally lean forward.

Easily Mistaken For
For a long time the similar Short-Snouted Spinner Dolphin (see above) was considered to be a variant of the Spinner Dolphin.

Other Names
Spinner, Longsnout, Long-Beaked Dolphin, Rollover (English); Spinner-Delphin, Langschnauzen Spinner-Delphin (German); Dauphin Longirostre, Dauphin à Long Bec (French); Stenella dal Lungo Rostro (Italian); Estenela Giradora (Spanish); Golfinho Rotador (Portuguese); Langsnuitdolfijn (Dutch); Skruedelphin (Norwegian); Spinnerdelfiini (Finnish); Spinnardelphin (Swedish); Langnæbbet Delphin (Danish); Hashinaga Iruka, (Japanese); Delphin Tornillón, Delfín Churumbelo (Latin Amer.).

Meaning of the Scientific Nomenclature
Stenella longirostris (Gray 1828) - *Stenella* - see *S. attenuata*. Latin *longirostris* (long-snouted).

The white colour on the belly of this Atlantic variant extends up to the flanks. Brazil.   Ralf Kiefner

Behaviour
Gregarious, lives in large groups of several hundred animals. Within these large groups are small family units with very tight social bonds. Highly developed intraspecies communication. In the Eastern Tropical Pacific the species is often seen together with Pantropical Spotted Dolphins, as well as yellowfin tuna and predator seabirds. Many thousand specimens die in the purse seine nets of the tuna fisheries each year. Examinations of stranded animals have shown that the species frequently associates with Short-Snouted Spinner Dolphins and other species of dolphin. Long-Snouted Spinner Dolphins are known for their acrobatic spinning leaps. They can leap 3 m out of the water and spin around their own axis seven times before landing flat on the surface. These twisting leaps are a form of territorial communication and the turbulence caused by the re-entry can have various meanings. Occasionally they will also perform normal leaps. The species is fond of bow-riding and will rush over as soon as a vessel approaches. The population in the eastern Antilles is rather shy and will rarely come near a boat. Approximately 300 resident animals (Fernando Spinners) live in the Brazilian archipelago of Fernando de Noronha, in the tropical Central Atlantic. They have a set daily schedule: Between 5 and 7 o'clock in the morning they arrive in the Baia dos Golfinhos, a shallow and protected bay on the main island. Here they rest, play and mate. Between 14 and 16 o'clock they leave the bay again and head out to the open sea for their nocturnal hunt. A similar pattern can be observed among populations in the tropical Pacific off the coast of Hawaii (Hawaiian Spinners). See SPINNING ACROBATS on page 216.

Diving
Hunts nocturnally at depths of 60-100 m. Usually surfaces at a sharp angle, snout first.

Feeding Habits
Feeds primarily on shoaling fish and squid.

General Information
First described as *Delphinus longirostris* by Gray in 1828 on the basis of a skull of unknown origin. Perrin and Gilpatrick (1994) recognised 3 geographically isolated subspecies: *S. l. longirostris*, most widely distributed; *S. l. orientalis*, Eastern Tropical Pacific (Mexico); *S. l. centroamericana*, west coast of Central America. Prefers the open sea. Population endangered worldwide due to fisheries.

Facts & Figures Long-Snouted S. D.

Size: 1.4-2.5 m
Weight: 45-75 kg
Longevity: 20 years
Sexual maturity: females at 4-7 years,
males at 6-9 years
Gestation period: 10-11 months
Calving interval: 2-3 years
Size at birth: 0.7- 0.8 m
Dive depth: to 100 m
Maximum speed: approx 20 km/h
Teeth: 88-128 small conical teeth in upper jaw,
88-124 in lower jaw
Group size: 5-200, occasionally up to 1,000
Population: unknown, endangered worldwide
due to tuna fisheries

Quick ID-Check Long-Snouted S. D.

High spinning leaps

Slender body

Slim snout with dark tip

High, upright, triangular dorsal fin

Long, pointed flippers

Usually lives in large groups

The Hawaiian Spinner is the largest variant of Long-Snouted Spinner Dolphin.   Helmut Debelius

Where & When

Cosmopolitan, found in warm-temperate to tropical waters of all oceans, both inshore and off-shore. Scarce in the subtropics. Tropical Pacific: Most common around Hawaii (Haw. Spinner), down to within 150 km of the west coast of Central America (Costa Rican Sp.), south of Baja California (Mexico) and all the way to the equator and the open seas to 125° W (E-Pacific Sp.). Atlantic: Most common along the southeastern coast of the USA and at Fernando de Noronha (Fernando Spinner).

Long-Snouted Spinner Dolphin, distribution: Inshore and off-shore in warm-temperate to tropical waters of all oceans.

215

SPINNING ACROBATS

Its common English name, Spinner Dolphin, is derived from the acrobatic aerial manoeuvres this dolphin performs. The slender and energetic-looking Spinner Dolphins can spin around their long axis up to seven times whenever they leap out of the water. It is quite easy to recognise them from a distance because of this characteristic leaping technique.

PHOTO: DOUG PERRINE

Spinner Dolphins have developed a highly complex form of social behaviour. It has recently been ascertained that their supposedly joyful pirouettes are more than just an emotional outburst. The spinning technique is actually a means of communicating, much like the characteristic clicking and whistling sounds that these animals make.

The manifestation of an "aerial communications behaviour" is especially evident in the twisting motion executed during the leap. The spinning bodies produce certain turbulences when they hit the surface of the water. This so-called "horizontal aerial communication" is used for close-range communion and can be repeated up to ten times at short intervals. "Vertical aerial communication," or fin slapping, is a short-distance signal for a very strong bond within a dolphin gathering. This form of communication is not only evident among Spinner Dolphins, but also among whales and other dolphins.

FRIENDS OF MANKIND

Their names are Freddy, Moses, Yoca and Fungi. They are a friendly bunch, always eager for some amusement. Tame dolphins are appreciated by the locals and attract tourists from faraway lands. Usually involved in these encounters between humans and marine mammals are Bottlenose Dolphins, three- to four-metre-long cetaceans known all over the world as a result of the popular "Flipper" television series and said to be as intelligent as the chimpanzees. Armin Maywald, a noted photographer, relates his experiences with some of these congenial animals.

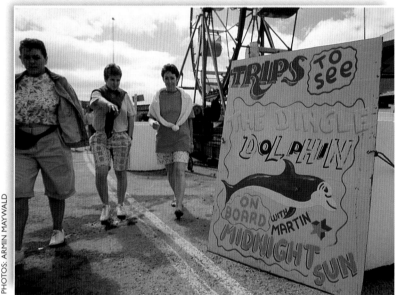

For the residents of Dingle, situated on the eastern coast of Ireland, Fungi, a Bottlenose Dolphin *(Tursiops truncatus),* is a gift from heaven: Fungi draws ready cash and pretty women to the town.

During the early nineties "Yoca" delighted both the residents and visitors of the Bay of Kotor, south of Dubrovnik; "Freddy" frolicked with his human pals in Amble in eastern England; "Moses" made his first grand appearance in the south of Spain in 1988; and "Fungi," a full-grown male, has been entertaining citizens and tourists nearby Dingle, which situated on the eastern coast of Ireland, since 1983.

According to numerous reports, tame dolphins often maintain contact with humans for many years. Generally, however, they will only make an appearance for a few minutes each day. "Yoca," for instance, used to wait until sundown before he would accompany the last sailboat headed for the harbour of Kotor. If he was in a good mood, he would cavort around the harbour basin, leap in the reflection of the streetlights, and play with the children who immediately sprang into the water as soon as he showed up. Then, as suddenly as he had come, he would vanish again.

"Fungi" was of a different mettle. Every time we

As soon as the pleasure boats arrive, Fuji swims over to each one and introduces himself.

At times he likes to leap over a diver who has brought him a paddle to play with...

entered his domain in the early morning hours he would first greet us by leaping out of the water and then proceed to follow our rubber dinghy around. As soon as the first tourist boats came into sight, Fungi's attention would shift. He would swim up to each boat and introduce himself to every newcomer, regardless of whether it was a paddler, a rower, or a swimmer. At times he would leap over the head of a diver who had brought him a paddle to play with. Eventually he would reappear alongside our craft again.

Fungi is obviously a ball of energy. He stays active from early morning until late at night and has been doing so for the past 18 years - an unusual record. What motivates these sensitive animals to seek the company of humans for such extended periods? Basically, this phenomenon remains a mystery up until today, but there have been a few attempts made to find a plausible explanation.

Friendly relations between humans and dolphins have been going on since antiquity, as is evidenced by prehistoric rock paintings in South Africa. These depict a man swimming among dolphins. Among numerous Mediterranean peoples, dolphins also play an important role as helpers and rescuers. The classical legends are replete with stories about tame dolphins.

Plinius writes about a close relationship between a boy and a dolphin. Every morning the dolphin would carry his friend over the water to a school in Pozzuoli, near Naples. When the

... at other times he will unexpectedly surface next to one of the pleasure boats.

boy suddenly died, the dolphin supposedly waited a long time for him at the accustomed meeting place and then finally died of sorrow when his friend failed to reappear.

British dolphin expert Christina Lockye feels that solitary or young animals that have either been separated or driven from their herds may actually seek the proximity of humans as an ersatz family.

Yoca is a case in point. This dolphin lady owes her life to the children of Kotor. Fishermen had killed her parents and wanted to dispose of her as well. The children

At the age of 40, Fungi is no youngster. Nobody knows why he likes the company of humans.

besieged the mayor to intervene and even threatened to burn down the houses of the fishermen if he failed to take action. Regardless of whether this is true or not, Yoca has been officially protected by law since 1987. The decree states explicitly that it is prohibited to hunt, hurt or kill the dolphin Yoca.

Dolphins are gregarious animals. They live in groups ranging from ten to several thousand individuals. But relations are not always harmonious within a herd of dolphins. If the social status of an individual is not clear, the others may harass and bite it until the unfortunate animal finally opts to abandon the herd altogether. This can happen to both female and male members regardless of age group.

There is also an assumption that there may well be a sexual connotation behind a dolphin's interest in swimmers and divers. In the course of numerous "swimming meets" with dolphins it has been observed that they tend to slide over the back of a swimmer's knee, which is precisely the spot where the sexual organs of a female dolphin would be located. Nevertheless, this does not really help to explain why a dolphin like Fungi should seek the company of humans for over 18 years.

Essential for any initial contact between humans and dolphins is the regular appearance of each party in the same ocean environment. A relationship usually begins as soon as dolphins decide to follow ocean-going crafts like fishing boats and ferries. "Percy," a tame dolphin in the vicinity of Cornwall, first developed the habit of accompanying the shrimp and lobster fishermen. He would halt next to each buoy that had been set by them and watch as the filled baskets were being hauled to the surface. It took another two years, however, for Percy to accept the presence of divers in the water.

Two things evidently have to occur simultaneously for an

Souvenir shops in Dingle are stuffed with dolphin knick-knacks, a bar appreciates Fungi's physiognomy.

encounter to take place: curiosity on the side of the dolphins and commitment and perseverance on the side of the humans. It also took two years before Fungi would allow his first contact person, one of the local divers, to touch him. Once the ice is broken, dolphins will often manifest a definite preference for certain human "pals" and can immediately recognise them, regardless of whether they are in the water or sitting on deck in summer apparel. Such "chosen" ones are usually deeply affected by the relationship. They say that dolphins are incredibly friendly and gentle. Those who have looked deep into their eyes swear that they reflect understanding, curiosity and a touch of impishness. Experts, on the other hand, tend to believe that humans attribute feelings to Bottlenose Dolphins because of what appears to be "laughter lines" on their faces. The arching groove running from the beak to the eyes makes it seem as if the dolphin were permanently smiling.

At the beginning of the 1990s, Dolphin-dame Yoca delighted people in the Bay of Kotor, which lies south of Dubrovnik, Croatia.

Dolphins really couldn't care less about human emotions. Frequent and regular contact with humans is much more significant to them. This is what really cements a relationship on the long run and keeps dolphins in the mood for more. At any rate, Fungi can hardly complain about boredom. Practically the entire village has adapted itself to his presence. The fishermen have given up fishing and now cart tourists to him on an hourly basis. Those who wish to do so are allowed to get into the water with him. The fishermen even promise to reimburse every guest should Fungi fail to make an appearance - something that has supposedly never occurred in the past 18 years. Each and every day dozens of people keep an eye out for the playful dolphin, ready to jump into the water with him as soon as he approaches the rocky shore. The souvenir shops are replete with dolphin statues, postcards and pins. As far as the inhabitants of Dingle are concerned, this particular dolphin is a gift of heaven. In their own words: "Fungi generates ready cash and brings pretty women to the village."

What does Fungi get out of the daily spectacle? Entertainment? Young dolphins practice their behaviour patterns while at play and thereby learn to cope with unfamiliar situations. In this fashion they gather new experiences that might someday be useful to them. But at almost 40 years of age, Fungi is certainly no longer a youngster.

Whatever it is that motivates Fungi and so many of his kind all over the world to maintain contact with humans still remains a mystery.

Yoca owes her life to the children of Kotor, who prevented the fisherman from killing her.

Bottlenose Dolphin, *Tursiops truncatus*

Encounter with a Bottlenose Dolphin on a Caribbean reef off Belize.   Howard Hall

Distinguishing Characteristics
Body long and somewhat stocky. Short, pointed snout clearly demarcated from the well defined melon by a fold. Dorsal fin falcate, clearly demarcated. Uniformly grey.

Description
Attains length of 3-4 m and weight of 600 kg. Smallest known mature specimen (1.5 m) found in the Mediterranean. Males somewhat larger than females (sexual dimorphism). In contrast to most other dolphins, its jawlines are slightly curved upwards into a characteristic "permanent smile." The dorsal fin is falcate and has a relatively broad base. The flippers are relatively long and slim, and have pointed ends. The back edge of the fluke is concave and has a well developed median notch. The colouration is variable, usually grey to dark-grey, underside blue-grey but fades with age. Often has a barely visible dark-grey blaze running from the melon to the eye, flippers and blowhole.

Easily Mistaken For
Other grey species of dolphin: Indo-Pacific Bottlenose Dolphins, Tucuxi, Spotted Dolphins, Atlantic Hump-Backed Dolphins and Rough-Toothed Dolphins. For differences see following species.

Other Names
Common Porpoise, Black Porpoise, Gray Porpoise, Atlantic/Pacific Bottlenose Dolphin, Grey Dolphin, Cowfish (English); Großer Tümmler (German); Grand Dauphin (French); Tursión (Spanish); Roaz Corvineiro, Nariz de Garrafa, Flipper (Portuguese); Tuimelaar (Dutch); Tumler (Norwegian); Pullonokkadelfiini (Finnish); Öresvin (Swedish); Öresvin (Danish); Taiseiyo Brando Iruka, Brando Iruka (Japanese); Delfín Naríz de Botella (Latin American Spanish).

Meaning of the Scientific Nomenclature
Tursiops truncatus (Montagu 1821) - The generic name *Tursiops* is made up of the Latin word *tursio* (dolphin-like animal/fish) and the Greek word *ops* (face, similarity, appearance). Latin *truncatus* (cut off) referring to short snout.

Behaviour

Very active on surface, often rides bow wave, leaps several metres out of the water, frequent lob-tailing. Occasionally observed surfing in the surge zone. Usually friendly towards swimmers. Group size 3-150, occasionally up to 1,000 animals. Size of group changes (smaller early mornings and late evenings). Groups separated by age and gender, occasionally mixed. Sexually active year-round, mating behaviour very variable, mutual touching of flippers, snout or teeth accompanied by rattling of jaws and different whistling sounds. Repeated copulation only lasts a few seconds, whereby partners usually swim side by side.

Hunts in groups, which assume different tasks. Shoaling fish are driven into tight bait balls just beneath the surface by warning cries, bubble nets and swimming manoeuvres. Prey is then killed with fluke or in direct attacks. The carousel hunting technique used by Bottlenose Dolphins (Black Sea), Dusky Dolphins (Argentina) and Killer Whales (Norway) has been described by Belkovitch and Würsing (1991). Prey is located optically or acoustically, often also herded together over sandy or muddy bottoms. Frequent resting phases, which only last a few minutes, take place throughout the day,

The display of teeth and gaping mouth are a threatening gesture aimed at the photographer.   Doug Perrine

whereby the animals remain 0.2-1 m under the surface facing in the direction of the current and only surface to breathe every 2-3 min. Often hunt for squid in association with Risso's Dolphins, Common Dolphins, both species of Pilot Whale and porpoises (in coastal regions). Observations of aggressive behaviour against porpoises with fatal outcome have become more frequent in recent years.

Cooperative behaviour is well developed with mutual aid provided during birthing and hunting, as well as in defence against attackers. Injured animals are brought up to the surface to breathe. Several reproductively immature females ("aunts") will frequently assist during birth. If a newborn calf does not immediately swim to the surface on its own, it will be brought to the surface by one of the "aunts" so that it can breathe. During the first days of its life a calf will maintain close physical contact to its mother, swimming laterally behind her where there is the least current. After 3-4 weeks, when its musculature is more developed, it will gradually increase the distance to its mother and independently surface to breathe or inspect its surroundings. It will remain in the immediate vicinity of its mother for the coming months, however, and all of its movements will be strictly monitored. Occasionally the mother will punish its calf by pressing it down against the sea bottom or roughly pushing it up to the surface. Although the nursing period lasts 12-18 months, the calves already begin to feed on fish when they are 6-7 months old. During the first 4 weeks

The photographer's patience has paid off: An unusual sunset.   Jasmine Rossi

the mother will turn on its side to nurse its young. Thereafter she assumes a normal swimming position. At first the calf is nursed every 15-30 min.

The species often accompanies other whales and dolphins, sea turtles and even shark species that only occasionally attack sick or injured animals. It has not been determined so far whether Killer Whales will attack Bottlenose Dolphins. Group size ranges from 1-15, but can comprise as many as 600 individuals on the open sea. Size varies depending on time of day (smaller early mornings and late evenings). Groups are separated by age and gender, occasionally mixed. Some animals only remain with a group for a few hours, others for days. Interbreeding takes place with Risso's Dolphins (evidence based on stranded animals), Rough-Toothed Dolphins and Short-Finned Pilot Whales (based on observations in the wild). The offspring (hybrids) is infertile.

Occasionally one can encounter solitary Bottlenose Dolphins that have lost contact with a group for some unknown reason. Whether they were cast out of a group or abandoned it on their own accord remains unclear. Only in rare cases will they rejoin a group. These solitary individuals, usually older males, will often remain in the same region for years and seek contact with humans and vessels. Regardless of whether they are fed or not, they will usually loose their shyness fairly quickly and sometimes even allow humans to touch them. They are often very friendly towards swimmers. In the wild they often accompany vessels and ride bow waves. See FRIENDS OF MAN-KIND (pp. 217-221) & THROUGH DONALD'S BLACK & WHITE LENS (pp. 266-272).

Bottlenose Dolphins surfing in South Africa.
Rod Haestier

In the saga "The Dolphin of Lassos," ancient Greek poet Aelian describes a close friendship between a boy and a dolphin. When the boy is mortally wounded by the dolphin's dorsal fin, the animal brings him to shore to die by his side. Studies conducted with captive specimens have shown that they can see quite well out of the water, as well as having and excellent echolocation and a broad vocalising spectrum. Stranding occurs very rarely. Since they can live in captivity for a long time and are very trainable, they will often be kept in sea aquariums. An estimated 2,800 animals were captured for delivery to aquariums or research purposes between 1860 and 1983.

Diving
Excellent swimmer. Two variants: A stockier offshore variant and a more slender coastal variant. The offshore variant has a higher concentration of red blood cells and two types of haemoglobin (the coastal variant only has one), which enables it to dive to much deeper depths (max around 500 m) and stay under longer (up to 10 min) than the coastal variant (6-7 min). Normal swimming speed around 6 km/h, max speed 30 km/h (short sprints).

Feeding Habits
Opportunistic feeder. Prey is seasonal and varies by region. Diverse species of fish, including shoaling fish and cephalopods up to 20 cm in length, as well as benthic crabs and other crustaceans. It will also remove fish from fishing lines and feed on the refuse of fishing fleets or organisms that are brought to the surface by the ships' movement. In some places the species will even drive fish onto the shore, grab it and then flop backwards into the water with its catch. Bottlenose Dolphins not only cooperate with each other while hunting, but sometimes also with humans. In Cameroon (West Africa) they drive fish into the fishing nets and get a share of the catch from the fishermen in recompense. When the mullet come close to the coast of Mauritania (West Africa) during their winter migrations, the local fishermen beat the surface of the water with sticks. Bottlenose Dolphins and Atlantic Hump-Backed Dolphins soon appear and begin to drive the fish into their nets. The dolphins then take what they need from the nets or catch the fish that manage to escape. During the1840s-1860s, the Aborigines of Moreton Bay in Australia also used to catch mullet with the assistance of Bottlenose Dolphins.

General Information
British naturalist George Montagu named the species *Delphinus truncatus* in 1821, perhaps with reference to its short snout (Latin *truncatus* = cut off). In 1843 British naturalist J. E. Gray established a new genus for this species, which he named *Tursio* (dolphin-like fish). The Greek term *ops* (appearance) was later added to the term to form *Tursiops*.

The population status of this species is unknown. Estimated at 1.5-2 million in 1930. Reduced to an estimated 100,000 + animals worldwide due to accidental killing by tuna fisheries. The television series "Flipper" and their presence in numerous aquariums have made Bottlenose Dolphins the

Wild Bottlenose Dolphin as a playmate of the photographer's children. Gulf of Mexico.   Donald Tipton

most famous of all species of dolphin. For many people they are the very prototype of a dolphin and the epitome of an intelligent and friendly animal. See also back cover (photo from the Gulf of Mexico) and the picture stories A RUN-IN WITH HONEY (on spages 258-260) and COOPERA-TIVE FEEDING IN A BRACKISH RIVER (on pages 285-286).

The male genitals of all cetaceans vanished into the hindquarters in the course of their evolution for the sake of streamlining. Bottlenose Dolphins were the first species of dolphin to be examined with a view of finding out how the males manage to produce active sperm cells in spite of a body temperature of 37° C . Sperm cells are very sensitive to temperature, which is why the testicles of terrestrial mammals are located outside of the body. Dolphins have developed a sort of "testicle cooler" that works on the basis of a countercurrent: Warm arterial blood is cooled by a capillary network carrying venous blood that was previously cooled in the non-isolated fluke. Consequently, the temperature of the testicles drops down to 1.3° C.

Facts & Figures Bottlenose Dolphin	Quick ID-Check Bottlenose Dolphin
Size: 1.5-3.9 m	Stocky, dark-grey body
Weight: 150-600 kg	
Longevity: 30-50 years	Conspicuous, falcate dorsal fin
Sexual maturity: females at 5-7 years, males at 10-15 years	Noticeable fold between snout and melon
Gestation period: 12 months	
Calving interval: 2-3 years	Usually appears in small groups
Size at birth: 1-1.3 m	
Weight at birth: average 20.4 kg	Frequent bow-riding
Nursing period: 12-18 months	
Dive depth: to 500 m	Very active on surface
Dive time: up to 10 min	
Maximum speed: 30 km/h	Not very shy
Teeth: 40-52 conical teeth in upper jaw, 36-48 in lower jaw	
Group size: 1-15, occasionally 600 (high seas)	
Population: unknown, estimated at 100,000+	

Where & When

A cosmopolitan species, which is found in all tropical to temperate oceans in both hemispheres. It is also frequently encountered in lesser bodies of water (North Sea, Mediterranean, Black Sea, Red Sea, Gulf of Oman, Sea of Cortez, Gulf of Mexico). The species frequents high seas and coastal areas with strong surge. It also swims into shallow lagoons no deeper than 1 m, as well as into shallow estuaries and harbours. The high seas variant is primarily found in temperate waters along the continental shelf. Depending upon the availability of nourishment, this variant migrates to the coast in spring and heads back to the high seas in fall. The coastal variant is usually found in resident populations.

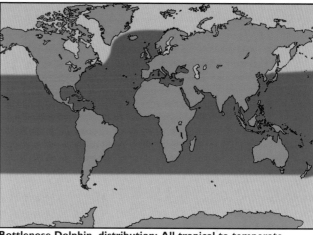

Bottlenose Dolphin, distribution: All tropical to temperate oceans in both hemispheres, inshore and offshore.

Indo-Pacific Bottlenose Dolphin, *Tursiops aduncus*

A Group of Indo-Pacific Bottlenose Dolphins off the coast of Japan.   Kazuaki Ichikawa

Distinguishing Characteristics

Short, pointed snout, somewhat angled downward, clearly demarcated from the well developed melon by a fold. Back uniformly grey to dark-grey, underside pale-grey with typical dark spotted pattern. Most common in coastal areas of the Indian Ocean and Western Tropical Pacific.

Description
Slender body, very similar to its closest relatives (Bottlenose Dolphins), but with a max length of 2.6 m it is markedly smaller. Males somewhat larger than females (sexual dimorphism). Jawlines differ from most other species of dolphin in that they are turned upwards slightly into a "permanent smile." Large, falcate dorsal fin. Flippers are relatively long, narrow and have pointed ends. Back edge of fluke is concave with a well developed median notch. Adolescent animals lack the spotted pattern on ventral side, which becomes clearly noticeable when the animals mature. Most have a grey band running from the base of the tail to the eyes, and another one from the middle of the snout over the melon to the blowhole.

Clearly visible: The typical spotted pattern.　　　K. Ichikawa

Easily Mistaken For
Difficult to distinguish from Bottlenose Dolphins (considered one and the same species until 2000), but it is darker and smaller. Bottlenose Dolphins have a more slender head with a pointed and slightly down-turning snout, as well as dark spots on the underside. They live primarily in inshore tropical waters of the Western Pacific and Indian Ocean. Adult Spotted Dolphins have conspicuous spots all over the body, not just on the belly, and different areas of distribution. Risso's Dolphins have a conspicuous hump, smaller dorsal fin and their range is relatively limited.

Other Names
Indian Ocean Bottlenose Dolphin (English); Indopazifischer Tümmler (German); Daupin á gros nez de l'océan Indien (French).

Meaning of the Scientific Nomenclature
Tursiops aduncus Ehrenberg 1832 - *Tursiops* - see *T. truncatus*. Latin *aduncus* (curved) with reference to snout.

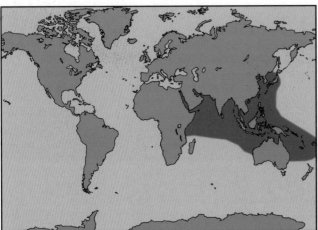

Behaviour
See Bottlenose Dolphin and A SINAI TALE, pp. 229-232.

General Information
First described by Ehrenberg in 1832. In 2000 *Tursiops aduncus* was recognised as a distinct species on the basis of DNA analysis. In addition to several genetic differences, there are also many anatomical distinctions from *T. truncatus*: smaller, various discrepancies in the shape of the head (e.g. narrower), less teeth, thinner and more downward-turning snout, darker back and dark ventral spots.

Indo-Pacific Bottlenose Dolphin, distribution: Inshore in tropical to temperate waters of the Indian Ocean and connecting seas.

A SINAI TALE

The oasis and settlement of Nuweiba at the east coast of the Sinai peninsula, right at the shoreline of the northeastern part of the Red Sea, the Gulf of Aqaba, is well known to many travellers, divers, and underwater photographers alike. All those people come to this enchanted place to experience the wonders of the Sinai desert which is exceptional in being surrounded by more or less deep tropical waters, harbouring a multitude of coral reef as well as open water organisms. This is the outstanding story of a friendship between man and one of those denizens of the deep that otherwise only rarely makes close contact with people. The tale is retold by marine biologist Ralf Hennemann who spent two years on Sinai's shores to explore its unrivalled wealth of submarine life.

Abdulla's friend Olline, a female Indo-Pacific Bottlenose Dolphin *(Tursiops aduncus)* that he met in the waters near Nuweiba.

The whole story began many years ago when Abdulla still was a child. Abdulla is a local Bedouin who was born in the Nuweiba area as the son of a fisherman. Because he was very young at the time actually his father had to recount the details. And this is what the old man had to say:

"When Abdulla was a small boy, one day he was playing with his friends around some old buildings in the village El Mouzina which belongs to oasis of Nuweiba. Together the boys climbed on top of the roof of one of the abandoned houses. But then, for some unknown reason one can only understand during childhood, the rest of the party left Abdulla behind, alone and lonely on the old house's roof. For some time he tried to find help by crying and shouting out as loud as he could, but nobody would answer his desparate calls and come to help him off the roof and back home."

It was around midday when his playmates had left Abdulla, but only when the sun settled down on the wild and ragged mountains on Sinai's western horizon his father, who meanwhile had been looking for him for a quite some time, finally found him on top of the building. Young Abdulla was very exhausted, and reportedly couldn't speak nor hear a word his father was saying. "The only part of this incident Abdulla remembers until today is that he was crying on the roof until darkness," his father said.

Then Abdulla himself started to speak and continued the narrative of the happenings during his later childhood years: "Only a few days after my mother had died, I also lost a very close uncle. Naturally this left me behind with great sadness in my heart and with tears in my eyes. But life went on and I had to go out at sea for fishing." While preparing his simple fishing gear he suddenly noticed a dolphin in the water which wasn't behaving normal at all. He goes on: "Soon I found out why the

229

Soon a dolphin statue was placed on the Nuweiba beach to show everybody where to find its totally free-living resident Olline.

dolphin didn't swim away. It was trapped and entangled in something that looked like a bent, thick and rigid wire it couldn't get rid off and which kept the animal fixed in one place. The dolphin was a female and I immediately decided to try everything to free the animal. It was very hard to remove the wire from the soft and sensitive skin of the dolphin but after some time I finally succeeded without hurting it. When the female was freely swimming around again I felt very happy to have saved the life of a living being, especially after having lost two beloved members of my family."

"A couple of days later, when I went out to sea again for fishing, I noticed another disturbance in

Snorkellers - young and old - come by the score to see the dolphin. Snorkelling is the only way allowed to approach the animal.

The sensation was perfect when Olline gave birth to a youngster. This event only added to her reputation as wild animal that seeks the company of man.

the sea, only a few feet below its surface. Without hesitation I went into the water and dived down to see what was going on there. To my amazement I found another dolphin, but this time it was a male. It also was trapped like the female I had freed only a few days ago, but this male was caught beneath the surface and couldn't reach it anymore in order to draw a breath. I soon found out that it was already very exhausted and close to death as it obviously hadn't had any fresh air for too long a period of time.

Desparately I tried very hard to save the life of this marine mammal by applying respiratory aid with my own breath until I almost fainted from lack of oxygen. Almost unconscious, I suddenly noticed the presence of a second dolphin which approached me, carefully pushed me away from the site, and carried me to the safe shore. At that moment I thought the dolphin that had saved me was crying."

At that point in his narrative Abdulla paused and tears started to appear in his eyes. After a little while he resumed to speak: "The second, male dolphin had literally died in my arms. And after my rescue by the other dolphin I had the very strong feeling that this one was the female I had relieved from its trap a short

Abdulla takes care that Olline and her offspring are safe and that they have a reason to come back: This time it is a freshly-caught juicy octopus.

while ago. The one that had died from suffocation most probably had been her mate but neither I nor the female had been able to save his life."

But sad as it was, since then a close relation, well, even a true friendship between Abdulla and the female dolphin has established. The dolphin was given the name 'Olline' and whenever Abdulla goes to the beach of the Nuweiba bay and touches the water she soon comes to play with him. During the years Olline became famous with many people from all over the world who come to see the tame dolphin swimming together and interacting with the Bedouin fisherman on the Red Sea's shore.

"Unfortunately sometimes there are so many visitors that I am afraid Olline will swim away and leave forever," Abdulla says. Meanwhile, however, Olline gave birth to a young which indicates that she has mated with another male in the past. Of course, the youngster is the favourite of all spectators and especially of the children who live in Nuweiba or are lucky enough to visit the desert oasis right next to the tropical coral reefs of the Red Sea. When the dolphin is grown up it can swim out to sea to carry further the unparallelled ways of its kind...

Olline now has to show her little one how to deal with a tasty morsel like the one presented by Abdulla.

Creating sand sculptures is not new - but the model is: Since Olline's appearance dolphin-casting is the prime occupation of some.

Atlantic White-Sided Dolphin, *Lagenorhynchus acutus*

Distinguishing Characteristics: Flanks pale-grey. White lateral stripe begins under the dorsal fin and turns conspicuously yellow or tan towards the tail. Very short snout (5 cm), dark-grey to black on top, pale-grey to white underneath, demarcated from the flat forehead. **Easily Mistaken For:** White-Beaked Dolphins, Common Dolphins, Long-Beaked Common Dolphins. White-Beaked Dolphins are similar is size and

The Gully, Nova Scotia, Canada. Sascha Hooker/Seapics.com

shape, but larger and stockier, with a uniformly pale snout and no bicoloured lateral stripes on the rump. Common Dolphins and Long-Beaked Common Dolphins are more slender, have a much longer snout, a lateral hourglass pattern and a yellow patch between the head and dorsal fin.

Other Names: Atlantic White-Sided Porpoise, Jumper (English); Weißseitendelphin, Atlantischer Weißseitendelphin, Nordischer Delphin, Springer (German); Dauphin à Flancs Blancs, Dauphin à Flancs Blancs de l'Atlantique (French und Canadian French); Lagenorinco Acuto (Italian); Delphin de Flancos Blancos (Spanish); Golfinho Branco do Atlântico, Roaz Malhado (Portuguese); Witflank-dolfijn (Dutch); Kvitkjeving, Springhval (Norwegian); Valkokuvedelfiini (Finnish); Vitsiding (Swedish); Hvitskæving (Danish); Taiseiyo Kama Iruka (Japanese); Lag, Jumper (Newfoundland, Canada).

Meaning of the Scientific Nomenclature: *Lagenorhynchus acutus* (Gray 1828) - *Lagenorhynchus* composed of Greek *lagenos* (bottle) and *rhynchos* (snout). Latin *acutus* (pointed, sharp).

Behaviour: Usually found offshore, but stranding occurs quite often. Very gregarious, usually in groups of 10-50 animals, occasionally 100-1,000 (during migrations, or because of abundance of nourishment). Oceanic groups larger than coastal groups (more protection). Fast swimmer, leaps and lob-tails frequently. Population along the coast of East Canada and New England often hunts in association with Long-Finned Pilot Whales and White-Beaked Dolphins. Also regularly spotted in company of Fin Whales and Humpback Whales, riding their bow waves. Nursing period is 18 months, calves live together with their mothers in breeding groups until they are about two years old and then join a bachelor group. When they reach sexual maturity (as of 6 years) they join a mating group. Rather unusual for dolphins, intraspecies cooperation has only been observed once (an animal was supported on the surface so it could breathe). Otherwise the species tends to be indifferent about relatives in distress. Even when a group is chased down and several animals harpooned, its fellow group members will not panic.

Diving: Presumably dives to depths of 200 m and normally remains under water for 10-20 sec (much longer if threatened).

Feeding Habits: Shoaling fish (herring, hake, cod, mackerel), cephalopods, shrimp, occasionally also other invertebrates.

General Information: First described as *Delphinus acutus* by J. E. Gray in 1828. Classified under the genus *Lagenorhynchus* in 1846. Vocalisations include whistling and clicks (1-24 kHz). Sharks and Killer Whales Natural are its natural enemies. During the 18th and 19th centuries hundreds of these animals were driven onto the shores of Cape Cod (Massachusetts, USA) and Trinity Bay (Newfoundland) along with Pilot Whales, and are still occasionally hunted there today. Exact population status unknown, but estimated at 30,000-50,000 specimens worldwide (24,000 of these in the NW-Atlantic).

Where & When: Only in the North Atlantic, exact range unknown, often associated with White-Beaked Dolphins.

White-Beaked Dolphin, *Lagenorhynchus albirostris*

Pieter Arend Folkens

Distinguishing Characteristics
Very short snout (5 cm), blunt, barely demarcated, white, sometimes dark-grey or speckled-brown. Back and flanks black to dark-grey with conspicuous white to pale-grey saddle patch.

Description
Robust, stocky body, max length of 3.1 m. Largest species of the genus. Dorsal fin conspicuously large, falcate, with a broad base. Colour of snout varies individually. Saddle patch extends from the back downwards past the flippers to the flanks. White or pale-grey blaze runs from above the eye to the base of the tail. Ventral side white. Flippers, dorsal fin and fluke black. Edge on underside of fluke occasionally covered with white spots. Ends of fluke pointed, back edge concave with well developed median notch. Sexual dimorphism or age-related colour variations unknown. Thickest layer of blubber of all members of the genus (ranges to the edge of the pack ice).

Easily Mistaken For
Atlantic White-Sided Dolphin is similar in size and shape and has the same range, but is slightly smaller, thinner. Bicoloured lateral stripes on rump. Both species often associate with each other.

Other Names
White-Nosed Dolphin, Squidhound, White-Beaked Porpoise (English); Weißschnauzendelphin (German); Dauphin à Nez Blanc, Dauphin á Bec Blanc (French); Lagenorinco dal Rostro Bianco (Italian); Delphin de Hocico Blanco (Spanish); Golfinho de Focinho Branco, Roaz de Bico Branco (Portuguese); Witsnuitdolfijn (Dutch); Kvitnos, Hvidnaese (Norwegian); Valkonokkadelfiini (Finnish); Vitnos (Swedish); Hvidnæse (Danish); Lag, Squid-hound (Newfoundland).

Meaning of the Scientific Nomenclature
Lagenorhynchus albirostris (Gray 1846) - Genus see *L. acutus*. Latin *albus* (white) and *rostrum* (snout).

Behaviour
Usually shies away from vessels, may occasionally bow-ride briefly. Usually appears in groups of 2-25 animals. When there is ample food sources or during long migrations 100-1,000 + individuals. Off the coast of Newfoundland and in the Gulf of St. Lawrence often occurs in groups of about 1,500 animals. Westerly groups larger than easterly groups. Trails a thin spray of water when swimming fast. Usually leaps out of the water entirely to breathe. Very active, especially when hunting and feeding. Often leaps high out of the water. Frequently in association with Bottlenose Dolphins, Atlantic White-Sided Dolphins, Fin Whales, Killer Whales and other cetaceans.

Diving
Presumably does not stay under longer than 6 min, max dive depth around 200 m.

Feeding Habits
Fish (herring, capelin, mackerel, hake, cod, plaice), squid and crabs. Hunts close to surface.

General Information
A specimen stranded close to Great Yarmouth (England) in 1846, which J. E. Gray named *Delphinus albirostris*. Later classified under genus *Lagenorhynchus*. The popular name is somewhat misleading as the snout of the westerly animals can be dark-grey to speckled-brown. Only white in the case of easterly population (appears in smaller groups).

Where & When
Northernmost species of the genus, only occurs in cold (to edge of pack ice) to cold-temperate waters of the N-Atlantic, inshore and offshore. Range overlaps with Atlantic White-Sided Dolphin.

Peale's Dolphin, *Lagenorhynchus australis*

Distinguishing Characteristics
Flanks pale-grey, separated from white belly by a dark line. A tapering grey-white stripe runs from the base of the tail to the blowhole. Brilliant white patch with grey borders at the upper base of the flippers ("armpits").

Description
Length 1.8-2.1 m, weight up to 120 kg. Largest specimen ever measured 2.16 m. Body relatively stocky for its size. Back generally dark-grey to black. Very large, falcate dorsal fin. Large fluke, small and pointed flippers, short and blunt snout uniformly dark-grey to black.

Easily Mistaken For
Dusky Dolphins. Range of both species overlaps at the southern tip of South America and the Falkland Islands. Difference: Peale's Dolphins have a dark snout and white patch at the "armpits."

Other Names
Blackchin Dolphin, Peale's Porpoise, Southern Dolphin (English); Peale Delphin, Süddelphin, Schwarzkinn-Delphin (German); Dauphin de Peale, Dauphin à Menton Noir (French); Lagenorinco di Peale (Italian); Delphin Austral (Spanish); Golfinho de Peale, Roaz Austral (Portuguese); Dolfijn van Peale (Dutch); Pealedelphin (Norwegian); Pealendelfiini (Finnish); Pealesdelphin (Swedish); Sydlig Hvidskæving (Danish); Delfín Austral (Latin American Spanish).

Falkland Islands, South Atlantic.   Todd Pusser/Seapics.com

Meaning of the Scientific Nomenclature
Lagenorhynchus australis (Peale 1848) - Genus see *L. acutus*. Latin *australis* (southern distribution).

Behaviour
Usually appears in groups of 3-10, occasionally up to 30 animals. Very fast and powerful swimmer. Frequent porpoising. Leaps high into the air repeatedly and lands on its sides. Rides the bow wave of larger vessels and often accompanies smaller craft. Presumably resident. Frequently in association with Risso's Dolphins in the surge zone.

Diving: Unknown.

Feeding Habits: Unknown. Presumably fish, squid (based on stomach content analysis of stranded animals).

General Information
First described as *Phocoena australis* by Titian Peale in 1848. The specimen identified was harpooned on February 12, 1839, by a member of the United States Exploring Expedition along the coast of Patagonia. No other sightings made until a second specimen was discovered in 1941. Till then species was considered to be extinct. This particular animal was examined by American zoologist Remington Kellogg of the Smithsonian Institution in Washington, who classified it in the genus *Lagenorhynchus*.

Where & When
Distribution relatively limited. Primarily found in coastal waters around the southern tip of South America, Golfo San Matías, Peninsula Valdés (Argentina) and Valparaíso (Chile). Usually frequents fjords and bays, but also found along the continental shelf from Argentina to the Falkland Islands. Most often sighted to the south of Puerto Montt in Chile, around the Falkland Islands, off the coast of Tierra del Fuego and in the Beagle Canal. One of the most common species of dolphin in the Magellan Strait. Southernmost sighting 57° S. Very rare in region of crab fisheries, where it is occasionally caught in nets or harpooned (meat used as bait for crab traps).

Hourglass Dolphin, *Lagenorhynchus cruciger*

Drake Passage, South of Cape Hoorn.   Robin Baird/Seapics.com

Distinguishing Characteristics: Black flanks with white hourglass pattern. Rare oceanic species, the only dolphins in the Antarctic and Sub-Antarctic seas that have a dorsal fin. **Description:** Length 1.5-1.8 m, weight 90-120 kg. Body relatively stocky for its size. Very large, falcate dorsal fin. Back edge of fluke concave with well developed median notch. Dorsal fin, fluke, flippers and short, blunt snout uniformly dark-grey to black. Dark flanks have conspicuous white patches fore and aft which are connected by a thin line running underneath the dorsal fin (hence the hourglass pattern). White ring surrounds the dark eye-patch. White belly. Cadavers of stranded animals quickly turn grey all over.

Easily Mistaken For: Dusky Dolphins and Peale's Dolphins. Dusky Dolphins are similar in size and shape, but have a bicoloured dorsal fin (dark on leading side, light on trailing side) and no hourglass pattern. Their areas of distribution only overlap along the southern tip of South America, around the Kerguelen Islands, New Zealand and the southernmost tip of Australia. Peale's Dolphins (southern tip of South America, Falkland Islands) are similar, but lack hourglass pattern.

Other Names: Southern White-Sided Dolphin, Wilson's Dolphin (English); Stundenglass-Delphin, Sanduhr-Delphin, Kreuzdelphin, Kreuzbanddelphin (German); Dauphin Crucigère, Dauphin Sablier (French); Lagenorinco dalla Croce (Italian); Delphin Cruzado (Spanish); Golfinho Ampulheta, Golfinho Cruzado, Roaz Cruzado (Portuguese); Zandloperdolfijn (Dutch); Korsdelphin (Norwegian); Tiimalasidelfiini (Finnish); Timglasdelphin (Swedish); Kors-hvidskæving (Danish); Dandara Kama Iruka (Japanese); Delfín Cruzado (Latin American Spanish).

Meaning of the Scientific Nomenclature: *Lagenorhynchus cruciger* (Quoy und Gaimard 1824) - Generic name see *L. acutus*. Latin *cruciger* made up of *crux* (cross), *gero* (I carry), meaning "carrier of the cross," refers to hourglass pattern.

Behaviour: Because of its remote distribution it is one of the least known species of dolphin. Appears singly or in small groups (2-10), occasionally 40, very rarely up to 100 animals. Large dorsal fin reveals that the species is a fast swimmer. Short sprints up to 40 km/h. Often rides bow and stern waves of fast boats, porpoising at the same time. Swims fast close to the surface without breaking through it. Shallow and long leaps on the surface to breathe, producing a lot of turbulence. Oceanic, only rarely encountered inshore (less than 200 m in depth). Sightings are rare, and then frequently seen in association with other cetaceans.

Diving: Unknown.

Feeding Habits: Preys on squid and pelagic shoaling fish.

General Information: First described as *Delphinus cruciger* by French zoologists Jean René Quoy and Jean-Paul Gaimard in 1824. Classified under Gray's genus *Lagenorhynchus* in 1846.

Where & When: Exact distribution unknown. Prefers cold offshore waters with temperatures ranging from 1-10° C. Circumpolar from 45°-65° S. Southernmost sighting close to Antarctic ice barrier, northernmost off the coast of Valparaíso (Chile). Occasionally spotted close to the Antarctic Peninsula and off the coast of South America in areas shallower than 200 m. Otherwise only encountered on the open seas. Of all species of dolphin, this one is best adapted to life on the high seas.

Dusky Dolphin, *Lagenorhynchus obscurus*

Distinguishing Characteristics
Dark base of tail has two white to pale-grey, wedge-shaped, forward-facing lateral patches ("stirrups"). Large, falcate dorsal fin, dark-grey to black on leading edge, the rest pale-grey. Belly and ventral side white, colour extends to top of the eyes and forehead.

Description
Length 1.6-2.1 m. Compact and stocky body. Back, flippers and fluke dark-grey to black. Short, dark and indistinct snout.

South Atlantic.   Jasmine Rossi

Flat forehead, region around eyes and throat white. Dark patch around the eyes.

Other Names
Fitzroy's Dolphin (English); Schwarzdelphin, Dunkler Delphin, Dunkeldelphin (German); Dauphin Sombre, Dauphin Obscur (French); Lagenorinco Scuro (Italian); Delphin Obscuro (Spanish); Golfinho Cinzento, Roaz Negro (Portuguese); Donkergestreepte Dolfijn (Dutch); Mørkdelphin (Norwegian); Eteläinenjuovadelfiini (Finnish); Mörkdelphin (Swedish); Mørk Hvidskæving (Danish); Harajiro Kama Iruka (Japanese).

Meaning of the Scientific Nomenclature
Lagenorhynchus obscurus (Gray 1828) - Genus see *L. acutus*. Latin *obscurus* (dark, flanks and back).

Behaviour
Very gregarious, often seen in association with other cetaceans, sea lions and seabirds. Frequently approach vessels and ride the bow wave. Size of group varies depending upon availability of food and season, up to 1,000 animals (max in summer). Hunting behaviour and social structure of a population in Valdés Peninsula was studied by biologists Melany and Würsing during the 1970s, whereby the technique of photo-identification was implemented for the first time. Group size ranges from 6-15, but may include up to 300 or more animals during hunt. During the day the groups tend to be larger and head for the open seas. It can swim at speeds of up to 15 km/h while feeding, otherwise it cruises around 6.5 km/h. Belkovitch and Würsing (1991) described this species' "carousel" hunting technique in Argentina (see section on behaviour of Indo-Pacific Bottlenose Dolphin). The herding together of prey in this fashion will attract many seabirds, which can be detected from afar.
Species is known for high and spectacular spinning leaps, as well as executing forward and backward somersaults. This will occur repeatedly, especially after feeding. Once one animal begins the others will invariably follow. Wide, arching bounds when swimming fast.

Diving: Stays under relatively briefly, max 200 m depth.

Feeding Habits: Squid, shoaling fish (sardines, anchovies), as well as reef fish and crustaceans.

General Information
First described as *Delphinus obscurus* by J. E. Gray in 1828 on the basis of a skull found at the Cape of Good Hope (South Africa). First description of Atlantic White-Sided Dolphin provided that same year. Classified under *Lagenorhynchus* after 1846. In Peru larger than in New Zealand.

Where & When
Temperate zones of the Southern Hemisphere, relatively common, primarily inshore. Presumably three isolated populations: Largest along the Pacific coast of Peru and Chile. Second in the Atlantic from the tip of South America to Valdés Peninsula (Argentina) and the Falkland Islands. Third in the South Pacific around New Zealand and Campbell, Chatham and Auckland islands. A fourth, smaller population lives around the Kerguelen Islands (French) in the Southern Indian Ocean. First confirmed sighting off the coast of South Australia in 2000.

Pacific White-Sided Dolphin, *Lagenorhynchus obliquidens*

California, USA.   Michele Hall

Distinguishing Characteristics

Large dorsal fin and flippers with conspicuous colouration: Leading edges dark, gradually fade towards trailing edges. Pale-grey lateral blaze running from the dorsal fin to the head, separated from the white underside by a dark stripe. Back and upper side of flanks with one or more pale-grey to white streaks ("suspenders") that expand from the base of the tail to form a lateral patch.

Description
Length up to 2.4 m, weight up to 140 kg. Front half of the body very stocky. Back edge of fluke slightly concave with an indistinct median notch. Fluke and back dark-grey to black. Dark and indistinct snout. Dark ring around the eyes.

Other Names
Lag, Hookfin Porpoise, Hook-Finned Porpoise, White-Striped Dolphin, Pacific Striped Dolphin (English); Weißstreifendelphin, Gestreifter Pazifikdelphin (German); Dauphin à Flancs Blancs du Pacifique (French); Lagenorinco dai Denti Obliqui (Italian); Delphin de Costados Blancos del Pacifico (Spanish); Golfinho do Pacífico, Roaz Listado (Portuguese); Witgestreepte dolfijn (Dutch); Kortsnutedelphin (Norwegian); Juovadelfiini (Finnish); Västamerikansk Vitsiding (Swedish); Stillehavs-hvidskæving (Danish); Kama Iruka (Japanese); Tikhookaen Skiy (Russian); Delfín Lagenorringo (Latin American Spanish).

Meaning of the Scientific Nomenclature
Lagenorhynchus obliquidens Gill 1865 - Generic name see *L. acutus*. Latin *obliquidens* ("slanting tooth") made up of *obliquus* (slanting, crooked) and *dens* (tooth).

Behaviour
Very active. Large schools draw attention from afar by their spray. Short sprints of up to 40 km/h. Very inquisitive, likes to ride the bow wave and follow in the wake of larger vessels. Leaps frequently, twisting around its own axis, executes somersaults. Very gregarious, lives in groups of 10-100, occasionally up to several thousand animals. Oceanic groups usually larger than coastal groups (better protection). Separates into smaller groups while hunting, regroups to rest or during migration. Little known about its social structure, however. Often hunts in cooperation with other cetaceans (Killer Whales, Dall's Porpoises, Risso's Dolphins, Northern Rightwhale Dolphins), as well as seals *(Eumetopias jubatus)*.

Diving
Little is known about its diving behaviour. Often swims close to the surface with dorsal fin out of the water like many species of shark. Analyses of stomach contents have shown that they dive to depths of 1,000 m.

Feeding Habits
Fast and agile hunter. Prefers squid and shoaling fish (herring, anchovies, hake). Hunts at dawn and during the night. Shoaling fish are chased by groups of 10-20 dolphins, which herd their prey together by slapping the water with their flukes and heads. Follows schools of sardines to the coast of California in summer and fall, returns to the open seas in spring and winter.

General Information: First finds (3 skulls) made near San Francisco in 1855. These were examined and classified by taxonomist Th. N. Gill in 1865. There may be two populations in the NE- and NW-Pacific. Few sighting made in between. Often caught accidentally in fishing nets.

Fishermen in North America and Japan view species as unwelcome competitor. Meat is consumed in Japan. Population status unknown. 30,000-50,000 (estimate) in NE-Pacific.

Where & When
Cold to temperate Northern Pacific. Ranges from Baja California to Alaska and Taiwan to the Aleutian Islands (northernmost distribution). Also north of 20° N from Alaska to the peninsula of Kamchatka (Siberia). Never seen in the Bering Sea. Usually on the open seas over the continental shelf, also found along steep coastline. A few populations Probably undertake seasonal north-south migrations, others are apparently resident.

Pacific White-Sided Dolphin in a delphinarium.   Ralf Kiefner

Fraser's Dolphin, *Lagenodelphis hosei*

Description: Pointed flippers, dorsal fin (slightly curved) and fluke relatively smaller than those of related species. Short and blunt snout is clearly demarcated. Flippers, fluke, tip of lower jaw, upper jaw, back and flanks black to blue-grey and grey -brown. Rest of lower jaw, throat, belly creamy-white to pinkish-white. Pale-grey to creamy-white line stretches from base of melon over the eyes and down to the venting area. Turns paler towards the base of tail. A dark lateral stripe runs parallel to and directly underneath this line. A thinner dark stripe extends from the jawlines to the flippers. Stocky body, length ranges from 2.3-2.6 m, weight from 150-200 kg. Back edge of fluke slightly concave with indistinct median notch. Complex facial patterns. Calves paler than adults.
Other Names: Sarawak Dolphin, Shortsnout Dolphin, Bornean Dolphin, White-Bellied Dolphin (English); Borneo-Delphin, Kurzschnabeldelphin, Frasers Delphin (German); Dauphin de Fraser (French); Lagenodelphino (Italian); Delphin de Fraser (Spanish); Golfinho do Bornéu, Roaz Malaio (Portuguese); Dolfijn van Fraser (Dutch); Borneodelphin, Sarawakdelphin (Norwegian); Fraserin-delfiini (Finnish); Frasers Delphin (Swedish.); Hvidskæving-delphin (Danish); Sarawaku Iruka (Jap.).
Behaviour: Shy, habits not well known. Usually encountered offshore in groups of about 100 animals, occasionally up to 500-1,000 migrating to nutrient-rich waters. Rarely close to shore. Very active on surface. Shies away from vessels, will flee as soon as one approaches and seek close contact with fellow group members. Often in association with other cetaceans on the high seas.
Diving: According to analyses of stomach contents, species hunts at depths of 200-1,000 m.
Feeding Habits: From the stomach contents of stranded animals: Fish, crabs, squid and isopods.
General Information: British naturalist Dr. Charles Hose first found a dead specimen on the beach of Sarawak (Borneo) in 1895. First scientific description provided by F. C. Fraser in 1956. For a long time this skeleton was the only proof for this species' existence, which was thought to be extinct. The first living specimens were not sighted until the beginning of the 1970s.
Where & When: Distribution not well known. Presumably in all tropical and warm-temperate oceans between 40° N and 40° S. The species prefers the open seas or islands with steep coasts. It is only rarely seen in inshore waters.

Pieter Arend Folkens

Irrawaddy Dolphin, *Orcaella brevirostris*

Irrawaddy Dolphin in the public aquarium at Jakarta, Indonesia   Helmut Debelius

Distinguishing Characteristics
Upperside of body dark-grey, underside pale-grey. Head is compact and round, with no beak. Large melon. Like a Beluga, this species' head and neck can move freely as only two vertebrae are fused. Very small dorsal fin, almost triangular, with rounded tips and located far down the back.
Description
Length 2-2.5 m, weight 100-150 kg. Head clearly demarcated from neck by a fold or slight indentation. Flippers long, wide, spade-like and markedly curved.

Other Names: Snubfin Dolphin (English); Irawadi-Delphin (German); Orcelle (French); Orcella (Italian); Delphin del Irrawaddy (Spanish); Golfinho do Irrawaddy, Boto de Bengala (Portuguese); Irrawady-dolfijn (Dutch); Irrawadydelphin (Norwegian); Iravadinvalas (Finnish); Iravadidelphin (Swedish); Irrawady-delphin (Danish); Pesut Mahakam (Indonesian); Lumba Lumba (Malayan).

Meaning of the Scientific Nomenclature
Orcaella brevirostris (Gray 1866) - *Orcaella* based on Latin *orca* (species of whale); *brevirostris* (short-snouted) made up of Latin *brevis* (short) and *rostrum* (snout, beak).

Behaviour
Due to the species' shyness and poor visibility in its natural habitat, very little is known about it. Best observed in captivity. Lives in small groups (2-15 animals), without separation by gender, in the rivers and coastal waters of Southeast Asia, Papua-New Guinea and North Australia. Swims up to 1,300 km upstream in larger rivers. Some populations in India, Cambodia and Borneo live exclusively in fresh-water lakes. Very slow and calm swimmer, difficult to spot on surface. Blow can be heard on calm days. Often spits out water (like untrained Belugas in captivity), which may be a way for the animal to knock down small prey sitting on overhanging branches.

Diving
Does not stay under long, up to 10 min when hunting. Bends base of tail sharply when sounding.

Feeding Habits
Benthic fish, cephalopods and crustaceans. Occasionally drives schools of fish into shallows in order to facilitate capture.

General Information
Classified in 1866 by John E. Gray on the basis of a skull that Sir Walter Elliot found in the harbour of Vishakhapatnam on the Bay of Bengal (Indian) and had been described previously as *Phocoena brevirostris* by Owen. First population discovered off Papua-New Guinea in 1948. Barnes (1984) classified it under Monodontidae, but genetic analyses excluded any relationship with Belugas. Animal is sacred to Vietnamese fishermen, who free animals accidentally caught in nets because these supposedly drive fish into their nets and traps. In parts of Borneo they are viewed as reincarnated ancestors. Nevertheless, due to dam construction and industry their natural habitat (tropical rivers, estuaries, shallow coastal areas) is severely threatened.

Where & When
Indo-Pacific region: Warm, shallow inshore waters, lakes and rivers from Bay of Bengal (eastern coast of India) to the west coast of Papua-New Guinea and north coast of Australia. Found in shallow, well-protected bays, muddy estuaries and mangrove swamps - never far from coast. Often encountered in major river systems of Ganges and Brahmaputra (India), as well as in rivers in Burma (Irrawaddy), Laos, Cambodia, Vietnam (Mekong) and Borneo (Mahakam).

DOLPHIN DANCE

Unlike the famous "Flipper", wild dolphins hardly play with divers. There are few dolphins on this earth who prefer the company of people. 'Normal' dolphins sometimes come to take a look at divers, or like to ride on the waves of fast boats, but that's about it. Underwater photographers Peter Verhoog and Georgina Wiersma, however, had the privilege of dancing with dolphins.

PHOTOS: PETER VERHOOG

A magnificent spectacle under the surface: Dolphins have driven a large school of sardines to the surface...

We are cruising at fast speed in the waters around the Portuguese island of Pico (Azores) in the Atlantic Ocean. This morning we have seen some dolphins, but when we very carefully entered the water they disappeared within seconds. The animals took a quick look at us, but there was no chance to have a good look at them, let alone take pictures of these beautiful creatures.

Then our skipper spots a large group of birds on the surface. We steer the boat towards the swarm to have a look. These birds often hunt schooling fish that are herded to the surface by dolphins. There could be a group of dolphins hunting! When we arrive near the birds, we see Atlantic common dolphins (Delphinus delphis) jump out of the water. We carefully choose our position, get cameras, masks and fins and glide into the water as slowly and silently as possible. Any wrong movement or noise can disturb the dolphins in their natural behaviour. The photographers in the boat are allowed to go first. We decide to stay away from each other: It is never a good idea to approach dolphins with a large group of people! Peter calmly swims into the direction of the dolphins and I follow a few minutes later, inhale, and dive down - snorkelling, because the bubbles of SCUBA-gear chase dolphins away. Under the surface, a magnificent spectacle unfolds. The dolphins have driven an immensely large school of sardines to the surface. The marine mammals have used the natural

...which they divide into smaller balls that are more easy to handle.

Dinner is ready! Now the dolphins wait for an opportunity to speed into the fishball and grab a fish.

The silvery ball of fish is boiling: From the surface, sea birds dive into the ball to a depth of 3 to 4 m, and have their pick.

After dinner, it's playing time. Like in the centre of a carefully designed dance we are approached by small groups of dolphins.

behaviour of these schooling fish perfectly. The surface serves as a natural barrier, which holds the fish together on one side. The dolphins approach the school of sardines from all other sides, which forces the fish to form a dense mass, in which they would normally be safe, but that has now become a deadly trap. A genuine case of fatal attraction...

The dolphins are speeding by all around me, grey silhouettes in a vast, blue underwater sky. The water is filled with their squeaking sounds. It is obvious that they are communicating intensely and cooperate during their hunt. They swim at great speed, and shoot to the surface every 20 to 30 seconds to breathe, and when submerging again, they create a long trail of tiny bubbles in the water.

There must be about 300 to 400 dolphins around us! Now they split up to divide the baitfish into smaller balls with a diameter of about one and a half metre, which are more easy to handle for the smaller groups of dolphins that actually start feeding. The silvery ball of fish next to me is boiling: Dinner is ready! Dolphin after dolphin speeds up to the ball, grabs a fish, and swims away. From the surface, the birds dive into the school, sometimes to a depth of 3 to 4 metres, and have their pick. Afterwards they return to the surface with extended legs, their wings folded closely to their body. One dolphin grabs a bird instead of a fish, and throws the poor animal away with an elegant swing. The whole spectacle lasts about 5 minutes, and ends because there is only a small ball of sardines left.

There is peace in the water again. But after dinner, it's playing time! Today, part of the game is looking at clumsy snorkellers. Small groups of two to four dolphins approach fast, almost stop, and watch me from a distance, a curious look in their black-rimmed eyes. I feel like part of a dance, in which I am the centre of a carefully designed series of movements. They do not come closer than a few metres. Suddenly, I see a dolphin mother and her baby. The youngster is only 70 centimetres long, and must have been born only recently. The female positions herself between me and her offspring. A last dolphin comes to take a look at us, but then they all have disappeared. The water is silent again, the sounds have faded, the sea seems to be deserted. When we climb into the boat, we realise that we are now part of a very small group of privileged people, who have had the wonderful opportunity to observe wild dolphins hunting.

STRANGERS IN FRESH WATERS

It is raining cats and dogs. We are diving in the Rio Negro, a branch of the Amazon River. Only during the rainy season can one expect up to 2 m of visibility here. At other times the Rio Negro carries so much sediment that it even becomes impossible to see one's own diving watch. In order to take uw-shots of the Amazon's fauna, photographer Scott Frier and the author ventured into the realm of anacondas, caimans and piranhas.

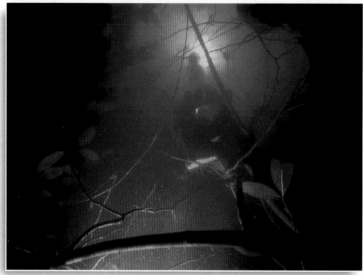

PHOTOS: SCOTT FRIER

Due to the decay of organic substances the water takes on a reddish hue, which allows for a minimum in visibility.

It is useless to dive in the Rio Negro (Black River) during the dry season. Its waters look like black coffee. Now that the rainy season has arrived, the river has risen some 20 m and over-flowed its banks. Its waters have flooded many square kilometres of rain forest. The heavy rainfall has also improved the visibility in the Rio Negro considerably. Because of the rapid decay of organic substances, the river has taken on a reddish colour. This process of decay is extremely important for the ecosystem of the rain forest as it provides the barren soil with many nutrients.

Our boat chugs across the lake. A few 4-5 metre long river-caimans doze along the sand banks. Their size impresses me. We are keeping a sharp lookout for signs of the progenitor of all dolphins. The origin of river dolphins predates that of their better known cousins in the ocean. The River dolphins has adapted perfectly to their life in these turbid waters. They are nearly blind, but a highly developed echolocation enables them to find their way in this murky 'soup.' Their unusually long beaks and flexible necks make it easier for them to catch even the tiniest fish trying to hide behind the sub-merged roots.

Suddenly we hear a soft blowing sound. Four

An anaconda lies in wait for prey 4 m below us on the bottom.

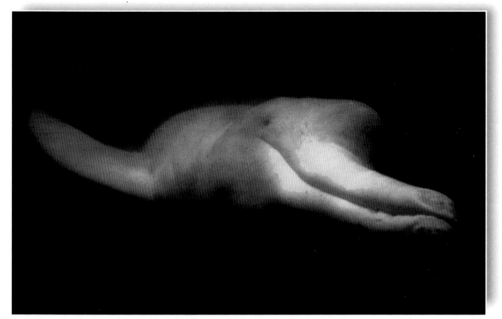
An inquisitive Boto or Amazon River Dolphin *(Inia geoffrensis)* scans us with its echolocation.

pink dorsal ridges break the surface just beyond our boat. We can clearly make out their small hump-like dorsal fins. Their compact dorsal fins, shorter beaks and smaller size reveal them to be Tucuxis *(Sotalia fluviatilis)*. The dolphins keep moving on, obviously unimpressed by our presence. No matter what we try, whether we speed up the boat or shut down the engine and let it drift, the dolphins always maintain about 20 metres between us. As soon as we move in closer they sound and then resurface some distance from us. After numerous abortive attempts, we decide to try our luck snorkelling. Scott and I glide silently into the murky water and swim in the direction where we last saw the dolphins.

We swim past a few uprooted trees and spot an anaconda lying in wait for prey on the bottom below us. I am amazed at how many different species of fish we can see in spite of the turbid water. "What do piranhas actually look like?" suddenly flashes through my mind.

A nosy caiman also watches every move we make.

I am troubled by a series of horrible images of skeletons that have been picked clean in seconds. "As long as you don't have any open or bleeding wounds, it is alright for you to get into the water," I recall the assuring words of our tour guide. "Hopefully the piranhas know that too," I think to myself.

I hardly have time to worry about it, however, as suddenly an Amazon River Dolphin surfaces directly in front of Scott. If I were not so certain that

245

Tucuxis are the only fluvial dolphins with a dorsal fin.

these dolphins are almost completely blind, I would say that it is giving us a thorough look over. It moves its head slowly and "scans" us with its echolocation. Its uncommonly long beak and very wide flippers give it a strange appearance. The Boto, as Amazon River Dolphins are also referred to here, turns its head sideways a little as if it were trying to decide what to make of us. It evidently feels somewhat uneasy about our presence. With a few strokes of its fluke it vanishes forever in the murky water.

We spend the next few days searching in vain for any signs of the pink dolphins. Seemingly out of nowhere, a young dolphin suddenly leaps out of the water before our bow. When it surfaces again we notice that there are two of them, a mother and her baby. The baby swims very close to its mother, almost riding her back. Tucuxi, as these animals are referred to here, are one of the smallest species of dolphins and easy to differentiate from other river dolphins. They are the only fluvial dolphins with a dorsal fin. They are also unique in that some of them live exclusively in coastal waters.

We get into the water as silently as possible and carefully make our way towards the two dolphins. Normally Tucuxis are extremely shy, but we interpret their leaping before the bow of our boat as an invitation to play. Almost as soon as we get into the water the dolphins begin to swim alongside of us. The mother slows down and halts directly in front of us. It is almost as if she wanted to introduce us to her baby. Scott and I try to remain immobile. The baby snuggles up close to its mother. After a while the baby becomes nervous and moves to its mother's opposite side. The attentive mother apparently interprets her baby's move as an indication to move on. Both gradually vanish in the turbid waters.

A Tucuxi dolphin mother and its baby appear to be swimming here.

The **Subfamily Long-Snouted Dolphins** comprises 4 species:
Tucuxi, *Sotalia fluviatilis*
Indo-Pacific Hump-Backed Dolphin, *Sousa chinensis*
Atlantic Hump-Backed Dolphin, *Sousa teuszii*
Rough-Toothed Dolphin, *Steno bredanensis*

Distinguishing Characteristics of this Subfamily
All species have a very long, narrow snout and a large, falcate dorsal fin.

Tucuxi, *Sotalia fluviatilis*

Distinguishing Characteristics
Small, stocky, rounded melon. Dorsal fin small, triangular, wide.
Description
Length 1.3-1.8 m, weight 35-45 kg. Flippers wide. Back grey, underside and flanks grey to pink. Dark line from eye to base of flipper. Second line below the dorsal fin backwards.
Easily Mistaken For
Boto (Amazon River Dolphin), but Boto less shy, paler, longer snout, smaller dorsal

Reserve Anhatomirim, Baia Norte, South Brazil.   Paulo Flores/Seapics.com

fin. In coastal areas: Bottlenose Dolphin, but this is larger, dorsal fin larger, more falcate, snout shorter. In its southern limits of distribution: La Plata River Dolphin, but juveniles with very small eyes, always accompanied by mother; adults darker, with longer snout and rounder flippers.
Other Names
Estuarine Dolphin (English); Amazonas-Sotalia (German); Sotalie (French); Sotalia (Italian); Bufeo Negro (Spanish); Tucuxi (Portuguese, Swedish, Danish); Amazonedolfijn (Dutch); Brasildeltadelphin (Norwegian); Amazoninvalkodelfiini (Finn.); Pirayaguara (Tupí & Yagua Indians); Boto Negro (Braz.).
Meaning of the Scientific Nomenclature
Sotalia fluviatilis (Gervais 1853) - Origin of *Sotalia* unknown. Latin *fluviatilis* (river-dweller, habitat).
Behaviour
Active, fast swimmer. Very gregarious, lives in groups of 2-30. Shies away from vessels. Lob-tailing, flipper-slapping, spy-hoping frequent. Leaps high and often. Fluvial variant smaller, paler, head and torso come high out of the water when surfacing, often associated with river dolphins (Platanistidae) in the Amazon region. Coastal variant larger, darker, oceanic, behaviour little known.
General Information
French zoologist and physician Paul Gervais first described a specimen from the Amazon in 1853 and named it *Delphinus fluviatilis*. Classified under genus *Sotalia* Gray, 1866 in 1884. *S. brasiliensis, S. tucuxi, S. pallida* and *S. guianensis* are merely colour- and age-variants of *S. fluviatilis*. However, the comparison between 22 characteristics on 104 skulls (92 from the Brazilian coast, 12 from the Amazon) produced the following result: No gender-based differences, but variations in form. Consequently, there may eventually be a subdivision into a coastal (*S. guianensis*) and Amazon (*S. fluviatilis*) species. "Tucuxi" (the other dolphin) refers to the fact that this species often appears together with (unrelated) Botos in the Orinoco and Amazon rivers. See also STRANGERS IN FRESH WATERS on pp. 244-246.
Where & When
NE South America to E Central America (Atlantic, Caribbean, rivers). Coastal variant close to shore from Florianopolis (Brazil) to Leimus Lagoon (Nicaragua), as well as several southern Caribbean islands. River variant found up to 250 km upstream in the Orinoco and 2,500 km upstream in the Amazon. Best observed at mouth of tributaries. Also in Lake Maracaibo (Venezuela).

Indo-Pacific Hump-Backed Dolphin, *Sousa chinensis*

Queensland Coast, Australia   Doug Perrine/Seapics.com

Distinguishing Characteristics
Pale, very long snout, wide dorsal hump (up to 30% of total length) with small dorsal fin.

Description
Robust, stocky. Length 2-2.8 m, weight 150-240 kg. Forehead clearly demarcated from long snout, but no fold. Flippers wide, triangular, with rounded tips. Dorsal and ventral ridges on peduncle of tail. Colouration varies depending upon population, age and individuals. Dorsally brown-grey, pale-grey, pinkish-white; ventrally paler. Some adults spotted.

Easily Mistaken For
Bottlenose Dolphin is similar in size and stature, but has a shorter snout, no dorsal hump and a larger dorsal fin. The Atlantic Hump-Backed Dolphin is very similar (number of teeth and vertebrae only anatomical difference), but ranges elsewhere.

Other Names
Chinese White Dolphin, Speckled Dolphin (English); Chinesischer Weißdelphin, Indopazifischer Buckeldelphin (German); Sousa de Pacifique, Dauphin à Bosse de l'Indo-Pacifique (French); Susa Indopacifica (Italian); Delphin Jorobado del Pacifico Negro (Spanish); Golfinho Branco Oriental (Portuguese); Chinese Witte Dolfijn (Dutch); Kinesisk Hvitdelphin (Norwegian); Kiinanvalkodelfiini (Finnish); Osbecks Näbbdelphin (Swedish); Indopacifisk Pukkeldelphin (Danish).

Meaning of the Scientific Nomenclature
Sousa chinensis (Ostbeck 1765) - Origin of generic name (J.E. Gray) unknown, perhaps it means dolphin (India); *chinensis* refers to its distribution.

Behaviour
Lives in groups of up to 7, occasionally 25 animals. Habitat is usually very murky, so the species communicates avidly with whistling sounds and has sophisticated echolocation. Very shy. Frequent spy-hopping. Slow swimmer, likes to float motionless on surface with one flipper extended out of the water. Younger animals leap often, however. Lob-tailing when animals are hunting. Courtship behaviour: Animals swim fast in circles. Often associated with Bottlenose and Spinner Dolphins.

Diving
Conspicuous surfacing (45° snout first) and sounding (back extremely curved, fluke sometimes visible) behaviour. Dives for about 1 min, longer if threatened. Max depth 50 m.

Feeding Habits
Shoaling fish (sardines, breams, herring, plaice, goatfish), occasionally cephalopods and river crabs.

General Information
First described as *Delphinus chinensis* by the Swede Per Ostbeck in 1765, who had observed the species in the China Sea in 1757. Population status unknown, probably very small.

Where & When
Tropical and subtropical coastal waters with depths of about 20 m. Along steeper coastlines it remains within the shallower surge zone. Rarely offshore, occasionally found a few kilometres upriver. Prefers mangroves, lagoons, estuaries, reefs and sandbanks. Found in Indic and Western Pacific (South Africa to North Australia, Borneo, Sumatra and Northern Japan). Three geographic variants, one of which, *S. plumbea* (South Africa to South China) may actually be a distinct species.

Atlantic Hump-Backed Dolphin, *Sousa teuszii*

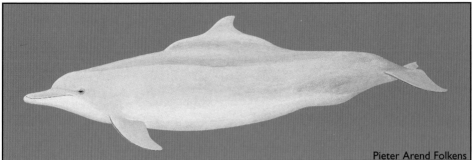

Pieter Arend Folkens

Description
Length 2-2.7 m, weight 100-150 kg. Slate-grey, ventrally paler. Melon of young animals less well developed, dorsal fin more falcate, no dorsal hump. Otherwise like *S. chinensis*.

Easily Mistaken For
Bottlenose Dolphin is similar in size and shape, but has a shorter snout, no dorsal hump and a larger dorsal fin. The Indo-Pacific Hump-Backed Dolphin is very similar (number of teeth and vertebrae only anatomical difference), but ranges elsewhere.

Other Names
Cameroon Dolphin (English); Kamerun-Delphin, Atlantischer Buckeldelphin (German); Sousa de l'Atlantique, Dauphin à Bosse de l'Atlantique (French); Susa Atlantica (Italian); Delphin Jorobado del Atlantico (Spanish); Golfinho de Bossa do Atlântico, Golfinho Branco Africano (Portuguese); Kameroendolfijn (Dutch); Kamerundelphin (Norwegian); Atlanninvalkodelfiini (Finnish); Kamerundelphin (Swedish); Atlanterhavs-pukkeldelphin (Danish).

Meaning of the Scientific Nomenclature
Sousa teuszii (Kükenthal 1892) - Origin of the generic name (given by Gray) unknown, *Sousa* probably meaning "dolphin" in India. Specific name *teuszii* given in honour of Edward Teusz, who found the first specimen.

Behaviour
Group size 2-10, only occasionally up to 25 animals. The members of a group communicate lively with whistling sounds. Their echolocation is very important for a survival in the partly murky and sediment-rich waters of their habitat and hence is highly developed. The species is very shy and hardly observed in the wild. If a boat approaches, all animals of a group immediately dive and disappear in different directions to resurface later at a safe distance together again. This dolphin is a slow swimmer that often moves lazily along the surface, but it can also be very acrobatic, especially juvenile animals frequently jump. Often seen in association with Bottlenose Dolphins. Behaviour otherwise like *S. chinensis*.

When the mullet migrate in winter, the fishermen living along Cape Timiris, situated north of Nouakchott on the coast of Mauritania (West Africa), beat the water with sticks. This will attract Bottlenose Dolphins and Atlantic Hump-Backed Dolphins which then drive the fish into their nets. The dolphins feed on some of the mullet caught in the nets or chase down those that manage to escape.

Diving see *S. chinensis*.

Feeding Habits
Shoaling fish (see *S. chinensis*), rarely also cephalopods.

General Information
First described by W. Kükenthal (Natural History Museum in Jena) in 1892 on the basis of a skull that Edward Teusz had sent him from Cameroun (West Africa). Long regarded as a vegetarian species of dolphin because the stomach contents of an examined sea cow (mangrove sprouts, seagrass and leaves) were erroneously attributed to it. Population status unknown, regionally quite common.

Where & When
Tropical Atlantic coast of West Africa from Mauritania over Senegal to Cameroun, perhaps all the way to Angola and even farther south. Especially frequent in the south of Senegal and the north-west of Mauritania. Prefers shallow, murky coastal waters no deeper than 20 m. In steeper coastal areas it remains within the shallower surge zone. Rarely offshore, sometimes several kilometres upriver (Niger, Bandiala). Prefers mangroves, lagoons, estuaries, reefs and sandbanks.

Rough-Toothed Dolphin, *Steno bredanensis*

Maui, Hawaii.   Jim Watt

Distinguishing Characteristics: Cone-shaped head with a very long and narrow snout that appears like a prolongation of the flat forehead. Eyes very black. Underside white or pink with conspicuous round pinkish-white or yellowish-white spots. **Description:** Slender, length 2.1-2.5 m, max 2.75 m, weight 130-160 kg. Females smaller than males. Flippers long and pointed, leading edge sickle-shaped. Dorsal fin falcate. Small saddle patch, usually only slightly darker than the dark-grey flanks. Flippers, dorsal fin and fluke black. Colouration variable. The typical spots were once though to be Cookiecutter Shark bites. Today it is believed that they are caused by parasites. Only cetacean to have fine longitudinal lines on the enamel of their teeth (hence name).

Easily Mistaken For: Species is similar in size and shape to Bottlenose Dolphins, Spotted Dolphins, Long-Snouted Spinner Dolphins and Short-Snouted Spinner Dolphins. However, it is rarely sighted and its head shape, black eyes and typical spots make it unmistakable.

Other Names: Slopehead (English); Rauhzahn-Delphin (German); Dauphin à Long Bec (French); Steno (Italian); Esteno (Spanish); Caldeirão (Portuguese); Snaveldolfijn (Dutch); Nebbdelphin (Norwegian); Rosohammasdelfiini (Finnish); Näbbdelphin (Swedish); Rutandet Delphin (Danish).

Meaning of the Scientific Nomenclature: *Steno bredanensis* (Lesson 1828) - *Steno* based on Greek *stenos* (narrow) <u>or</u> in honour of famous 17th-century Danish anatomist Dr. Nikolaus Steno. *Bredanensis* in honour of artist Van Breda, who made the first drawing of a specimen (Brest, 1823).

Behaviour: Little known species. Group size 10-20, rarely 100+ (seasonal migrations). Pelagic, also ranges over the continental shelf, occasionally inshore (e.g. Mauritania). Swims very fast, skimming shark-like along the surface. Porpoising infrequent. Often in association with Bottlenose Dolphins, Pilot Whales, Short- and Long-Snouted Spinner Dolphins. Biologist Fabian Ritter recently observed a case of solicitous concern (La Gomera, Canary Islands): A female kept its dead calf on the surface for five days, whereby it was assisted by other dolphins. A trainable species that adapts well to life in an aquarium, where interbreeding with Bottlenose Dolphins has occurred.

Diving: Up to 15 min and depths of 80 m. Surfaces in opposite direction of where it sounded.

Feeding Habits: Pelagic fish, squid and other invertebrates.

General Information: For a long time the species was only known on the basis of a few skull finds. Desmarest first described it as *Delphinus rostratus* in 1817 (name invalid). Classified as *D. bredanensis* in 1828 by Lesson, who based his decision on Cuvier's material and Van Breda's drawings. Placed in Grey's genus *Steno* after 1846. Fraser and Purves (1960) gave *Steno, Sousa* and *Sotalia* their own family, Stenidae. Today, however, these are classified as a subfamily of long-snouted dolphins (Steninae) within the family Delphinidae. Communicates with whistling sounds of 4-7 kHz echolocation with clicks of 14-25 kHz. Frequently involved in mass stranding.

Where & When: Pelagic cosmopolitan, found in tropical to warm-temperate waters (22°-25° C) of all oceans. Range between 40° N and 40° S. Sightings: Indic: South Africa, Gulf of Aden, Gulf of Bengal, Indonesia; Pacific: Ogasawara (Japan), Hawaii, Galapagos; West Atlantic: Virginia, Georgia, Florida, Caribbean islands, Gulf of Mexico; East Atlantic: Ivory Coast, Senegal, Mauritania.

The **Subfamily Rightwhale Dolphins** comprises 2 species:
Northern Righwhale Dolphin, *Lissodelphis borealis*
Southern Righwhale Dolphin, *Lissodelphis peronii*

Distinguishing Characteristics of this Subfamily
Only two species of dolphin without a dorsal fin. Found in cold to temperate waters of both hemispheres.

Northern Rightwhale Dolphin, *Lissodelphis borealis*

The finless back is characteristic. East Pacific, California.   Todd Pusser/Seapics.com

Distinguishing Characteristics: Unmistakable within its area of distribution: No dorsal fin (hence popular name), slender, streamlined, typical black-and-white colouration.
Description: Adults average 2-3 m in length, 50-100 kg in weight. Males larger than females (max 2.3 m). Short, pointed snout clearly demarcated from forehead. Lower jaw longer than upper one. Primarily black. Thin lines connect a white ventral patch to a white patch on the belly that varies in size and is wider in case of males. Chin and underside of fluke are white. Newborn calves are grey-brown or cream-coloured, attain permanent colouration after one year.
Easily Mistaken For: Southern Rightwhale Dolphin, but different distribution.
Other Names: Pacific Rightwhale Porpoise (English); Nördlicher Glattdelphin (German); Lisso-delphe Boréal, Dauphin á dos Lisse Boréal (French); Lissodelphino Boreale (Italian); Delphin Liso del Norte (Spanish); Roaz Baleeiro Boreal, Golfinho Setentrional (Portuguese); Noordelijke Gladde Dolfijn (Dutch); Nordlig Slettdelphin (Norwegian); Pohjoinenvalasdelfiini (Finnish); Nordlig Rätvalsdelphin (Swedish); Nordlig Rethvalsdelphin (Danish); Kiti Demi Iruka (Japanese); Delfín Liso (Latin American Spanish).
Meaning of the Scientific Nomenclature: *Lissodelphis borealis* (Peale 1848) - Greek *lissos* (smooth), referring to lack of dorsal, *delphis* (dolphin). Latin *borealis* (northern), distribution.
Behaviour: Fast (up to 40 km/h) and tireless swimmer. Group size 100-200, occasionally up to 3,000 animals. Usually swim behind each other. Long (up to 7 m) and flat leaps, usually simultane-ously. Leaping, lob-tailing and flipper-slapping frequent. Relatively shy. Often in association with Atlantic White-Sided Dolphins, Risso's Dolphins, Short-Finned Pilot Whales and large whales (Fin Whales, Gray Whales - rides their bow waves). Follows preferred prey (cephalopods) along the coast and southwards in seasonal migrations from October-June.
Diving: Dive depth to 200 m, max dive time 10 min.
Feeding Habits: Hunts close to surface, primarily squid and lanternfish.
General Information: Titian Peale first described a specimen from the NW coast of North America as *Delphinapterus borealis* in 1848. Species name was given in order to differentiate it from Southern Rightwhale Dolphin, which had already been known for 44 years. Later in *Lissodelphis*.
Where & When: Deep, cold to temperate waters of the Northern Pacific. Prefers deeper regions over the continental shelf and the open seas between 30°-50° N. Inshore only along steep coastlines. Northwestern Pacific: Kamchatka (East Siberia) to Japan; Northeastern Pacific: British Columbia (Canada) to Baja California (Mexico).

Southern Rightwhale Dolphin, *Lissodelphis peronii*

Kaikoura, New Zealand   Ingrid Visser/Seapics.com

Distinguishing Characteristics: Unmistakable within its area of distribution: No dorsal fin (hence popular name), slender, streamlined, with a black-and-white colouration characteristic for this species.

Description: Adults 1.8-2.9 m in length, average weight 60-100 kg. Males larger than females (max 2.3 m). Short, pointed snout clearly demarcated from forehead. Lower jaw longer than upper one. Black back from the eyes downward, upper side of fluke grey. Snout, forehead, flippers, ventral side (including fluke) and flanks white. Leading or trailing edge of flippers can be dark. Calves are grey or spotted. Individuals distinguished by colouration of flippers, head and body (Cruickshank and Brown, South Africa).

Easily Mistaken For: Northern Rightwhale Dolphins, but different distribution.

Other Names: Mealy-Mouthed Porpoise (English); Südlicher Glattdelphin (German); Lissodelphe Austral, Dauphin Aptère Austral (French); Lissodelphino Australe (Italian); Delphin Liso Austral (Spanish); Roaz Baleeiro Austral, Golfinho do Perú, Golfinho Austral (Portuguese); Zuidelijke Gladde Dolfijn (Dutch); Sørlig Slettdelphin (Norwegian); Eteläinenvalasdelfiini (Finnish); Sydlig Rätvalsdelphin (Swedish); Sydlig Rethvalsdelphin (Danish); Delfín Liso (Latin American Spanish).

Meaning of the Scientific Nomenclature: *Lissodelphis peronii* Lacépède 1804 – Generic name see *L. borealis*. Peronii in honour of Francois Peron (see below).

Behaviour: Because of its remote habitat, species is little known. Group size 2-200, rarely up to 1,000. Often in association with Dusky Dolphins, Hourglass Dolphins and Pilot Whales. Swimming behaviour like *L. borealis*. Usually very shy, avoids vessels, occasionally rides bow wave.

General Information: Species discovered by French naturalist Francois Peron during his expedition to southern Tasmania (1800-1804) on board the ship "Géographe." He also provided the first description.

Where & When: Circumpolar, deep, cold to temperate waters of the Southern Hemisphere. Limits of range to the north 19° S; varies in south depending upon water temperatures and season, but does not extend to cold waters of the Antarctic. Prefers high seas, inshore only along steep coastlines (200+ m, volcanic islands). Most frequent sightings: Chile, in Falkland Stream between Patagonia and the Falklands, South Africa, Australia, New Zealand.

The **subfamily Black-and-White Dolphins** encompasses 5 species:
Commerson's Dolphin, *Cephalorhynchus commersonii*
Black Dolphin, *Cephalorhynchus eutropia*
Heaviside's Dolphin, *Cephalorhynchus heavisidii*
Hector's Dolphin, *Cephalorhynchus hectori*
Risso's Dolphin, *Grampus griseus*

Distinguishing Characteristics of this Subfamily
All species stocky with a cone-shaped head (round in case of *G. griseus*). Tip of snout poorly defined. Rounded dorsal fin, fluke concave with median notch. Colouration black and/or white.

Commerson's Dolphin, *Cephalorhynchus commersonii*

Delphinarium Duisburg (Germany).   Ralf Kiefner

Distinguishing Characteristics: Typical black-and-white colouration. Leading edge of flippers serrated (see below).
Description: Length up to 1.5 m, resembles a porpoise. Lower jaw extends further than upper one. Flippers oval. Leading edge of left flipper usually serrated in case of 50% of males and 80% of females. Among 5% of males the right flipper also serrated. Reason unknown, perhaps the animals use them to plow through the sea bottom in search of prey. Dorsal fin small, located just behind the middle of the back. Head, lower jaw, flippers, dorsal fin, fluke and base of tail black. Black surfaces on head and flippers connected, surround a large white ventral patch. Fluke and dorsal fin linked by a black stripe. Throat and rest of body white. A black horseshoe-shaped genital patch on females; a tear-shaped black genital patch on males. At birth black, grey and brown.
Easily Mistaken For: Similar to Dall's Porpoise, but different distribution.
Other Names: Piebald Dolphin, Jacobite, Skunk Dolphin, Black-and-White Dolphin, Puffing Pig (English); Commerson-Delphin, Jacobiter (German); Jacobite (French); Cefalorinco di Commerson (Italian); Tonina Overa (Spanish); Jacobita (Portuguese); Commerson-dolfijn (Dutch); Commerson-delphin (Norwegian); Commersonindelfiini (Finnish); Commersons Delphin (Danish, Swedish.); Delfín de Magellanes (Latin American Spanish).
Meaning of the Scientific Nomenclature: *Cephalorhynchus commersonii* Lacépède 1804 - Greek *cephalos* (head), *rhynchos* (nose); *commersonii* in honour of Philibert Commerson (see below).
Behaviour: Intensive studies by Natalie Goodall off Tierra del Fuego in the 1970s. Group size 2-15, rarely 100+ animals. Very swift, agile and active swimmer, rolls around its own axis. Often breaches, porpoises, bow rides and surfs in the surge.
Diving: Dives for short periods of time, does not go very deep, changes course under water.
Feeding Habits: Shoaling fish, squid and benthic shrimp uncovered by tidal currents.
General Information: Species was discovered by French physician Philibert Commerson in 1787 as he circumnavigated the globe with Louis Bougainville. A few animals rode the bow wave of his ship in the Magellan Strait, off Tierra del Fuego. Because of their black-and-white colouration he named the species "Le Jacobin" (Jacobean). First description in 1804 by French naturalist Lacépède based on Commerson's notes. Population status unknown. Regionally quite common, elsewhere severely endangered. Population (subspecies?) found off Kerguelen Island (S-Indic).
Where & When: Cold and temperate coastal waters of the Southern Hemisphere. Prefers tidal zones, harbours, natural preserves and beds of seaweed. Atlantic: Golfo San Mathias (Argentina) to Tierra del Fuego, Magellan Strait, Falkland Islands. Also frequents deep fjords, bays and rivers.

Black Dolphin, *Cephalorhynchus eutropia*

Pieter Arend Folkens

Distinguishing Characteristics: Back and flanks dark-grey to black. Very large and rounded dorsal fin. White belly and throat, white "armpit" under flippers. Pale-grey "cap" over the melon.

Description: One of the least known and smallest species of cetacean. First accurate description by Natalie Goodall (1970s). Length 1.2-1.7 m, weight 40-60 kg. Females smaller than males. Lower jaw extends farther than upper jaw. Black banded flippers, fluke and dorsal fin dark-grey to black.

Easily Mistaken For: Spectacled Porpoise (throughout entire range), but this species has spectacle-like black rings around the eyes and white flippers. Black Porpoises (southern range), but this species is almost uniformly dark-grey to black with pale ventral patch. Both species are larger, lack an "armpit" patch and have a differently shaped fluke.

Other Names: Chilean Dolphin, White-Bellied Dolphin (English); Weißbauch-, Flachkopf-, Chile-Delphin (German); Dauphin Noir, Dauphin du Chili (French); Cefalorinco Nero (Italian); Delphin Chileno (Spanish); Toninha Oveira Negra (Portuguese); Witbuikdolfijn (Dutch); Chiledelphin (Norwegian); Chilendelfiini (Finnish); Vitbukig Delphin (Swedish); Chilensk Delphin (Danish).

Meaning of the Scientific Nomenclature: *Cephalorhynchus eutropia* (Gray 1846) - Generic name see *C. commersonii; eutropia* made up of Greek *eu* (beautiful) and *tropidos* (keel), head form.

Behaviour: Hardly known. Very few sightings, usually stranded animals. Apparently likes to surf in the surge, rarely breaches. Population in southern range very shy, only local fishermen have seen living specimens; those in northern range are more approachable, occasionally ride bow wave. Group size in south 2-8, rarely up to 50 animals; in the north up to 400, max 4,000 (unconfirmed estimate). Often in association with large flocks of seabirds. Seasonal migrations not known.

Feeding Habits: Fish, cephalopods, shrimp (stomach contents of stranded animals).

General Information: First described as *Delphinus eutropia* by Gray in 1846. Dall classified it as *Cephalorhynchus* in 1874. Recently deceased animals turn dark very quickly, which may have led to false identifications. Still illegally hunted in Chile and used for crab-bait, which means the species may be threatened. Hunted earlier by the Indians of Tierra del Fuego.

Where & When: South America: In shallow coastal waters, fjords, bays, estuaries and regions with strong tidal currents off the coast of Chile between 33°-55° S (Valparaiso to Tierra del Fuego), as well as in Magellan Strait. Common at Playa Frailes (Gulf of Arauco) and Chiloe Island.

Heaviside's Dolphin, *Cephalorhynchus heavisidii*

Distinguishing characteristics: Small, conspicuous colouration.

Description: Length 1.6-1.7 m, weight 40-80 kg. Colouration only known since 1969 as a result of three South Africa. Rod Haestier

accidental captures and a find of recently stranded animals before they turned dark. Flippers small, dark, with rounded tips and bent slightly backwards. Leading edge of flippers usually serrated. Dorsal fin small, dark, triangular. Rear half of body and fluke blue-black; front half of body grey. Three dark oval spots around the eyes and blowhole. A finger-shaped patch extends from the white belly along the flanks down to the fluke. Three white, teardrop-shaped patches extend from the belly towards the tail and down to the venting area in case of females and somewhat further in case of males. Rhombus-shaped, white ventral patch is separated from the white belly by a grey band running between the flippers. White "armpits."

Other Names: South African Dolphin, Benguela Dolphin (English); Heaviside-Delphin (German); Dauphin du Cap (French); Cefalorinco de Heaviside (Italian); Delphin de Heaviside (Spanish); Golfinho de Heaviside, Toninha Oveira (Portuguese); Heaviside-dolfijn (Dutch); Heavisidedelphin (Norwegian); Heavisidendelfiini (Finn.); Heavisides Delphin (Swed.); Sydafrikansk Delphin (Danish).

Meaning of the Scientific Nomenclature: *Cephalorhynchus heavisidii* Gray 1828 - Generic name see *C. commersonii; heavisidii* in honour of Captain Haviside (not Heaviside, see below).

Behaviour: Hardly known since species is scarce and inaccessible. Usually appears in pairs, smaller groups, rarely up to 20 animals. Shy, does not breach often (up to 2 m high), executes fast forward somersaults that terminate in lob-tailing, occasional porpoising.

Feeding Habits: Squid, pelagic and benthic fish (stomach contents of stranded animals).

General Information: Little is known about this species to date. Scientific name is based on an error: It was assumed that the first specimen (see above) stemmed from the anatomical collection belonging to fleet physician Heaviside, which had just been auctioned off in 1827. As it turned out later, however, the skull used for the first description stemmed from Captain Haviside, an employee of the British East Indian Company, who brought the skull and skin of a specimen back to England after a sea voyage in 1827. During the accidental capture in 1969 (see above) voicing was also recorded: Only clicks, no dolphin-like whistling. Population presumably very small. Occasionally caught in nets and traps of South African and Namibian fishermen.

Where & When: Only occurs along the West African coastline from Cape of Good Hope (South Africa) to Cape Cross (Namibia), perhaps as far as Angola. Few sightings within 10 km of the coast, max depth 150 m. Range is probably dependent upon the cold Benguela Current.

Hector's Dolphin, *Cephalorhynchus hectori*

Distinguishing Characteristics: Large, round, blue-grey spot with dark border on forehead. Dorsal fin dark-grey to black, very large and markedly rounded ("Mickey Mouse Dolphin").

Description: One of the smallest species of dolphin, length 1.2-1.67 m, weight 35-60 kg. Flippers large, dark, very rounded tips. Fluke dark-grey. Tip of snout black. Elongated black patch running from the eye to the tip of flipper. White, finger-shaped lobe extends from the belly across the flanks to the fluke. Sexual dimorphism: Males are smaller than females and have a large dark-grey patch in the genital region. Both have a white, teardrop-shaped patch extending from the belly over the venting region down to the tail. White belly separated Kaikoura, New Zealand. Ingrid Visser/Seapics.com

from white throat by a grey band running between the flippers. Small white "armpit." Back and flanks dark-grey. Calves paler.

Easily Mistaken For: Species unmistakable within its area of distribution due to spot on forehead and rounded dorsal fin.

Other Names: Little Pied Dolphin, New Zealand Dolphin, White-Front Dolphin (English); Hector-Delphin (German); Dauphin d'Hector (French); Cefalorinco di Hector (Italian); Delphin de Hector (Spanish); Golfinho da Nova Zelândia (Portuguese); Hector-dolfijn (Dutch); Hektordelphin (Norwegian); Hectorindelfiini (Finnish); Hectors Delphin (Swedish); Hectors Delphin (Danish).

Meaning of the Scientific Nomenclature: *Cephalorhynchus hectori* (van Beneden 1881) - Generic name see *C. commersonii; hectori* in honour of New Zealander zoologist Sir James Hector, who collected the first specimen in 1869 (see below).

Behaviour: Best known species of genus. Very curious, highly active on surface (breaching, lob-tailing, spy-hopping), likes to surf in surge and ride the bow wave of slower vessels. Group size usually 2-8, only rarely up to 100+. Rest motionless and parallel to each other on the surface.

Diving: Poor diver. Dive time usually 1-2 min, if longer than 1 min then it needs the same amount of time to recuperate on surface. Occasionally several animals will sound simultaneously.

Feeding Habits: Shoaling fish (tuna, cod), stargazers (benthic fish), squid.

General Information: First specimen erroneously described in 1869 as *Electra clancula*. Worldwide one of the rarest species of dolphin. Population not endangered, but many accidental deaths in fishing net. Between 1984-1988 almost 30% of the estimated 750 members of the "Banks Population" (Banks Peninsula, New Zealand) were killed in this fashion. Region was declared a protected area thereafter. Pesticides pose another threat to coastal populations. Often in oceanariums.

Where & When: Coastal waters of New Zealand (depth of 300 m). Regionally quite common, entirely lacking elsewhere. Inshore during summer (within 1 km). Frequents rocky shores, shallow bays, murky estuaries and penetrates rivers. Rarely on high seas. Appears frequently in Cloudy Bay

and between Kawhia and Manukau harbours. Whale watching tours available as of Kaikoura (North Island), a famous harbour for such activities.

New Zealand. Todd Pusser

Risso's Dolphin, *Grampus griseus*

Distinguishing Characteristics: Grey, older animals almost white due to numerous long scars (see below). Head blunt with no beak (appears "chopped off" in profile). Dorsal fin dark, slightly rounded and up to 50 cm high.

Description: Length 2.5-4 m, weight up to 650 kg. Mouth slants upwards. Flippers long, narrow, crescent-shaped, with pointed ends. Tips of fluke arrow-shaped and curved backwards. Only species in the family without teeth in upper jaw, only has 4-14 teeth in front of lower jaw, older animals often toothless (typical squid feeder). Colouration varies with age and gender. Dark-grey to grey-black, ventrally paler. Scratches and scars more numerous as animal ages, thereby turning almost-white. Only dorsal fin, fluke and flippers remain dark. White, anchor-shaped patch on thorax. Males more scarred than females. Scars inflicted by teeth of rivals (intraspecies aggression), as well as the beaks of cephalopods. Patterns of scars used to identify individuals. Newborn calves are dark-grey, no scars.

Easily Mistaken For: Belugas are similar, but lack a high dorsal fin and have a different area of distribution. Bottlenose Dolphins have a demarcated snout and no scars.

Other Names: Grey Dolphin, White-Head Dolphin, Grey Grampus (English); Risso-Delphin, Rundkopfdelphin (German); Dauphin de Risso, Grampus (French); Golfinho de Risso (Portuguese); Grijze Dolfijn, Gramper (Dutch); Rissodelphin (Norwegian); Rissondelfiini (Finnish); Rissos Delphin (Swedish); Rissos-delphin, Halvgrindehval (Danish); Hana Gondo Kujira (Japanese); Delfín de Risso (Latin American Spanish).

Azores, Atlantic Ocean.   Doug Perrine/Seapics.com

Meaning of the Scientific Nomenclature: *Grampus griseus* (G. Cuvier 1812) - Latin *grampus* (large) and *griseus* (grey), meaning "Large Grey One." Also based on old French *graspeis,* which stems from Latin *piscis* = "large fish."

Behaviour: Some specimens are shy, others readily follow vessels. Not infrequently solitary, but also quite gregarious. Group size 20-50, sometimes a few hundred. Long, flat leaps when swimming fast. Occasional lob-tailing, flipper-slapping, spy-hopping, bow-riding. Rests motionless and side-by-side on surface. Associates with other dolphins and Pilot Whales. Often involved in mass stranding. Prefers deep waters, also found along steep coastlines.

Diving: Usually stays under 2-3 min, but can remain at greater depths for up to 30 min.

Feeding Habits: Diverse cephalopods, very rarely also fish.

General Information: First described as *Delphinus griseus* in 1812 by French anatomist Baron George Cuvier, who based his observations on a specimen that was found in the vicinity of Brest (France). Skeleton still housed in Natural History Museum of Paris. Classified under *Grampus* (Gray 1828) by Hamilton in 1837. The Italian amateur naturalist discovered a stranded specimen near Nice in 1811 (hence Risso's Dolphin), and sent drawings to Cuvier. Still hunted in South America, Sri Lanka, Indonesia, Japan and Philippines, but population not considered endangered.

Where & When: Cosmopolitan species found in all tropical to temperate oceans as well as in the Mediterranean, Red Sea, North Sea, Baltic Sea. Atlantic: Northern limits of distribution in

Newfoundland and the British Isles, southern limits Tierra del Fuego to South Africa. Pacific: Kurile Islands in the north, Australia, New Zealand in the south. Indic: South Africa to Australia. Sinai, Red Sea.

Helmut Debelius

257

A RUN-IN WITH HONEY

On numerous occasions solitary toothed whales - especially Bottlenose Dolphins - became close friends of humans. This has happened in locations on the coasts of almost all the world's oceans. The animals then stayed in a specific region for a long time where one can regularly see them. Often they have become well-known attractions, too. The author had a run-in with one of these seemingly friendly creatures along the Lighthouse Reef on the Caribbean coast of the Central American country of Belize.

PHOTOS: RALF KIEFNER

The female dolphin Honey seeks the close company of humans...

Our chartered sailing yacht anchors in the turquoise lagoon before Lighthouse Reef. The water here seems clearer and bluer than anywhere else in the Caribbean. Its beautiful hue and crystall-clearness motivates me and my female companion to go snorkelling. The water here is a good 10 metres deep and thus we have a wonderful panoramic view of the corals on the bottom.

Our snorkel tour takes us past a small buoy or fender which is used to tie down the boats at night. My snorkel partner and I decide to take a brief rest here and grab on to the line holding the buoy.

But it appears as if someone has already staked out a claim on our chosen place of rest - its is private property, so to say. We are startled by a loud splash close by, followed by a barrage of bubbles. Once the bubbly obstruction has faded I manage to make out who is responsible for all this commotion. A dolphin!

The perpetrator is Honey, a female dolphin that has been living in the vicinity of Lighthouse Reef for several years. Although she has never been trained or regularly fed, she still chose to reside here of her own free will. Honey frequently accompanies her old friend Pete, the lighthouse guard from neighbouring Sandbourne Caye, when he goes fishing along the offshore reef. Sometimes she also joins up with a school of roving dolphins, only to return to her favourite lagoon before Northern Caye a few days later.

We try to get her attention by pushing the buoy around. Honey takes hold of the line a couple of times and tugs the buoy under water. At the same time, she bares her conical teeth at us. Suddenly, without warning, Honey rams my companion in the chest with her blunt nose. This is the way dolphins normally attack aggressors or potential enemies, such as sharks, either to kill or drive them away. Our game has obviously become a serious matter. Honey makes it perfectly clear to us that this is her very own buoy and we are not to touch it. Obligingly, we give up the idea of resting on the buoy.

We decide to abandon the buoy altogether and continue snorkelling as if nothing had happened.

...and impatiently waits for her "playmates".

Honey appears to understand that we have gotten her message. At first she circles us a few times to look us over and then evidently makes up her mind to play with us. Again and again she swims alongside us or darts from one to the other. Of course, we hardly stand a chance in this one-sided game of catch. She seems to acknowledge our awkward attempts with a wry face.

I could spend hours romping with Honey in the water. Obviously we are welcome as playmates, just as long as we leave her buoy alone. It is only with a great deal of cunning and several mistrials that we finally manage to get out of the water again. Or was it that Honey finally took pity on us? Every time we wanted to end the play session and back climb on board, she would purposely block our way

This buoy is Honey's "private property" and nobody else is allowed to play with it.

Honey shows great patience while "modelling" for the photographer.

to the ladder. On the long run we had head for the nearby beach, where the water was too shallow for her to follow, before we managed to get some well-earned rest.

We spend the greater part of that day in the water with Honey. After sunset she continues to circle our boat as if she still had not seen enough of us. A couple of divers told us later that she had the bad habit of pinching their chemical lights during night dives.

Recently I received the news that, after so many years of living alone, Honey decided to join up with a wandering school of dolphins again.

Worldwide List of Docile Dolphins

Name	Geographical Location
Bottlenose Dolphins:	
Percy	Cornwall, southwestern England
Donald & Beaky	Isle of Man, southwestern England
Nina	La Coruna, Spain
Simo	Solva, Wales
Fungi	Dingle, east coast of Ireland
Jean-Louis	Bretagne, France
Charlie	Eastern shore of England to Northumberland, Scotland
Yoka	Kotor, south of Dubrovnik, Croatia
Honey	Belize (Caribbean)
Freddy	Near Amble, east coast of England
Moses	Southern Spain
Opo	Opononi, New Zealand
Dolly	Key West, Florida
Carolina & Snowball	South Carolina to Georgia, east coast USA
Nudgy	Philip's Inlet, Florida
Georgy Girl	Florida, USA
Horace	New Zealand
Dobbie	Eilat, Israel (Red Sea)
Other species:	
Tammy (Black Dolphin)	Tamaki, New Zealand
Sandy (Spinner Delphin)	San Salvador, Bahamas
Pelorus Jack (Risso's Dolphin)	Cook Strait, New Zealand
Old Tom (Killer Whale)	Twofold Bay, eastern Australia

The **Family Porpoises** encompasses 6 species:
  Spectacled Porpoise, *Australophocaena dioptrica*
  Finless Porpoise, *Neophocaena phocaenoides*
  Harbour Porpoise, *Phocoena phocoena*
  Vaquita, *Phocoena sinus*
  Burmeister's Porpoise, *Phocoena spinipinnis*
  Dall's Porpoise, *Phocoenoides dalli*

Distinguishing Characteristics of this Family
Max length 2.2 m. Poorly defined snout. Teeth spatula-shaped (not conical like dolphins), cross-section oval. Well developed dorsal fin (except Finless Porpoise). Small, swift swimmer. Very shy, sightings rare, behaviour little known. Only Dall's Porpoise and Finless Porpoise will not sound as soon as they are approached. Distribution of species hardly overlaps, therefore easily identifiable. High concentration of toxic materials in tissues of all (inshore) species. Alarming decrease in population.

Spectacled Porpoise, *Australophocaena dioptrica*

Pieter Arend Folkens

Distinguishing Characteristics: One of the largest porpoises, conspicuously coloured (see below). Found in extremely remote southern regions.
Description: Length 1.3-2.2 m, weight 60-85 kg. Sexual dimorphism: Females max 2 m, males 2.2 m. Dorsal fin of male very large, rounded, almost oval; that of female smaller, almost triangular. Back is black, in marked contrast to white flanks and ventral side. Flippers white, dorsal fin black, fluke black on upper side and white on lower side. Black ring around the eye bordered by a white spectacle-like line (hence name). Thin, black "lips" on white background. One to two thin, dark lines running from the corner of the mouth over the leading edge of the flipper to tip of tail.
Easily Mistaken For: Burmeister's Porpoise is similar and distribution overlaps along the coastline from Uruguay to Argentina. Flippers and belly of this species not white, however.
Other Names: Brillenschweinswal (German); Marsouin à Lunettes (French); Focena dagli Occhiali (Italian); Marsopa de Anteojos (Spanish); Boto de Lunetas (Portuguese); Brilbruinvis (Dutch); Brillenise (Norweg.); Silmälasipyöriäinen (Finn.); Glasögontumlare (Swed.); Brillemarsvin (Danish).
Meaning of the Scientific Nomenclature: *Australophocaena dioptrica* (Lahille 1912) - Greek *phokaino* (porpoise), Latin *australis* (southern); Greek *dioptra* (spectacles), refers to eye ring.
Behaviour: Most descriptions stem from stranded animals. Sightings are few and far between. According to Natalie Goodall's observations in Tierra del Fuego the species is shy, a very swift swimmer and avoids vessels. Its white flanks are clearly visible just beneath the surface. Singly, in pairs or small groups. Breaching has never been observed. Analyses of stomach contents indicate that the species also ranges offshore. Population status, intermixture and migrations are unknown.
Feeding Habits: Preys primarily on fish and squid (stomach contents of stranded animals).
General Information: First find (a stranded specimen) made in the Rio de La Plata near Punta Colores (Argentina) in 1912. First described as *Phocaena dioptrica* by Argentinian zoologist Fernando Lahille (Buenos Aires) that same year. Barnes placed it in *Australophocaena* in 1985. Considered extinct until additional discoveries were made in the mid-1970s (ten specimens). Natalie Goodall examined 112 stranded animals. Population status unknown.
Where & When: S-Atlantic: Coast of South America from Uruguay to Tierra del Fuego and Falkland Islands, perhaps also circumpolar in the Antarctic. Strandings/Sightings: South Georgia, Kerguelen Island, Macquarie Island, McDonald Island, S-Tasmania, Auckland Island, Campbell Island.

Finless Porpoise, *Neophocaena phocaenoides*

Distinguishing Characteristics: Only porpoise without a dorsal fin, body pale-grey to white. **Description:** Length 1.2-1.8 m, weight 30-50 kg. Females smaller. Flexible neck. No dorsal fin, low dorsal ridge with tubercles. Back teeth wider than front teeth. Dead animals quickly turn black. Eyes often bright pink. **Easily Mistaken For:** Belugas, but different

Pieter Arend Folkens

areas of distribution. Irrawaddy Porpoises, but species has dorsal fin. River Dolphins have a long snout. **Other Names:** Black Finless Porpoise, Jiangzhu (English); Indischer Schweinswal, Glatt-Tümmler (German); Marsouin de Aptère, Marsouin de Cuvier (French); Neofocena (Italian); Marsopa Lisa, Marsopa sin Aleta (Spanish); Boto do Indico (Portuguese); Indische Bruinvis (Dutch); Indianise (Norwegian); Rosopyöriäinen (Finnish); Indisk Tumlare (Swedish); Finneløst Marsvin (Danish); Sunameri (Japanese); Haichu (Chinese); Bhulga (Hindi); Tabi (Urdu).
Meaning of the Scientific Nomenclature: *Neophocaena phocaenoides* (G. Cuvier 1829) - *Phocaena* see *A. dioptrica*. Greek *neos* (new), *oides* (similar), meaning "similar to a porpoise."
Behaviour: Group size 1-10, max 50 animals. Very active, seldom breaches, shy. Swiss biologist Pilleri observed that species often associates with Indo-Pacific Hump-Backed Dolphin in Chinese rivers. Seasonal migrations depend upon availability of food and water temperatures. Tubercles on dorsal ridge enable calves to ride their mothers' backs during first months of their lives. **Diving:** Dive time 1-2 min, during which animals can cover a great distance. **Feeding Habits:** Squid, shrimp, small fish. **General Information:** First described as *Delphinus phocanoides* in 1829 by George Cuvier. Theodor Palmer (USA) placed it in *Neophocaena* in 1899. Might be 2 distinct species (Pilleri & Gihr, 1971). Three subspecies: 1. Yang Tse, China; 2. Coast of Japan, Korea; 3. Rest of Asia. Still hunted in Pakistan, India and China. Protected in China since 1980. **Where & When:** Coastal waters, estuaries of the Indo-Pacific from Kuwait (Gulf of Oman) over Southeast Asia to Japan. In the south: Sunda Islands to New Guinea and North Australia. Never sighted farther than 5 km from shore. Also found in warm rivers, lakes and mangrove swamps.

Harbour Porpoise, *Phocoena phocoena*

North Sea.   Florian Graner

Distinguishing Characteristics: Unmistakable, smallest cetacean within its area of distribution. Dorsal fin small and triangular, snout short. **Description:** Length 1.3-1.8 m, max 2 m; weight 25-90 kg, max 100+ kg. Black Sea populations smaller than those in the Baltic Sea. Females up to 20 cm smaller. Leading edge of flippers with tubercles. Back dark-grey to black, underside white. Colours merge in front half of body, demarcated in back half. Lower jaw white with dark "lip," upper jaw black. One to three dark stripes running from corner of mouth to base of tail. Flanks vary individually, asymmetrically coloured. Flippers always black. Albinism rare. **Other Names:** Common Porpoise, Puffing Pig (English); Gewöhnlicher Schweinswal, Kleiner Tümmler (German); Marsouin,

Marsuin Commun (French); Focene Comune (Italian); Marsopa Comun (Spanish); Boto (Portuguese); Gewone Bruinvis (Dutch); Nise (Norweg.); Pyöriäinen (Finnish); Vanlig Tumlare (Swedish); Almindeligt Marsvin (Danish); Nezumi Iruka (Japanese); Morskaya Svin'ya (Russian). **Meaning of the Scientific Nomenclature:** *Phocoena phocoena* (Linnaeus 1758) - See *A. dioptrica.* **Behaviour:** Most thoroughly studied species in family. Lives singly, in pairs, occasionally groups of 5, max 100+ animals. Young males live in "rowdy groups," mature males in

Sognefjord, Norway.   Florian Graner "singles groups," females
with offspring in "nursery

groups" in shallow waters. Bond between mother and its calf very strong, solicitous behaviour, vocalisation of stress sounds when separated. Intraspecies conflicts involve lob-tailing, head-nodding, open beak, short clicking sounds. Mating behaviour: Males chase females, mutual "caressing," "love bites" on dorsal fin. Copulation vertically on the surface, takes only a few seconds. From May-June the testicles swell from 400 g to nearly 2,000 g. Very active, swift swimmer (22+ km/h). Breaching, porpoising (rarely high). No bow-riding. Blow seldom visible, but can be heard quite well. Animals rest parallel to each other on surface for 1-2 min. Very shy. Clicks range around 2 and 110-150 kHz (communication, orientation). Auditory range 1-150 kHz, double that of Killer Whales, which are unable to register all high-frequency vocalisations of porpoises. Seasonal migrations to and from the coast in pursuit of prey. Some populations resident. **Diving:** Dive time 2-6 min, dive depth to 100 m. **Feeding Habits:** Shoaling fish (cod, herring, sardines, mackerel) as well as benthic sole, squid, shrimps, worms, snails. Calves are nursed 8-9 months. At 5 months they are fed small fish, at 7 months their teeth are fully developed. **General Information:** Designated as *porcus piscus* (pig-fish) in ancient Rome. First scientific designation, *Delphinus phocoena,* by Linnaeus in 1758. Cuvier placed it in *Phocoena* in 1817. Three subspecies under proposal: North Atlantic, *P. p. phocoena;* Northern Pacific, *P. p. vomerina;* Black Sea, *P. p. relicta* (smallest subspecies, does not occur in Mediterranean). Because of its inshore habitat and increasing industrialisation of coastal regions the population status of this numerous and widely distributed species has been diminishing markedly in recent years. More and more animals are being caught in fishing nets and killed, and the fishing industry is quickly depleting its food sources. Examinations of specimens from Fundy Bay (East Canada) showed high concentrations of PCB and DDT in the blubber, as well as high doses of heavy metals like lead, cadmium and quicksilver in the muscles, liver and other organs. The percentage of Harbour Porpoises involved in stranding is quite high for an inshore animal. The actual population status of the species is unknown, but considered threatened due to increasing pollution of the seas. Estimates vary considerably, e.g. the European population is estimated at 20,000-95,000 animals. **Where & When:** Exclusively inshore, in temperate to cold, ice-free subarctic waters of the Northern Hemisphere. Rarely roams farther than 10 km from shore or in waters deeper than 200 m. Often encountered in shallow bays, estuaries, tidal channels and sometimes also far upriver or deep into fjords (see photograph). In the eastern part of the Northern Pacific the species ranges from the coast of Los Angeles (California) to where the McKenzie River empties into the Beaufort Sea. In the western regions of the Northwestern Pacific its distribution extends from the Yellow Sea to the Chukchi Sea. In the eastern regions of the North Atlantic the species occurs from the coastal waters of West Africa to Iceland; in the western part of the North Atlantic its is found from Cape Cod to Davis Strait and the southern tip of Greenland, occasionally also as far as Thule (North Greenland). Occasionally sighted off the Azores, Madeira, Cape Verde Islands, Canaries. Also lives in the North Sea, Baltic Sea (endangered), Mediterranean and Black Sea (see above). In the Mediterranean it can be encountered along the coasts of Morocco, Algeria, Tunis and Spain.

Vaquita, *Phocoena sinus*

Distinguishing Characteristics: Unmistakable, distribution limited. Only species in family to live exclusively in the northern end of the Sea of Cortez (Mexico). Small size and shy behaviour further ease identification. **Description:** Length 1.2-1.5 m, weight 30-50 kg. One of the smallest cetaceans. Head is more rounded than that of other species in family, but it also has a poorly defined snout.

Pieter Arend Folkens

Females larger than males. Dorsal fin slightly falcate, very large in comparison to other porpoises, and almost shark-like in form. Leading edge with tubercles in case of adult animals, recognisable as white dots in case of young animals. Flippers short, wide. Belly grey-white; back, dorsal fin, fluke and flippers pale-grey to dark-grey. Conspicuous dark "lips," dark eye ring. Two pale-grey stripes running from chin to flippers. Young animals similar, only darker.

Other Names: Gulf of California Porpoise, Cochito (English); Kalifornischer Schweinswal, Golftümmler (German); Marsouin de Californie, Cochito, Marsouin du Golfe de Californie (French); Focene del Golfo della California (Italian); Vaquita (Spanish); Boto do Pacífico (Portuguese); Californische Bruinvis (Dutch); Kalifornianise (Norwegian); Kalifornianpyöriäinen (Finnish); Kalifornisk Tumlare (Swedish); Golfmarsvin (Danish); Cochita (Latin American Spanish).

Meaning of the Scientific Nomenclature: *Phocoena sinus* Norris & McFarland 1958 - Generic name see *A. dioptrica*. Latin *sinus* (bay) refers to distribution. **Behaviour:** Small groups of no more than 4 animals. In contrast to other porpoises, calm and slow swimmer, hardly visible on surface. Like its relatives, species is shy, avoids vessels. Behaviour little known. Breaching unobserved so far. **Diving:** Blow hardly visible, but clearly audible (snorting). Forward roll when sounding. Short surface interval to breathe, usually dives again immediately. **Feeding Habits:** Small fish (e.g. redfish), squid. **General Information:** In 1950 scientist Ken Norris discovered the skull of a new species of porpoise in the northern part of the Sea of Cortez. After several additional skulls were found, the species was first described by Norris and William McFarland in 1958. Population (estimated at a few hundred individuals) has a very small area of distribution (protected as of 1993). Due to damming projects on the Rio Colorado, heavy pesticide contamination and accidental deaths in fishing nets (up to 30 animals annually) it is presumably the most threatened species of cetacean. **Where & When:** This species has the smallest area of distribution (with a radius of only 50 km) of all cetaceans. Today it is only found in the northern end of the Sea of Cortez and the estuary of the Rio Colorado, but it probably ranged farther down the Mexican coastline just a few decades ago. The species prefers shallow waters which are not deeper than 30 m. Occasionally it is also found in shallow, murky lagoons along the coast that are susceptible to strong tidal action. At low tide the animals sometimes find themselves stranded in small tidal ponds until the high tide comes in again. Then their backs will be visible on the surface and are exposed to the burning sun.

Burmeister's Porpoise, *Phocoena spinipinnis*

Distinguishing Characteristics: Unmistakable, the smallest species of cetacean within its area of distribution. Other than a grey patch on the belly, the species is dark-grey to black with a paler underside. Dorsal fin is small, triangular and slightly bent backwards. Leading edge with 2-4 rows of small tubercles. Extremely swift swimmer. **Description:** Length 1.4-1.8 m, weight 40-70 kg. Flippers

This specimen died in a fishing net. Peru.   Robert Pitman/Seapics.com

large, wide. Dorsal fin set farther down the back than among other members of family. Leading edge straight, trailing edge sickle-shaped. Animals found in Atlantic coast of South America larger than those in the Pacific. **Other Names:** Black Porpoise (English); Burmeister-Schweinswal (German); Marsouin de Burmeister (French); Focena di Burmeister (Italian); Marsopa Espinosa (Spanish); Boto de Burmeister (Portuguese); Bruinvis van Burmeister (Dutch); Svartnise (Norwegian); Burmeisterinpyöriäinen (Finnish); Burmeisters Tumlare (Swedish); Pigfinnemarsvin (Danish); Marsopa Espinosa (Latin American Spanish). **Meaning of the Scientific Nomenclature:** *Phocoena spinipinnis* Burmeister 1865 - Generic name see *A. dioptrica*. Latin *spina* (spine), *pinna* (feather, flipper), or "spiny finned" (tubercles on dorsal fin). **Behaviour:** Hardly known as species is extremely shy. Presumably most common small cetacean in South American waters. Group size 2-5, rarely up to 8 animals. Seldom breaches. **Diving:** Unknown. **Feeding Habits:** Preys on small shoaling fish (anchovies), squid, shrimp. **General Information:** As director of the Museo Argentino de Ciencias Naturales in Buenos Aires, German scientist Karl Conrad Burmeister established a large whale research centre around 1860. First description of species in 1865, based on a specimen that local fishermen caught live at the mouth of the Rio de La Plata. The tubercles might possibly afford calves a better hold when they "ride" on their mothers' backs. Peruvian and Chilean fishermen occasionally sell the meat of this species in the local markets. **Where & When:** In shallow, cold, temperate to subpolar coastal waters and estuaries of South America. Their range extends from Peru in the Pacific to Southern Brazil in the Atlantic, including Falkland Islands. It appears that the species is more numerous in the Pacific than in the Atlantic.

Dall's Porpoise, *Phocoenoides dalli*

Distinguishing Characteristics: Unusual behaviour: Very active, bow rides, produces "rooster tail" (see below) when swimming fast. **Description:** Length 2 m, weight 220+ kg. Females smallest. Tireless swimmer. Black-and-white body with variable ventral patch (harlequin pattern). Uniformly white or black animals are rare. Flippers small, conspicuously near the head. Dorsal fin triangular, upright, dark at the base, grey or white on top. Fluke small,

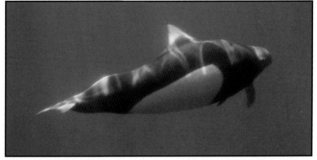

In the Northern Pacific.   Robert Pitman/Seapics.com

back edge convex, upper side dark, back edge and tips bordered by band of white. **Easily Mistaken For:** Often in association with Atlantic White-Sided Dolphins, which also produce a "rooster tail," but breach often. Colouration and dorsal fin different. **Other Names:** True's Porpoise, Spray Porpoise, White-Flanked Porpoise (English); Dall-Schweinswal (German); Marsouin de Dall (French); Focenoide (Italian); Marsopa de Dall (Spanish); Marsopa de Porto Dall (Portuguese); Dall-bruinvis (Dutch); Stillehavsnise (Norwegian); Dallinpyöriäinen (Finnish); Stillahavstumlare (Swedish); Hvidsidemarsvin (Danish); Delfín de Dall (Latin American Spanish). **Meaning of the Scientific Nomenclature:** *Phocoenoides dalli* (True 1885) - *Phocoena* see *A. dioptrica*; *oides* based on Greek *eides* (similar to). Species name in honour of American zoologist William Healey Dall, who discovered the first specimen as member of the Humboldt Expedition to Alaska. **Behaviour:** Group size 10 to several hundred animals. Max speed of 65 km/h just beneath the surface. Its head and back produce a bow wave, or "rooster tail," when swimming fast. Preyed on by Killer Whales and sharks. **Diving:** Down to 200 m when hunting. **Feeding Habits:** Shoaling fish (capelin, mackerel, herring, anchovies, lanternfish), shrimp, squid. **General Information:** First described by Frederick True (American Museum of Natural History) in 1885. First find made in Japan by Roy Chapman in 1909. Andrews later classified it under *Phocoenoides*. Two subspecies: *P. d. dalli,* also found offshore, white patch begins behind flippers; larger and slimmer *P. d. truei* only inshore, white patch larger, begins in front of flippers. Population status unknown, estimated at 900,000-2,000,000 animals. Several thousand are accidentally caught by Japanese fisheries and consumed. **Where & When:** Cold and cold-temperate waters (3°-20° C). Northern Pacific: *P. d. dalli* found in Sea of Okhotsk, Bering Sea to Southern Japan and Baja California; *P. d. truei* in coastal waters of Northern Japan, Kurile Islands. Depending upon water temperatures, it undertakes short, seasonal north-south migrations, also to and from the coast.

THROUGH DONALD'S BLACK & WHITE LENS

Donald Tipton lives in the moment. He believes that everything will work itself out. Some would call him naive but Donald sees the world in a different light and he hears hidden notes in the blaring music. This is a man who combines his fervent belief in the divine word of scripture with his understanding of the scientific proof of natural selection and who will explain to you at great length why these two beliefs are not incongruent. His friend Joe Cocozza writes about him.

There is an impressive backstory to this man who takes underwater photographs. His roots are in the southern United States. Donald's first passion was and is classical music. Donald majored in music and fine arts at the University of Georgia. But as the fates often circumvent mortal plans, Donald did not become a concert pianist but became fascinated in the world of photography. Just as the cord structure of a Beethoven Sonata can paint a picture, in the same way, the tonal shading of a photograph can sing a song. Donald has the ability to make music with light.

He is a firm believer in contrast. To quote him: "This life we lead is a journey between the sacred and the profane". This contrast he brings together with light and shadow. The ocean realm tends to reduce the contrast range but this makes the subtly of greyscale even more important. As both in music and photography it's Donald subtle use of tone that expresses his vision and incarnates his reality.

In 1986 Donald discovered scuba diving. The sport of scuba diving completed his personal trinity, music - light - the sea. He immersed himself into diving and within two years was a scuba instructor and cave diver. With his passion for the sea and its creatures, underwater photography was a natural progression for Donald. Very quickly his star soon rose in the constellation of renown underwater photographers.

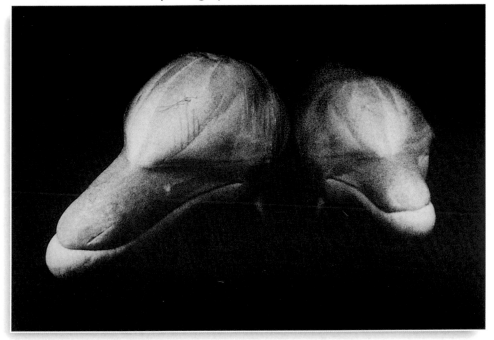

Today, with the explosive growth of the sport of scuba diving and the advent of cheap underwater cameras, the standard of great underwater photography is no longer defined by technology. It is talent that is the determining factor in the artistic merit of an underwater photograph. What makes Donald's photographs special, is the range of his experience, his beliefs and the passions that he brings to his photographic canvas.

Sometime he finds it appropriate to express his vision through boisterous and discordant colours but most of the time Donald takes a retro approach, expressing his vision through the soft and subdued tones of black and white photography. Using this simplicity of approach, he expresses his unique vision of marine mammals in images that evoke moods and feelings that I struggle to describe in prose and verse.

I have been with Donald when he shot these photos and I still find it hard to describe them in words. His images are like that awaking time, just before dawn when some issue has been resolved in your dreams. In that brief moment before consciousness, there is an understanding of the universe. The understanding is fleeting as the mind passes into the modern world and the filters of experience diffuses understanding. As such, Donald Tipton's photos have passed between these worlds, and have captured the twilight quality of the ocean realm.

Distinguishing Characteristics of this Family

The least known cetacean family (taxonomy still in process), with approximately 20 species, some of which are known on the basis of skeletal finds, others (undescribed) only through sightings. Spindle-shaped, length 4-12.8 m. Snout (beak) long and narrow. Lower jaw extends further than upper jaw. Two separate, V-shaped throat grooves. Fluke usually lacks median notch. Dorsal fin, if at all present, is set far down the back. Cervical vertebrae are joined. Head asymmetrical, except for *Berardius* spp. Form and position of teeth vary with each species, usually only well developed in case of males. Two *(Mesoplodon, Ziphius, Hyperoodon)* or four *(Berardius)* teeth erupt in lower jaw, upper jaw toothless (typical for squid feeders). But both sexes of *Mesoplodon grayi* and *Tasmacetus shepherdi* have rows of small teeth. Some *Mesoplodon* spp. have "pockets" into which the flippers can be retracted in order to enhance streamline flow. Round scars on many animals are caused by cookiecutter shark bites or parasites. Bulls frequently have paired scars (same pattern as front teeth) as a result of altercations with rivals. Colour varies individually, not helpful for identification.

Northern Bottlenose Whale, *Hyperoodon ampullatus*

The Gully, Nova Scotia, Canada.   Boris Paulmann

Distinguishing Characteristics: The head is the most unique feature of this species. Males have a clearly demarcated snout and a bulging melon (older animals) that overhangs the snout. These features are less developed in females and calves. **Description:** Body is cylindrical, stocky. Sexual dimorphism in size and shape of head (see above): Males attain a max length of 9.8 m and weight 6.5-7.5 t; females grow up to 8.7 m in length. Females and calves toothless. Males have 2-4 conical, overlapping teeth at the tip of the lower jaw. These tend to break off when the animal reaches an age of 15-17 years, or long after maturity. Occasionally rudimentary teeth in both sexes. Flippers small, pointed; dorsal fin up to 30 cm high. Brown to black body (paler with age). Melon and snout pale-grey to white; ventral side cream-coloured to pale-grey. Head of older males pale-grey to white (hence known as "Greyhead" in Norway). Some animals have a pale stripe running from the melon to the throat. **Easily Mistaken For:** Bulging melon makes this species unmistakable within its area of distribution. **Other Names:** Bottlehead, Steephead, Flathead (English); Nördlicher Entenwal, Dögling (German); Grand Souffleur á Bec d'Oie, Hyperoodon Boréal (French); Iperodonte Boreale (Italian); Ballena Nariz de Botella del Norte (Spanish); Bico de Garrafa (Port.); Butskop (Dutch); Bottlenosen, Nebbhval (Norwegian); Pohjoinennokkavalas (Finnish); Vanlig Näbb-

The Gully   Sascha Hooker

val, Dögling (Swedish); Nordlig Døgling (Danish); Andhvaler (Icelandic). **Meaning of the Scientific Name:** *Hyperoodon ampullatus* (Forster 1770) - Generic name means "teeth in upper jaw" (erroneous observation by Lacépède in 1804, species is toothless). Composed of Greek *hyper* (on top), *odon* (tooth). Latin *ampullatus* (with a flask) refers to bottle-shaped snout. **Behaviour:** Found where waters reach a depth of 1,000 m (-2°C to 17°C). Migrates and lives in groups of up to several hundred animals that are segregated by age and sex. Nursing cows often live alone with their calves. Unusual for beaked whales, younger animals will approach noisy vessels. Very gregarious. Under protection since 1977. **Diving:** Deepest (approx 1,000 m) and longest dives of all cetaceans. Dive time 14-70 min, max 2 hours. Surface interval 10+ minutes, breathes 1-2 times per minute. Sounds and surfaces vertically. Blow bushy, 1-2 m high, angled slightly forward, easy to spot on calm day. **Feeding Habits:** Deep-sea squid, rarely fish (herring). Also takes starfish, sea cucumbers, mussels and other benthic invertebrates. **General Information:** First described as *Balaena ampullatus* by Forster in 1770. *B. rostrata* by Müller in 1776; to *Hyperoodon* by Lacépède in 1804. Numbers severely depleted prior to 1970s as a result of whaling. Frequent stranding. Killer Whale is its natural enemy. **Where & When:** In deep, cold, temperate waters of North Atlantic and Arctic. From N-Europe over Greenland to Davis Strait. Larger population resident in The Gully, a deep-sea canyon north of Sable Island, off the coast of Nova Scotia, Canada (see photos). Also common in northern polar waters between Iceland and Jan Mayen, as well as Davis Strait. South to the Azores. See photo on p. 9 (The Gully, by Boris Paulmann).

Southern Bottlenose Whale, *Hyperoodon planifrons*

Southwest Indian Ocean.

Robert Pitman/Seapics.com

Length 6-7.2 m (males), 7.8 m (females); weight 6-8 t. Otherwise like *H. ampullatus*. Associates with Arnoux's Beaked Whales and Long-Finned Pilot Whales, but its characteristic snout and melon make any confusion unlikely. **Other Names:** Flathead or Antarctic Bottlenose Whale (English); Südlicher Entenwal (German); Hypérodon Austral (French); Iperodonte Australe (Italian); Ballena Nariz de Botella del Sur (Spanish); Boto Gladiador (Port.); Zuidelijke Butskop (Dutch); Sørnebbhval (Norwegian); Eteläinennokkavalas (Finnish); Sydlig Näbbval (Swedish); Sydlig Døgling (Danish); Gran Calderón (Lat. Am.). *Hyperoodon planifrons* Flower 1882. Latin *planifrons* (with flat forehead). Very shy. Little known about its behaviour. Diving, Feeding Habits like *H. ampullatus*. Circumpolar in deep, cold and temperate offshore waters of the S-Hemisphere from the Antarctic to 29° S.

Arnoux's Beaked Whale, *Berardius arnuxii*

Pieter Arend Folkens

Distinguishing Characteristics: Small and bulbous melon, long snout, two protruding teeth on tip of lower jaw. **Description:** Length 8-10 m, weight 7-10 t. Both sexes have 2 additional teeth located about 20 cm behind the front teeth, which is a fairly unique feature in the family (Baird's Beaked Whales only other species to have them). Front teeth exposed outside the closed mouth, little used, often covered with barnacles, but usually worn down to the gums in older animals. Flippers are short and wide, leading and trailing edges almost parallel. Small dorsal fin slightly falcate. Skin may have a pale-brown shimmer due to algae growth. Few scars on speckled pale-grey or white underside. Older animals can also be pale-grey or off-white. Young animals are slate-grey, little evidence of scars. Blow is low, bushy, inconspicuous. **Easily Mistaken For:** Young Southern Bottlenose Whales similar, but always accompanied by distinctly coloured adults. **Other Names:** Large Beaked Whale, New Zealand Beaked Whale, Southern Four-Toothed Whale (England); Arnoux-Schnabelwal (German); Bérardien d'Arnoux (French); Berardio di Arnoux (Italian); Ballenato de Arnoux (Spanish); Baleia de Bico de Arnoux (Portug.); Zuidelijke Zwarte Dolfijn (Dutch); Arnouxnebbhval (Norwegian); Arnouxinvalas (Finnish); Arnuxis Näbbval (Swedish); Arnouxs Næbhval (Danish). **Meaning of the Scientific Name:** *Berardius arnuxii* Duvernoy 1851 - Generic name in honour of a vessel that plied between France and New Zealand. Species name in honour of the physician Arnoux, who discovered it (skull find). **Behaviour:** Little known. Groups of 6-10, max 80 animals, swim in close formation, breathe and dive simultaneously. Slow swimmer, very shy. **Diving:** Dive time 15-25 min, max 60 min. Max dive depth about 1,000 m. **Feeding Habits:** Squid, occasionally deep-sea fish (stomach analyses of stranded animals). **General Information:** First observations of a live specimen during the Antarctic summer of 1956/57. A single animal was locked in by the ice together with 120 Pygmy Killer Whales and 60 Killer Whales. **Where & When:** Circumpolar in all deep, cold, inshore waters of the Southern Hemisphere south of 30° S. Most sightings in Tasmanian Sea, during the southern spring/summer frequently in the Cook Strait (South Pacific). Also occurs in Southern Atlantic, off South America and South Africa. Stranding reported in New Zealand. Southernmost sighting at 64° S, close to Antarctic peninsula. During the summer the species probably ranges near the ice barrier, during winter even farther north.

Baird's Beaked Whale, *Berardius bairdii*

The meat of Baird's Beaked Whales is eaten in Japan. Boso Peninsula.   Mako Hirose/Seapics.com

A school of Baird's Beaked Whales. Baja California, Mexico. Todd Pusser/Seapics.com

Distinguishing Characteristics: See *Berardius arnuxii*. Slate-grey to brown in colour.
Description: Length 11–13 m, weight 11-14 t. Forehead of male wider, more rounded. A small dent around the blowhole becomes visible when species is viewed in profile. Flippers and dorsal fin small, rounded. Otherwise like *B. arnuxii*.
Other Names: Northern Giant Bottlenose Whale, North Pacific Four-Toothed Whale (English); Baird-Schnabelwal (German); Baleine a' Bec de Baird, Bérardie Boréale (French); Berardio di Baird (Italian); Zifio de Baird (Spanish); Baleia de Bico de Baird (Portuguese); Zwarte Dolfijn (Dutch); Bairdnebbhval (Norwegian); Berardinvalas (Finnish); Bairds Näbbval (Swedish); Bairds Næbhval (Danish); Tsuchi Kujira, Tsuchimbo (Japanese).
Meaning of the Scientific Name: *Berardius bairdii* Stejneger 1883 - Generic name see *Berardius arnuxii*. Species name in honour of Stejneger's colleague, the naturalist Spencer Baird (Smithsonian Institution, Washington, DC, USA).
Behaviour: Groups segregated on the basis of sex, size 3-50 animals, stay close together in open waters with depths ranging from 1,000-2,000 m. Difficult to approach. Blow low, bushy, inconspicuous. Occasional spy-hopping, lob-tailing, breaching. Sounding, surfacing, resting simultaneously.
Diving: Dive time 20-35, max 60 min. Dive depth 1,000-2,000 m. Usually remains no more than a few minutes on the surface.
Feeding Habits: Squid, other deep-sea cephalopods and fish, as well as benthic crustaceans.
General Information: In 1882 the scientist Leonhard Stejneger found a skull on Bering Island in Alaska (first description see above). The species had long been hunted with hand-held harpoons in Japan. Today 40-60 animals are still caught each year. Populations have since decreased dramatically. Gestation period is 17 months (Boso Peninsula, Japan), the longest of all species of whale.
Where & When: Deep (1,000-3,000 m) offshore waters in the temperate and subarctic latitudes of the N-Pacific (30° N to the southern part of the Bering Sea). Also inshore. Frequently encountered in the Aleutian Islands (Alaska), California, Emperor Seamount (NW of Hawaii), Vancouver Island, Boso Peninsula, SW of Hokkaido and Tobayama Bay (Japan) and Sea of Okhotsk (Russia).

Tropical Bottlenose Whale, *Indopacetus pacificus*

Pieter Arend Folkens

Description: This is one of the least known species of cetacean. So far all information is based on two skull finds and a few stranded animals. Length up to 7.6 m. Head form is typical for the family, with two small holes at the tip of the lower jaw through which two small oval teeth protrude. Two unidentified pale-grey whales were sighted in the vicinity of the Seychelles in 1980, which may have been representatives of this species. The whales were approximately 7.5 m and 4.5 m long respectively, and they had long snouts and broad flukes with straight back edges. Their dorsal fins were small and set far behind the middle of the back.

Meaning of the Scientific Name: *Indopacetus pacificus* (Longman 1926) - Generic name means "whale in the Indo-Pacific."

General Information: The first skull belonging to this species was found along Mackay Beach (NE-Queensland, Australia) in 1882. On the basis of this find, Longman described the species as *Mesoplodon pacificus* in 1926. In 1955 fishermen found a second skull (1.1 m) on Danane Beach (NE-Somalia). After a number of recently stranded animals from the Indic were examined in a DNA laboratory, it was generally assumed that the previous finds were in fact the remains of *Indopacetus*. This would mean that the genus *Indopacetus* is more closely related to *Hyperoodon* than to *Mesoplodon*.

Where & When: In deep, offshore waters of the Indo-Pacific. Very shy.

Sowerby's Beaked Whale, *Mesoplodon bidens*

Azores, Atlantic.   Ralf Kiefner

Description: Slimmer than other beaked whales. Length 4-5 m, weight 800-1,000 kg. Males probably larger than females. Slate-grey on top, ventral side and flanks blue-grey to white. Young animals paler.

Meaning of the Scientific Name: *Mesoplodon bidens* (Sowerby 1804) - Greek *mesos, hopla* and *odon* ("tooth in the middle of the mouth"). Latin *bidens* (two-toothed) refers to teeth in lower jaw of male animals.

Behaviour: Little known, few sightings. Probably prefers the open seas. Close to 100 reports of stranding worldwide, more than any other species of beaked whale. More than 2 specimens never sighted together, probably lives singly or in pairs.

General Information: A stranded animal was found in the Moray Firth (N-Scotland) in 1800. This was the first discovery of a beaked whale. Skull housed in the Oxford University Museum.

Where & When: NE-Atlantic: Finland to Bay of Biscay and Azores. NW-Atlantic: Newfoundland (Canada) to Cape Hatteras (USA), occasionally also father south to Florida (stranded animal in Gulf of Mexico). Most often encountered in the northern regions of the North Sea and around Norway, where most stranded animals were found.

Andrew's Beaked Whale, *Mesoplodon bowdoini*

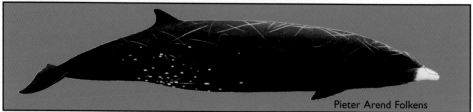

Pieter Arend Folkens

Description: Spindle-shaped. Length 4-4.7 m, weight 1,000-2,500 kg. Uniformly dark-grey to blue-black. Only the short, thick snout is white.

Meaning of the Scientific Name: *Mesoplodon bowdoini* Andrews 1908 - Generic name see *Mesoplodon bidens*. Species name in honour of Bowdoin, who found the first specimen.

Behaviour: Unknown. There are no confirmed sightings and only about 20 stranded animals have been found so far.

Feeding Habits: Results from a few analyses of stomach contents and the typical teeth of a beaked whale indicate that the species preys primarily on squid.

General Information: Roy Chapman Andrews, an American who launched his career as a naturalist with the first description (1908) of this still little known species, also examined and identified the first skeletal find. A clear identification on the high seas is very difficult, and even stranded animals have been wrongly classified by whale experts. Due to numerous similarities in the shape of the head and lower jaw, as well as the position of the two teeth in the lower jaw and the colouration of the body, some hold this species to be only a Southern Hemisphere variant of Hubbs' Beaked Whale.

Where & When: Presumably in the cold-temperate to warm waters of the Indo-Pacific. A few animals stranded along the southern coast of Australia, New Zealand and Tasmania. Reports of a stranded specimen in the Kerguelen Islands (Southern Indic) unconfirmed.

Hubbs' Beaked Whale, *Mesoplodon carlhubbsi*

Pieter Arend Folkens

Description: Length 5-5.3 m, weight 1,000-2,000 kg. Dark-grey to black. Males have small, pale spots on the body, a white "cap" around the blowhole and a white rostrum. This facilitates identification on the open seas. Adult females and calves are medium-grey on top, with pale-grey flanks and white undersides. Lack a white "cap."

Meaning of the Scientific Name: *Mesoplodon carlhubbsi* Moore 1963 - Generic name see *Mesoplodon bidens*. Species name in honour of biologist and pioneer whale researcher Carl Hubbs, who discovered the species.

Behaviour: Unknown, as sparse information on this species is based on a few stranded animals and a single dependable sighting on the high seas.

Feeding Habits: A few stomach content analyses revealed remains of squid and deep-sea fish.

General Information: Biologist Carl Hubbs found the first fully preserved remains of this species on a beach near La Jolla (California) in 1945. Because of certain similarities in colouration and head shape, a few earlier scientists believed that it might be a subspecies of Andrews' Beaked Whale. Today it is known that these cetaceans live in isolation from each other and are consequently regarded as two distinct species.

Where & When: Offshore in the cold-temperate waters of the Northern Pacific between 30°-50° N. Eastern Northern Pacific: California (most cases of stranding) to Queen Charlotte Islands (British Columbia, Canada). Western Northern Pacific: Only a few stranded animals in Ayukawa and Honshu (Japan).

Blainville's Beaked Whale, *Mesoplodon densirostris*

Big Island, Hawaii.   Jim Watt

Description: Length 4.5-5.8 m, weight 2,000-3,500 kg. Ash-grey to dark-grey. Besides scars from altercations with rivals, the species has irregular light-brown or pale-grey marks primarily on the belly and genital region (more common in case of females) that were probably caused by cookiecutter sharks. Females are about one metre shorter than males. Calves have a blue-grey back and cream belly.

Meaning of the Scientific Name: *Mesoplodon densirostris* (de Blainville 1817) - Generic name see *M. bidens*. Species name (dense beak) refers to the extremely dense jawbone (see below).

Behaviour: Hardly known, even though this is one of the most common species of beaked whale with a wide area of distribution. Stranding of single specimens only. According to sightings, it lives in tropical regions in groups of 3-7 animals. Observations made off Hawaii imply that the species prefers offshore waters with depths of 700-1,000 m.

Feeding Habits: Most stomach contents revealed squid and other cephalopods, but fish remains were found in the stomach of a specimen that stranded in South Africa.

General Information: First described as *Delphinus densirostris* by Henri de Blainville in 1817 on the basis of a skull fragment. The species has the densest bone structure of all vertebrates (hence the name). In 1846 Grey described a skull found in the Seychelles as *Ziphius seychellis,* but Flower discovered in 1875 that it actually belonged to this species. In 1992 a live male specimen stranded along the shore of New Jersey (USA). James G. Mead of the Smithsonian Institution tried in vain to save the animal, which lived for another three days.

Where & When: Widely distributed in deep tropical to temperate regions of all the world's oceans between 60° N and 50° S. Most sightings occurred along the Atlantic coast of the USA and around Hawaii (especially Waianae Coast in the southwestern part of Oahau). Occasionally also encountered in South Africa.

Gervais' Beaked Whale, *Mesoplodon europaeus*

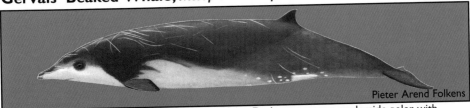

Pieter Arend Folkens

Description: Length 4-5.2 m, weight 600-1,500 kg. Dark-grey on top, underside paler with irregular white spots around the navel. Females 0.5 m longer than males. Belly of calves white.

Meaning of the Scientific Name: *Mesoplodon europaeus* (Gervais 1855) - Generic name see *Mesoplodon bidens*. Species named after continent where it was first sighted.

Behaviour: Hardly known. Presumably prefers deep tropical to subtropical seas.

Feeding Habits: Stomach analyses of three specimens only revealed the remains of cephalopods.

General Information: First find of a cadaver in the English Channel in 1840. Gervais described it as *Dioplodon europaeus.* Second specimen, a stranded animal, found near Atlantic City (New Jersey, USA) in 1889. Another 54 animals stranded here by 1989. One report of stranding in Ireland.

Where & When: Offshore deep waters of warm-temperate and tropical latitudes of Atlantic (New York to Florida & Caribbean). Follows Gulf Stream to N-Europe, ranges south to Canaries.

Ginko-Toothed Beaked Whale, *Mesoplodon ginkgodens*

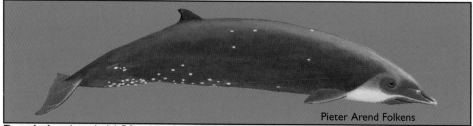

Pieter Arend Folkens

Description: Length 4.6-5.2 m, weight 1,500-2,000 kg. Males dark-grey, without scars, tip of rostrum pale, genital region with white spots about 3-4 cm in size. Females have a paler head, medium-grey back and pale-grey belly. **Meaning of the Scientific Name:** *Mesoplodon ginkgodens* Nishawaki & Kamiya 1958 - Species name refers to shape of the teeth, which resemble the leaves of the ginkgo tree. **Behaviour:** Unknown. Only 13 stranded animals reported, never observed on the high seas. **Feeding Habits:** Squid and deep-sea fish. **General Information:** The first specimen was found in Japan and described by the Japanese scientists Nishiwaki and Kamiya in 1957. **Where & When:** Presumably in deep, offshore warm-temperate to tropical waters of the Indo-Pacific. Stranded animals: Northern Pacific 10, Indian Ocean 2, Chatham Islands 1.

Gray's Beaked Whale, *Mesoplodon grayi*

Stranded Gray's Beaked Whales in Whangarei, New Zealand.   Ingrid Visser/Seapics.com

Description: Length 4.5-5.6 m, weight 1,000-1,500 kg. Females larger than males. Latter have characteristic triangular teeth erupting from the front of the lower jaw. Upper jaw of both sexes with 34-44 rudimentary teeth (see also Shepherd's Beaked Whale). Blue-grey to black on top, belly pale-grey, snout white and long, jawlines straight. **Meaning of the Scientific Name:** *Mesoplodon grayi* Haast 1876 - Generic name see *M. bidens*. Species name in honour of Gray. **Behaviour:** Not as shy as other species of beaked whale. One observation of breaching. Group size 1-5, rarely more. One mass stranding of 28 animals along Chatham Islands (east of New Zealand) in 1874. **Feeding Habits:** Primarily squid. **General Information:** Gray's Beaked Whales and Shepherd's Beaked Whales have also been classified together in the genus *Oulodon* because of the teeth in their upper jaws. Only one reported stranding in the Northern Hemisphere: A disoriented animal washed ashore on the North Sea coast of Holland in 1927. **Where & When:** Presumably offshore, deep, cold and temperate waters of the Southern Hemisphere south of 30° S. Only a few confirmed sightings in the Southern Indian Ocean, most of them south of Madagascar. Most occurrences of stranding in New Zealand and the Chatham Islands. A few reports of stranded animals from the Falkland Isles, Tierra del Fuego (Argentina), Chile, South Africa and Australia.

Hector's Beaked Whale, *Mesoplodon hectori*

Pieter Arend Folkens

Description: One of the smallest species of beaked whale, length 4-4.5 m, weight 1,000-2,000 kg. Blowhole is slightly sickle-shaped rather than round. Snout relatively short, pale-grey to white. Dark-grey to brownish-grey on top, belly pale-grey (that of male occasionally white). **Meaning of the Scientific Name:** *Mesoplodon hectori* Gray 1871 - Generic name see *M. bidens*. Species name in honour of Hector, who discovered the first specimen. **Behaviour:** Hardly known. Rare oceanic species, only two confirmed sightings off the coast of California in 1976 and 1978, one in Catalina Island and the other west of San Diego. Both involved a pair of animals that showed little fear and even approached the vessels inquisitively, a totally atypical behaviour for beaked whales. **Feeding Habits:** Primarily squid. **General Information:** First find in 1866, only 7 skulls or cadavers discovered in the Southern Hemisphere thereafter. In 1978 a cow with its young and bull stranded on the coast of Southern California. First concrete knowledge obtained from these well-preserved specimens. In March of 2001 a 4.5-m-long female and its 2-m-long calf stranded along the eastern shore of Tasmania. Both were in an excellent condition and taken to be examined at Hobart's Tasmanian Museum, where the skeletons are on display today. **Where & When:** Presumably offshore, deep, cold-temperate waters of the Southern Hemisphere. Most reports of stranding stem from New Zealand, Tasmania, South Africa and South America (Tierra del Fuego and Falkland Isles). Since there four cases of stranding and two sighting in California between 1975-1979, it may well be that the species also occurs in the Northern Pacific.

Strap-toothed Whale, *Mesoplodon layardii*

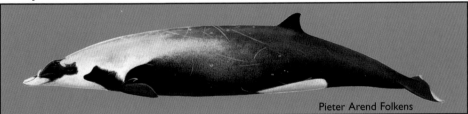

Pieter Arend Folkens

Description: One of the largest species of beaked whale, length 5-6.2 m, weight 1,500-3,000 kg. Females larger than males. Latter have two unique, up to 30-cm-long teeth in the lower jaw that curve over the upper jaw. Dark-grey to blue-black, lower jaw and tip of upper jaw white. Dark "mask" covering the melon and eyes. Pale-grey blaze from the melon almost down to the dorsal fin. Throat and genital region white. **Meaning of the Scientific Name:** *Mesoplodon layardii* Gray 1865 - Generic name see *M. bidens*. Species name in honour of Layard, who discovered the first specimen. **Behaviour:** Hardly known. Oceanic species, very shy, rests inconspicuously on the surface as if sunbathing. **Feeding Habits:** Primarily squid. **General Information:** The teeth of adult males pose somewhat of a mystery. They curve over the upper jaw, preventing it from opening fully. Perhaps this enables the animal to pull squid from their hiding places by suction, much like a vacuum cleaner. Most likely the teeth are a secondary sex characteristic that serve a function when the animal is vying for a mate. The variability of the teeth led to a subdivision into 4 species in the past. Today, only one species is recognised. With more than 150 occurrences of stranding and/or sightings, this is one of the most frequently reported species of beaked whale in the Southern Hemisphere. **Where & When:** Judging from reports of stranding and sightings, the species lives in deep, offshore cold-temperate waters of the Southern Hemisphere. The southern limit of its distribution lies around 55° S. The northernmost sighting occurred near 30° S. Most reports of stranding and sightings stem from New Zealand, Australia and Tasmania. Also encountered off South Africa, Namibia, Argentina, Chile, Uruguay and the Falkland Isles.

Pygmy Beaked Whale, *Mesoplodon peruvianus*

Pieter Arend Folkens

Description: By far the smallest species of beaked whale, length 3.4-3.7 m, weight unknown. Females smaller than males, both sexes without protruding teeth in lower jaw (males have two very small conical teeth). Snout short, narrow, with dark tip. Upper jaw dark, throat pale-grey. Dark-grey on top, colour merges with pale-grey to white on ventral side. Bulls have very few scratches or scars, which implies that there are few intraspecies altercations. **Meaning of the Scientific Name:** *Mesoplodon peruvianus* Reyes, Mead and Waerebeek 1991 - Generic name see *M. bidens*. Species name recalls site in Peru where first skull was found. **Behaviour:** Hardly known. All information about species is solely based on 5 sightings at sea (in pairs, once with a calf) and 10 stranded specimens (exclusively single animals). **Feeding Habits:** Primarily squid living at moderate depths. **General Information:** In 1976 scientists made a chance discovery of the first skull in a fish market in San Andrés, Peru. The first complete specimen (a female) was found in a fish market south of Lima in 1985. The most important specimen, in terms of classification, was a bull that stranded to the north of Lima in 1988. **Where & When:** Off- and inshore in moderate to deep tropical waters of the Pacific on both sides of the equator between 25° N and 20° S. Most stranded animals were found along a 400-km stretch of coastline from Ica to Lima (10-15° S). The two northernmost specimens were discovered near La Paz, Mexico in 1990.

True's Beaked Whale, *Mesoplodon mirus*

Pieter Arend Folkens

Description: Species has not been clearly identified in its natural habitat so far. Length around 5 m, weight 1,000-1,500 kg. Females barely smaller than males. Latter have a small tooth exposed on either side of the lower jaw. Living colour of species only known on basis of a female that stranded east of the Cape of Good Hope in 1984. Neck, dorsal fin, posterior half of the body, underside of fluke and genital region white. Sides of lower jaw and throat pale-grey and flecked with bluish-black. Back, flanks and belly in anterior half of body a dark blue-black. **Meaning of the Scientific Name:** *Mesoplodon mirus* True 1913 - Latin *mirus* (wonderful). **Behaviour:** Unknown. Species has never been observed at sea. Presumably oceanic as there have been no sightings close to shore and no more than 20 cases of stranding have been reported. **Feeding Habits:** Squid (based on stomach content analysis of female specimen found in South Africa). **General Information:** On July 26, 1912, American biologist Frederick True found a stranded female (4.87 m) of a hitherto unknown species of cetacean on Bird Island (Beaufort Harbor, NC, USA) and provided the first description on the basis of its skeleton. Presumably there are two distinct variants: North Atlantic (Gulf Stream region) and Southern Hemisphere. Slight differences in head shape, size of flippers and colouration of males. **Where & When:** In deep, offshore, temperate waters of North Atlantic and Southern Hemisphere (South Africa, Australia, New Zealand).

Stejneger's Beaked Whale, *Mesoplodon stejnegeri*

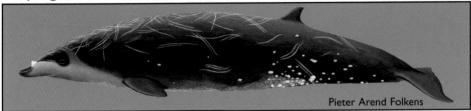

Pieter Arend Folkens

Description: Arched lower jaw, two large erupted teeth about 20 cm behind the tip of the snout of male specimens. Length 5-5.3 m, weight 1,000-1,500 kg. Males and females equal in size. Top almost uniformly dark-grey, brown or black. Underside paler and flecked with scars. Throat and lower jaw white. Long scratches indicate that rivalry occurs between male animals. Young animals can have pale stripes along the neck. **Meaning of the Scientific Name:** *Mesoplodon stejnegeri* True 1885 - Generic name see *M. bidens*. Species name in honour of Stejneger, who found the first specimen. **Behaviour:** Like most other beaked whales, this species is shy and unapproachable. Very few sightings so far. Inconspicuous surface behaviour. Usually swims in small groups composed of animals of various ages and sizes, as well as both sexes. These swim in tight formations and dive simultaneously. **Diving:** Sounds with a slow forward roll. Dive time about 10-15 min, dive depth to 1,600 m. **Feeding Habits:** Analyses of stomach contents revealed deep-sea squid. According to observations by Japanese fishermen it also preys on salmon. **General Information:** Known primarily on the basis of stranded specimens. This is one of the species of beaked whale that is most frequently misidentified. Consequently, its distribution is still uncertain. **Where & When:** Distribution in the Northern Pacific probably limited to 30°-60° N, presumably in deep waters over the continental shelf. Most reported sightings stem from Alaska and along the Aleutian Islands. There may be smaller populations off Honshu and southern Hokkaido in the Sea of Japan. Also may occur in the southern part of the Bering Sea.

Shepherd's Beaked Whale, *Tasmacetus shepherdi*

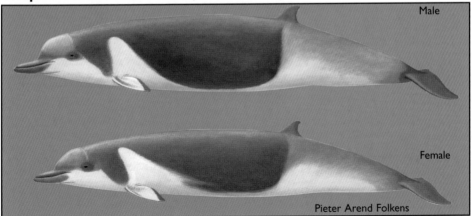

Male

Female

Pieter Arend Folkens

Description: Most information about this species stems from stranded animals. Consequently, little is known about its actual appearance. Females grow 6.6 m long, males 7 m. Weight 2,000-3,000 kg. Snout long, narrow and pointed. Melon steep, rounded and somewhat paler. The only species of beaked whale with a full set of teeth in both jaws of both sexes. Adult males have two large teeth at the tip of the lower jaw. Top is dark-grey or tan to black, underside white. Flanks have pale, diagonal bands. These were missing in an animal stranded in New Zealand in 1951 (younger specimen?). **Meaning of the Scientific Name:** *Tasmacetus shepherdi* Oliver 1937 - Generic name means "whale from the Tasman Sea." Species name in honour of G. Shephard, curator of the New Zealand Museum, who provided the first description in 1933. **Behaviour:** Little known. The reason why there have been so few sightings could be its inconspicuous surface behaviour or its avoidance of vessels. On the basis of one observation off the coast of New Zealand, it is assumed that its blow is inconspicuous. **Diving:** Unknown. **Feeding Habits:** The stomach content analysis of 1 specimen indicates that the species preys on fish rather than squid or crustaceans. This would also explain why both sexes have a complete set of teeth in both jaws, which is highly unusual for a beaked whale. All of the fish found in the stomach of the stranded specimen were deep-sea species. **General Information:** Oliver first described the species in 1937 on the basis of skeletal remains conserved in the Wanganui Alexander Museum. It is one of the least known species of cetacean. Only about 20 cases of stranding and one sighting at sea have been registered so far. Because of the presence of teeth, the species was once classified in the genus *Oulodon* together with Gray's Beaked Whales. **Where & When:** Presumably in deep, cold-temperate waters of the Southern Hemisphere. Most stranded animals found in New Zealand. As of 1970 reports of stranding also from Chile (Juan Fernandez Archipelago), Argentina, Tierra del Fuego, Australia.

Cuvier's Beaked Whale, *Ziphius cavirostris*

In the Atlantic off Cape Hatteras, North Carolina, USA.   Todd Pusser/Seapics.com

Description: Adult males have a white head and two exposed, conical, 4-6-cm-long teeth at the tip of the lower jaw. In contrast to other beaked whales, this species is very long and stocky. Both sexes average 5-7.5 m in length and weigh 2,000-3,000 kg. Snout is short and not clearly demarcated from the melon. Jawlines short and slightly curved at the back. Dorsal fin sickle-shaped to triangular, 30-40 cm high. Flippers small, with "flipper pockets." Fluke is atypical, with a concave back edge and slight median notch. Adults of both sexes white on the head and back down to the fluke. Belly and flanks dark. Younger animals uniformly pale-grey to tan, topside somewhat darker than underside. Depending on sex and age, colouration varies from grey, brown, white, gun-metal blue to black. Back and head begin to turn white when the animal reaches sexual maturity. Very old animals can occasionally be white all over. Males have scars from altercations with rivals. **Meaning of the Scientific Name:** *Ziphius cavirostris* Cuvier 1823 - Generic name from Greek *ziphia* (sword-shaped). Latin *cavirostris* (hollow rostrum) refers to a basin on skull. **Behaviour:** Relatively frequently sighted at sea. Frequent stranding for an oceanic species. Widest distribution of all beaked whales, presumably also largest population. Inconspicuous, shy, but resident population off Hawaii is curious and has been observed breaching. Lives in offshore waters (1,000-3,000 m) in groups of 2-5, occasionally up to 25 animals. Solitary individuals rarely encountered (older males). **Diving:** Dive time 20-40 min, dive depth to 1,000+ m. **Feeding Habits:** Deep-sea squid and fish. **General Information:** First described by Georges Cuvier in 1823 on the basis of a skull that was found in the French Mediterranean in 1804. Second Mediterranean specimen discovered near Les Aresquires in 1850. Bone structure of skull extremely dense in case of males. In English species also known as Goose-Beaked Whale because of shape of head. Japanese refer to it as "Akabo Kujira" (Baby-Faced Whale) with reference to white head. **Where & When:** Worldwide in all deep, offshore waters with exception of polar regions. Frequent stranding: NW-Atlantic (Massachusetts, Rhode Island), Europe (W-Scotland, England, Ireland, French Mediterranean coast)

COOPERATIVE FEEDING IN A BRACKISH RIVER

The purpose of a visit of the photographer Patrick Kelly to the Homosassa river in Florida, as initially intended, was to photograph the endangered West Indian Manatee that frequents springs in the winter months to take advantage of their warm water. The manatee story is an interesting one that any reader so interested should pursue. This writing, however, is of a specific incident the writer witnessed while on his visit to Homosassa.

It was my second trip to the Homosassa river. Homosassa, in fact, is both a town and the river deriving its name from the Homosassa Springs, located about 60 miles north of Tampa on the gulf side of Florida. Like many of the other fabulous springs within Florida's borders, the Homosassa is fed from a freshwater aquifer very deep into the earth. The spring generates millions of gallons of water at a constant 72 degrees Fahrenheit forming the river that about 5 miles downstream blends into the saltwater gulf coast along Florida's western shore.

One afternoon while working my way down river after a successful manatee shoot I noticed some disturbances in the water 20 m off the bow of my boat. At first I thought, perhaps this was a mother and baby manatee at the surface but realised in an instance that this animal was moving too fast to be a manatee. I wondered what other animal of such size would frequent this inter-coastal waterway. At that moment the unmistakable dolphin dorsal fin broke the surface. I quickly counted four Bottlenose Dolphins *(Tursiops truncatus)*. All of us had heard of freshwater dolphins and rare cases of dolphin sightings in freshwater.

The sightings, however, were only the beginning. I watched in amazement as the four animals separated in a deliberate manner, backtracked and in a choreography that would rival Olympic synchronised swimming teams, accelerated toward the shoreline. This was teamwork at its finest.

For a split second all four animals disappeared under the surface. The water ahead of them quickly boiled as the object of their attention became evident. About 20 mullets jumped into the air as they were herded into the shallows, their only other choice was certain doom in the mouths of the pursuing dolphins. Fact is, the jumping reaction was just what the dolphins desired. Once airborne the fish were helpless as the dolphins too broke the surface and simply snatched the mullets from the air as they fell back toward the water.

This process was repeated over and over, my dilemma trying to guess where the schooling mullets would swim to and which shore would the dolphins drive them towards. Although I saw as many as 20 sequences I succeeded only in getting close enough to film three.

I would later find that seeing dolphins in the Homosassa though not common is also not rare. Witnessing such tenacious herding, however, was unusual. As we headed back up the river I again was thankful for the fortune of being able to witness and photograph such a natural phenomenon. Until I saw the final images I was uncertain whether I really would capture anything useful from the event. As the saying goes, it is better to be lucky than good...

Bottlenose Dolphins pursue jumping mullets in Florida's Homosassa river.

The four dolphins act together in a choreography that would rival Olympic synchronised swimming teams.

These Bottlenose Dolphins lunge onto a mud bank to feed fish that they have driven ashore. South Carolina, USA.

Distinguishing Characteristics of this Family

This family comprises three species that live exclusively in fluvial and brackish waters. An additional species (Franciscana) is also found in coastal waters. It is included in the same superfamily as the three species of "true" river dolphins because there is a phylogenetic connection between them. The geographic isolation of these species makes their identification an easy matter. Since visibility is extremely limited in murky rivers, their eyes are tiny. They have a very long snout with numerous, small teeth and a highly developed system of echolocation. Their cervical vertebrae are unconnected, their body colouration is pale (also pink) and they are slow swimmers.

Boto, *Inia geoffrensis*

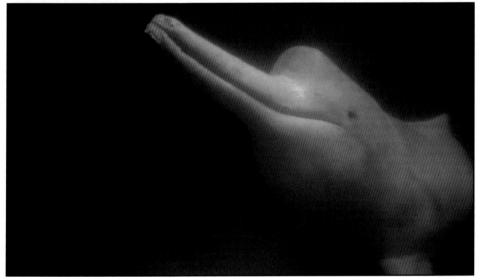

Amazon River.   Scott Frier

Description: Largest of all river dolphins, length 1.8-2.8 m (females up to 2.3 m), weight 80-160 kg. Very long snout, cylindrical, with a slight downward angle. Blowhole sickle-shaped, low dorsal ridge (no dorsal fin) and uniformly blue-grey, white or pink in colour. There are 46-70 small teeth in each jaw; posterior molar-like teeth are flat. In addition there are 50 bristly hairs growing on the external side of each jaw (vibrissae), which have a tactile function much like a cat's whiskers. It has "cheeks" beneath its eyes that obstruct its downward view, which is why it frequently swims on its back or sides. **Meaning of the Scientific Name:** *Inia geoffrensis* (de Blainville 1817) - Generic name: The Guarayo Indians of Bolivia call the animals living in the San Miguel River "Inia." Species name in honour of French biologist Etienne Geoffrey Saint-Hilaire. **Behaviour:** Lives singly or in pairs, occasionally in groups of up to 15 animals. Depending on region, species is more or less shy. Slow swimmer, but capable of swift, short sprints. Most active at dusk. Due to obstruction by the "cheeks" beneath its eyes, species often swims on its back or sides in order to find prey on the bottom. In rich feeding grounds it often associates with Tucuxis or giant otters. **Feeding Habits:** At least 50 different species of fish, including catfish, as well as invertebrates and crustaceans that it can detect in the muddy bottom with its vibrissae. **General Information:** First described as *Delphinus geoffrensis* by de Blainville in 1817. Contemporary taxonomists divide it into three distinct subspecies: *I. g. humboldtiana* in the Orinoco Basin, *I. g. geoffrensis* in the Amazon Basin, *I. g. boliviensis* in the upper Madeira River Basin. Exact population status difficult to establish because of the extent and inaccessibility of its natural habitat. A few Indians and settlers still hunt Botos even though an ancient Indian legend warns that he who makes use of lamp oil extracted from these beings will be struck with blindness. **Where & When:** This species has the widest distribution of all river dolphins. It lives exclusively in fresh water and prefers calm, slow-flowing, brown or black waters of the Orinoco River and its tributaries. The Boto is also found in many regions of the Amazon Basin. The area of distribution of this species extends over Venezuela, Ecuador, Columbia, Peru, Bolivia, Guyana and Brazil. This fresh water dolphin occurs in rivers up to 3,000 km from shore.

Yangtze River Dolphin, *Lipotes vexillifer*

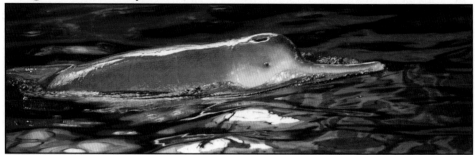

Yangtze River, China.   John Wong

Description: Length 1.5-2.4 m (males up to 2 m), weight 100-150 kg. Very long snout, not spade-shaped like other river dolphins, but slightly pointed. Triangular dorsal fin sits on a very broad base. Eyes are tiny and sit high up on the sides of the head. As with all river dolphins, its eyes are practically useless. There are 62-68 conical teeth in the upper jaw and 64-72 in the lower one. Top and flanks are pale-grey to bluish-grey, underside is off-white to white. Pale-grey upper jaw has a white border on each side, the lower jaw is white. **Meaning of the Scientific Name:** *Lipotes vexillifer* Miller 1918 - Generic name based on Greek *leipo* (abandoned), refers to the extreme geographic isolation of the species. Latin *vexillifer* (flag carrier) refers to dorsal fin. **Behaviour:** Hardly known, as species is shy and very difficult to observe in its natural habitat.

Aquarium Shanghai, China.   Scott Frier

Lives singly or in pairs, seldom up to 6 animals in a group. Slow swimmer, often rests for 5-6 hours in deep-water eddies. Most active from dusk to dawn. Swims backwards and on its sides in order to improve its chances of finding prey on the bottom. Blow somewhat resembles a sneeze. **Feeding Habits:** Various species of fish, preferably catfish, also crustaceans. **General Information:** Long honoured in China as a reincarnation of a drowned princess. Known there as "Baiji" (White Dolphin) for over 2,000 years. First described by Gerrit Smith Miller in 1918. The species has been under protection since 1949, was declared a national heritage in China in 1975, but its numbers are still depleting because of dam construction, expanding shipping traffic and intensive river fishing. It is one of the world's 12 most threatened species! **Where & When:** Only found in China in the lower course of the Yangtze River to Yichang. Most common along the approximately 1,700 km from Zicheng (upriver) to Nanking (downriver).

Ganges River Dolphin, *Platanista gangetica*

Description: Length 1.5-2.6 m (males up to 2 m), weight 70-90 kg. Narrow, very long snout, makes up 20% of its total body length. Wide flippers with wavy edges and finger-like segmentation. Instead of a dorsal fin species has a low dorsal ridge or "hump." Head asymmetrical, elongated blowhole offset to the left. Like all river dolphins, its cervical vertebrae are not connected at the neck, allowing for free movement of the head. It has 52-78 long, sharp teeth in the upper jaw and 52-70 teeth in the lower jaw, which are still exposed when its mouth is closed. Back and flanks are uniformly light-blue, grey-blue to medium-grey. Belly is paler. **Meaning of the Scientific Name:** *Platanista gangetica* Roxburgh 1801 - Origin of generic name unknown. In the first century AD, Pliny the Elder described a "fish with the beak of a dolphin" from the Ganges River and named it "Platanistes." Species name refers to its distribution in the Ganges River. **Behaviour:** Singly or in pairs, group size rarely more than 10. Not very active during the day. Continually

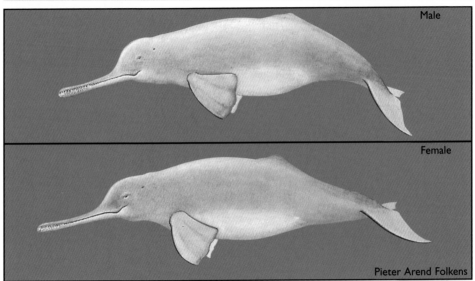

Male

Female

Pieter Arend Folkens

sends out echolocation signals while swimming in order to orient itself in the murky water. Hunts at dusk or during the night. Often swims sideways along the bottom, whereby it drags its lower flipper through the mud to uncover hiding prey. **Feeding Habits:** Catfish, carp, gobies, crustaceans. **General Information:** First described in 1801 by the British physician and biologist William Roxburgh, and independently named *Delphinus gangeticus* by the Dutchman Heinrich Julius Lebeck. In 1830 Johann Wagler classified it as *Platanista*. The very similar, geographically isolated and severely threatened Indus River Dolphin (formerly known as *P. minor*) is now considered to be identical with *P. gangetica*. **Where & When:** In the Ganges, Brahmaputra and Meghna rivers in India, Bangladesh, Nepal and Bhutan, as well as in the Karnaphali River in Bangladesh. Also found in the Indus River between Kotri Dam (Sind Province) and Jinnah Dam (NW Punjab, Pakistan).

Franciscana, *Pontoporia blainvillei*

Pieter Arend Folkens

Description: Length 1.2-1.7 m, weight 30-50 kg (males up to 1.6 m and 45 kg). Only member of family with a high dorsal fin. Small eyes, but very well developed, which is atypical for a river dolphin. Top grey-brown, flanks and belly paler. Older animals sometimes uniformly white. **Meaning of the Scientific Name:** *Pontoporia blainvillei* (Gervais & d'Orbigny 1844) - Greek *pontos* (ocean) and *poros* (passage), the first river dolphin ever found in the ocean. Species name honours French naturalist Henri de Blainville. **Behaviour:** Hardly known. Very shy, lives singly or in groups of up to 5 animals. Catatonic seizure when confronted with natural enemies (sharks). **Feeding Habits:** Fish, squid, octopus, shrimp. **General Information:** First described in 1844 as *Delphinus blainvillei* by Gervais and d'Orbigny. Later changed to *Stenodelphis blainvillei*. J. E. Gray classified it under *Pontoporia* in 1846. Population severely threatened by fishing nets. **Where & When:** Atlantic: Shallow coastal waters of Brazil, Uruguay, Argentina. Also found in the estuary of the Rio de la Plata between 19°-42° S, and around Valdéz Peninsula (Argentina) to the mouth of the Doce (Brazil).

PATAGONIA HUNTERS

When the sea lions of Argentina's Peninsula Valdes are basking too close to the water they are occasionally taken by orca whales directly on the beach. But if the hunters throw their massive bodies too far onto the sloping gravel beach, they risk their lives because they have to reach the water again with one of the next waves. The American wildlife photographer Jasmine Rossi has documented their risky and spectacular hunting technique.

The Valdes Orcas are the only whales in the world that snatch pinniped prey directly from the beach.

Gently, the surf pounds against the pebbled beach. Barks from the bustling sea lion colony echo across the coast. It is summer on Patagonia's Atlantic shore, and the two month old pups are just learning how to swim. Inquisitive and carefree, they duck into the surf, just to be rolled around and spewed back out again, snuffling and yapping, they scramble up the beach – but a few minutes later they are back on the water's edge for another try.

While the sea lions watch their doom closing in they only reluctantly turn away to safe ground.

Unbeknown to them the emerald swells bear a sinister presence: A massive orca whale is hiding in the depths, listening carefully to their clumsy splashes.

Most sea lion colonies on the Valdes peninsula are protected by long, green reefs that protrude far out into the ocean, but at Punta Norte, a wide channel allows the peninsula's orca whales to swim right up to the beach when the tide is high. The older seals are well aware of the danger: Here and there,

Too late the sea lion started its flight. If surf conditions permit, the Orca will soon lunge at its prey.

shiny wet heads pop through the surface, and nervously crane their necks scanning the surface for a telltale fin, before they quickly sprint across the channel. In an effort to avoid detection, the orca swims side-ways to hide its giant dorsal fin. It is a large bull, known as Mel, a solitary, but seasoned hunter. Occasionally, he comes up for air, deceptively swimming out to sea, and soon the older seals appear to fall for the trick and regain their calm.

Leisurely, two yellow females swim along the coast, their elongated dark shapes shimmering trough the glassy green. But there is something else, a shadow, the size of a boat, trailing their path. The orca is swimming parallel to them, just a few metres away. Unaware, the two seals reach the safety of the shallow reef, and the orca makes a sharp turn and veers off. Again and again Mel follows an unsuspecting seal, but for unknown reasons aborts the attack. As he comes up for air, a group of seals detect the whale and make their way across the channel on land. A little black pup clumsily hops behind them, calling out

With the next wave the Orca covers the short distance in no time - and closes in for the kill.

Riding the wave, the orca has grabbed its hapless prey in the menacing grip of up to 28 teeth.

for its mother. Suddenly the water appears to curve, and a massive wall-like wave thunders in from the ocean. Crashing with full force onto the beach, it parts, revealing Mel's enormous black and white body. Dangling helplessly between his huge conical teeth is the tiny pup. Mel's tall dorsal fin shakes violently as he bashes the pup against the pebbles, shaking it from side to side to separate the flesh from the hide. Then he flexes his body and turns sideways. With powerful beats of his tail, he inches slowly through the shallows until an incoming wave lifts him back out to sea. For a long while Mel circles far out in deeper waters, eating his catch while flocks of hungry gulls and petrels flutter overhead, greedily awaiting the leftovers.

To home in on a tiny pup, at the right spot and moment, requires perfect timing and co-ordination, and only every third of Mel's attacks ends in success. There is nothing more difficult or dangerous for an orca than to strand itself against its natural instincts to survive, for once it has lost all buoyancy, the orca risks becoming fatally stuck on shore. Only two groups of orcas in the world have learned how to master this lethal hunting technique: The nineteen whales of the Valdes peninsula, and a small pod living in the Crozet Islands of the South Pacific, eight thousand kilometres to the east. But the shoreline in the Crozet Islands is not as steep as at Valdes, and consequently only the smaller females are able to swim up to the beach, and even they do not come fully out of the water as they do in Patagonia.

Orcas mature slowly. They live in tightly knit family groups and many aspects of their behaviour are not genetically encoded but must be learned over time, from the unique vocal repertoire or "dialect" which distinguishes each orca family, to all hunting techniques, which are passed on from one generation to the next.

Beaching can be a serious problem for such a heavy animal, only experienced orcas hunt this way.

Often the prey is not seriously wounded and tossed about by the orca, much like cats do with mice.

Killer whales are agile like dolphins, they can bite like sharks, and are amongst the ocean's fastest creatures, manoeuvering at speeds of up to 55 kilometres an hour. But it is the orca's intelligence and cunning, that allows it to overpower much larger animals, and dangerous prey. Orcas co-operate much like a pack of wolves, and have been known to even attack giant blue whales, which can grow to 30 metres in length. But a single orca can also be a formidable opponent; and off the coast of California a female was recently observed feeding a large white shark to her offspring.

At Valdes, I witnessed how three orcas attacked a much larger right whale, - large enough to break their bones with a single flick of its massive tail. The orcas cut off the right whale's path by zigzagging in front of him. From the shapes of their fins and the saddle-patches on their backs, I soon recognised Ishtar, an adult female from the local pod. She was accompanied by two young orcas, Jasmine and tiny Tania. Turning sharply, Ishtar manoeuvered herself onto the whale's head. Terrified, it lifted its tail and dove away. Minutes later it resurfaced. Immediately Ishtar swam back on top of its head. Clearly she was trying to block the much larger whale's blow-holes to deprive it of air, an assault move designed eventually to kill it. Natural mimics, the two juniors soon followed suit. They took turns as they rode and rolled on top of its body, as if they were scratching their bellies on its callosities. Whenever the whale surfaced, an orca would already be draped over its enormous head like a headband – it was a sorry sight. Eventually the orcas let the whale go, but it is this kind of ingenious techniques which sets the largest member of the dolphin family at the crest of the marine food chain.

When hunting in pairs or as a group, the Valdes orcas always coordinated their attacks, each member playing a specific role. One favourite hunting strategy was for a larger whale to act as a decoy, sailing past the sea lions in full view whilst the others engaged in a sneak attack. Another tactic was for

Juvenile orcas test their impressiveness as they charge a large sea elephant bull almost their size.

the smaller orcas to patrol the reefs on either side of the attack channel, cutting off the sea lions' escape route to shallow water above the rocks. Others would form a wall in deeper water to keep the prey from fleeing towards the open ocean. A third group would swim sideways, flashing their white bellies, to herd the sea lions together. Corralled inside the channel, or against the beach, the hapless animals were usually captured by one or two of the older and more experienced hunters.

From an early age, the Valdes orcas are taught how to intentionally beach themselves. On calm mornings, several members of the pod can be observed practicing on the steeply sloping beach of the Bay of Medina. There they strand themselves simultaneously, arching their backs, and lifting their flukes, before wriggling their way out to sea with great thumps of their tails.

Even seasoned hunters like Mel come here regularly to sharpen their skills, much like an athlete training for a big event, but despite all this practice, accidents do occur: In 1989, Sparky and Nadia became stuck on the Punta Norte reef, while pursuing sea lions, and last December a large female, Maga, stranded

As the adult elephant seal is too large and not as vulnerable as sea lion pups the orcas veer off and leave the beach.

In other regions, e.g. the Pacific Northwest, orcas prey on large fish like this Pacific salmon.

when hunting in unfamiliar territory in the Gulf of San Jose. On both occasions, the whales were kept wet by rangers and fishermen, until the tide returned and they were able to swim to safety.

What makes orcas so successful is their incredible ability to adapt to different marine environments and to exploit a vast variety of prey by changing their hunting strategy according to the type of prey they are pursuing. As in other parts of the world, much of the orca's activity at Valdes coincides with the seasonal availability and movements of their prey. During the austral spring they scour the shores of the river-like Caleta Valdes inlet for recently weaned elephant seal pups and yearlings. Like at Punta Norte, there are no protective reefs and the orcas can swim right up to the beach during high tide. During the summer months they move 50 km up the coast to Punta Norte, for the sea lions' breeding season.

Orcas are highly specialised. In the Pacific Northwest, for example, two separate groups have evolved to exploit different types of prey in the same area. The "resident" whales specialise in fish and catch spawning salmon by corralling them into coves, against rocks, and other underwater barriers. The "transient" group, on the other hand, specialises in the capture of warm-blooded marine mammals such as seals, dolphins, and the incredibly speedy Dall's Porpoise, which the orcas chase down by leaping several body lengths through the air at a time.

The differences in behavioural skills not only reflect the orcas' adaptation to available food resources, but also influence their group competition and birth rate. Transient whales for example, communicate little, because marine mammals possess excellent hearing and must be stalked quietly, while "resident" whales co-ordinate their hunting manoeuvers through an elaborate vocabulary of whistles, squeals and shrieks since fish are not alerted by their calls. Marine mammal hunters seem to be more efficient when co-operating in tight groups of 2-7 individuals. They produce fewer calves than their fish–eating cousins, which live in tightly-knit family units that can reach several dozen individuals. The Valdes orcas behave much like their "transient" cousins. They travel alone or in small groups of varying size and composition. Occasionally as many as nine killer whales will hunt together, but groups of 5 or 7 whales that include calves are common. They use few calls as not to alert their prey, and rely mainly on sonar clicks to assess the position of the other members of their pod. Only immediately after a kill does the sea reverberate with their triumphant cries.

Sometimes, as if to celebrate their success, the orcas play with their prey. One afternoon, I watched Sparky drag off a plump yearling. In an explosion of foam, she breached victoriously, her victim helplessly locked between her jaws. Then she let the seal go. As it tried to swim away, Sparky swam up to it, and delivered a loud sideways smack with her paddle-like flipper that sent the seal flying through a cloud of spray. A second, explosive blow with her large tail catapulted the seal so high into the air that it soared with outstretched flippers amongst the petrels and gulls waiting for scraps. As soon as it hit the surface, she snapped it up again, towing it further offshore where the kill was finally shared with the rest of the

Top predator of the colder seas and the largest member of the dolphin family: An orca at sunset.

pod. This may appear cruel and senseless, but these apparent "games" are a means to survive and to sharpen their hunting skills. Adult whales often capture a seal and release it again to be recaptured by the younger members of the pod. One time I saw a wild, playful race take place with all younger members of the pod chasing the main hunter, prey in mouth, while attempting to snatch his catch. Finally, with a light flick of its head, the adult orca flung the seal to one of the calves, as if playing some kind of ballgame. The next day an unsuspecting penguin was caught and released as a live training target for the budding hunters. Equally, although one out of five of the 400 pups born each season at Punta Norte will fall prey to orcas, the 19 Valdes orcas pose no threat to a growing population of 19,000 sea lions and 43,000 elephant seals. On the contrary, it is the orca population and their extraordinary hunting technique that appears to be at risk: During the last three years attacks at Punta Norte have become increasingly rare. Two whales, Ruby and Bernd, were last seen with tumors before they disappeared and Mel, Punta Norte's main hunter, is suffering from a jaw-infection and showing signs of malnutrition. Last year he was seen only once in a six-month period and researchers fear that he, too, may soon disappear and die.

One day, I had a most memorable experience. When I got to the blind, the sun was still under the horizon, but its first tentacles were already stretching across the sky tinting the thin, streaky clouds in pale shades of rose. Mel was swimming back and forth inside the attack channel. Just as the morning sun rose, bathing everything pink, three sea lion pups clumsily hopped and paddled through the surf along the beach. Accelerating like a powerboat, Mel surfed in on a wave, swiftly snapping up one of the pups. It was so tiny that it disappeared entirely inside Mel's mouth. As always, he immediately turned sideways and wiggled his way out to sea. There he circled briefly, then swam slowly back to shore. At the beach, he opened his mouth, and the pup fell out onto the sand. With unbelievable tenderness and care, giant, fearsome Mel nudged the tiny fellow up the beach with his snout, until the startled pup wobbled away into the morning light.

I watched the pup for a while, but it appeared unharmed and healthy. We cannot judge other species by human standards, and shall never fully comprehend their actions. Yet I wondered for a long time whether Mel had been playing, sharpening his hunting skills, or whether this had been a true act of mercy...

THE LEGEND LIVES ON

Dieter Paulmann, a German UW-cinematographer, had already spent two months off the coast of Madeira on board his ship the "Foftein" because this is the site where Sperm Whales once abounded. Local whalers had already severely decimated the whale population by the end of the previous century, but Madeira is still the nearest place for Europeans to go to if they want to sight a Sperm Whale. In 1990 Paulmann sailed to Madeira in search of Sperm Whales, but is still convinced today that Moby Dick only took pity on him back then because the whales kept him waiting for such a long time.

ALL IMAGES OF THE WHITE WHALE WERE SCANNED FROM DIETER PAULMANN'S FILM

Moby Dick is clearly distinguishable from other Sperm Whales by his unusual colour.

In order to gain some preliminary experience, I had invited former chief whaler Eleuterio Riis on board, who killed more than 5,000 Sperm Whales in his lifetime. More or less forced to abandon his calling following the sanction placed on whale imports by the EC in 1984, he accepted the position as director of the first whale museum in Madeira. Together we sailed around Madeira's coastline for three weeks and I learned a lot from him, among other things how not to approach a Sperm Whale as photographer and observer. Whalers only know one way to get close to a whale, namely to sneak up behind it as quietly as possible and drive the harpoon deep into its neck. He did tell me much about the behaviour and feeding habits of Sperm Whales, however, so that all in all our Madeira voyage proved to be very productive. But we did not get near a single Sperm Whale on the surface, let alone under water. As it had occurred on so many previous sailing turns, I was suddenly overwhelmed by a strong impulse. Right in the midst of shooting footage in the harbour of Funchal I decided to stop filming and set sail for the Azores.

I still don't know today what prompted me to do so. With me were a boatswain, a friend and two godsons of mine. We were not adequately prepared for a trip to the Azores, but relished the

An extremely rare photo-documentation of a white Sperm Whale off the Azores.

idea of venturing 700 miles westward across the Atlantic. As we detected Pico, the second-largest island of the Azores, about 30 miles ahead, we also spotted our first group of Sperm Whales. They not only allowed us to come within a few hundred metres of them just like we had trained and practised earlier, but even steered our way as we drifted on the ocean in wait for them. This made us very happy, as we had finally found a way to get close to Sperm Whales. To approach them in the usual manner by ship is practically useless. Their sharp senses enable them to take note of every movement in or on the water. Almost imperceptibly, they always manage to keep a distance of 300-500 m between themselves and a vessel.

At 6 o'clock the next morning - before we had checked in at the nearest harbour - I could already hear the characteristic clicks on our hydrophone and assumed that there were several Sperm Whales within a radius of about 5 km. Indeed, after no more than an hour's search we found a pod of Sperm Whales and let the "Foftein" drift along quietly so as to allow them time to get used to us. Suddenly my friend asked me if it were unusual for a white container to be floating around this part of the ocean. I had to answer in the negative because unfortunately such containers were occasionally lost by ships passing through here. He then inquired whether there was such a thing as a container that could produce a blow like a whale. All of us became frantic when we saw the huge white whale floating on the surface just as another tremendous blow rose up high in the air. I recognized at once that this enormous bull was the spitting image of Moby Dick. It should be pointed out here, that Herman Melville's famous novel is still the best guide for anyone wishing

Moby Dick's "dancing troupe": The calves circle each other and rub their bodies together.

to observe Sperm Whales. My own experience has shown that the factual information contained therein is accurate and it has proven to be extremely helpful to me. But never in all those years of intensive study did I dare to imagine that I would someday come across a living white Sperm Whale. It should not be forgotten that only one large white Sperm Whale has ever been mentioned in historical records, namely Mocha Dick. This animal actually sank the English whaler "Essex" (see Owens's famous account) by ramming it repeatedly with its head. The tragic fate of the crew came to be known all over the world through the account written by one of its few survivors. After 104 days at sea and an erratic journey covering 4,000 nautical miles, only four members of the crew had managed to survive because they had consumed the flesh of their less fortunate shipmates. This was the first recorded case of cannibalism on the high seas. Mocha Dick was probably responsible for the deaths of about 34 seamen. Numerous harpoons still protruded from its body when Scandinavian whalers finally killed the aged and nearly blind animal around 1840. Melville heard the story while serving on board American whaling ships and used it as the basis for his great novel. Since then, no one has ever seen, photographed or even killed a white Sperm Whale bull. In the estimation of all whale experts we consulted, the ancient and huge Sperm Whale bull that appeared before us so unexpectedly was a singular occurrence. Only albino calves have been spotted here and there.

"My" Moby Dick immediately approached our

German UW-cinematographer Dieter Paulmann during his successful quest for Moby Dick.

BORIS PAULMANN

BORIS PAULMANN

As darkness closes in on the Atlantic the "Foftein" is still surrounded by whales.

boat, dove underneath it as if to take a good look at everything and then circled us at a depth of about 2 m. It should be noted that Sperm Whales have a unique flight strategy. When threatened they can swim very fast at a shallow depth of 2-5 m and cover distances of up to 5 km before surfacing for air. In this way they were able to elude whalers again and again. It also happened to us on numerous occasions that Sperm Whales would come close for a brief moment and then suddenly disappear again. Moby Dick behaved in much the same way, but he moved off at such a slow pace that we had no trouble keeping up with him. Since he kept close to the surface we could always see his white body shimmering in the water. Once in a while he changed course and then stopped abruptly, as if he wanted to make sure that we were still following. It appears that this was intentional on his part because after about a half an hour 30 to 50 Sperm Whales suddenly surfaced next to him. It was a large group of Sperm Whales, led by a female as usual and basically consisting of females, adolescents and calves only. Sperm Whale bulls will only temporarily join up with such a group and then go about their solitary ways again. Why did Moby Dick lead us to this particular group? And then the unimaginable took place: The entire group whiled away the time with us on this tiny spot in the middle of the ocean and not only allowed us to film it under water, but also to observe various social activities. We had the privilege of seeing an "underwater ballet" performed by the calves, for instance, in which the animals circled each other and rubbed their bodies together. We were also treated to demonstrations of spy-hopping and breaching. Only when darkness approached did the group of whales finally leave us to go in search of food.

I am still convinced today that Moby Dick lured me from Madeira to the Azores in order to show off his family and to compensate us for the three frustrating months of futile searching. Even though we spent an additional two years observing Sperm Whales in other regions, never again was I able to get so close to so many of these friendly and beautiful creatures. Perhaps Moby Dick was aware of the fact that we were wholly unprepared for such a momentous meeting. We neither had a second diver on board nor a photographer with a decent UW-camera to take pictures of the rare event. But I think that the images of Moby Dick scanned from the footage I shot that day fully convey the magic of that unbelievable encounter. It was undoubtedly very fortunate that there wasn't a second diver in the water with me, as then I would probably not have been able to document the event on film. I had no idea at the time that Sperm Whales tend to accept the presence of a single diver in the water, whom they tend regard as a harmless piece of driftwood. As soon as two or more divers appear, however, they will feel threatened and immediately veer off. As I floated on the wide ocean all by myself the great white bull and its relatives swam towards me and my heart began to beat furiously. But on they came, took a good look and then decided to keep me company for a while. My film proves that the legend lives on.

Not likely to be mistaken for a container from close up: Moby Dick of the Azores.

INDEX: SCIENTIFIC &

COMMON NAMES

BIBLIOGRAPHY

Cafiero, G. & M. Jahoda (o.J.) Giganten der Meere. Wale und Delphine. Karl Müller Verlag, Erlagen.

Carroll, R.L. 1988 Vertebrate paleontology and evolution. W. H. Freeman and Company, New York.

Carwardine, M. 1995 Eyewitness Handbooks: Whales, Dolphins & Porpoises. Dorling Kindersley Ltd, London.

Carwardine, M., E. Hoyt, R.E. Fordyce & P. Gill 2000 Wale, Delphine & Tümmler. Könemann, Köln.

Deimer, P. 1990 Das Buch der Wale. Wilhelm Heyne Verlag, München.

Dizon, A., C.S. Baker, F. Cipriano, G. Lento, Palsbøll, R. Reeves 1999 Molecular Genetic Identification of Whales, Dolphins and Porpoises: Proceedings of a Workshop on the Forensic Use of Molecular Techniques to Identify Wildlife Products in the Marketplace. NOAA, La Jolla, California.

D'Vincent, C. 1990 Reisen mit den Walen. Wilhelm Heyne Verlag, München.

Ellis, R. 1996 The Book of Whales. Alfred A. Knopf, New York.

Evans, P.G. 1987 The Natural History of Whales & Dolphins. Facts on File Publications, New York.

FAO/UNEP 1981 General Papers and Large Cetaceans. Mammals in the Seas, vol. 3, FAO Fisheries Ser. N° 5.

Figueiredo, J.M. 1996 Introdução ao estudo da indústria baleeira insular. Museu dos Beleeiros, Pico, Açores.

Flindt, R. 2000 Biologie in Zahlen. Spektrum Akademischer Verlag, Heidelberg, Berlin.

Gohier, F. 1999 A pod of gray whales. EZ Nature Books, California.

Hetzel, B. & L. Lodi 1993 Baleias, Botos & Golfinhos. Nova Fronteira, Rio de Janeiro.

Jefferson, T., S. Leatherwood & M. Webber 1993 Marine Mammals of the World. FAO Species Identification Guide. FAO, U.N. Environment Program, Rom.

Keller, J. (Hrsg.) 1988 Wale und Delphine. Jahr-Verlag, Hamburg.

Klinowksa, M. 1991 Dolphins, Porpoises and Whales of the World - The IUCN Red Data Book. IUCN, Gland, Switzerland and Cambridge, UK.

Leatherwood, S. & R. Reeves 1983 The Sierra Club Handbook of Whales and Dolphins. Sierra Club Books, San Francisco.

May, J. 1990 Das Greenpeace Buch der Delphine. Interbook, Hamburg.

McKenna, V. 1992 Into The Blue. Harper Colllins, New York.

Melville, H. 1999 Moby Dick. Manesse Verlag, Zürich.

Milinkovitch, M.C. 1995 Molecular phylogeny of cetaceans prompts revision of morphological transformations. Trends in Ecology and Evolution 10(8):305-345.

Norris, K.S. 1977 Whales, Dolphins & Porpoises. University of California Press, Los Angeles, CA.

Pack, A.A. & K. Basin 1998 Male humpback whale dies in competitive group. Marine Mammal Science, 14(4):873-881 (October 1998).

Reyes, J.C., K. Van Waerebeek, J.C. Cardenas & J. Yañez 1995 A new species of beaked whale, *Mesoplodon bahamondi*, of Juan Fernández islands. Bol. Mus. Nac. Hist. Nat. (Chile) 45:31-34.

Rice, D.W. 1999 Marine Mammals of the World - Systematics and Distribution. Society for Marine Mammalogy, Special publication Number 4, 231 pp. SMM, Lawrence, Kansas.

Robineau, D., R. Duguy & M. Klima 1994 Handbuch der Säugetiere Europas. Meeressäuger Teil IA: Wale und Delphine 1. Aula-Verlag, Wiesbaden.

Robineau, D., R. Duguy & M. Klima 1994 Handbuch der Säugetiere Europas. Meeressäuger Teil IB: Wale und Delphine 2. Aula-Verlag, Wiesbaden.

Slijper, E.J. 1962 Whales. Hutchinson, London.

Soury, G. 1997 Das große Buch der Delphine. Delius Klasing, Stuttgart.

Viallelle, S. 1997 Golfinhos e baleias dos Açores. Espaço Talassa, Pico, Açores.

Wandrey, R. 1997 Die Wale und Robben der Welt: Vorkommen, Gefährdung, Schutz. Kosmos, Stuttgart.

Wilson, D.E. & D. Reeder 1982 Mammal species of the world. A taxonomic and geographic reference. Smithsonian Series in Comparative Evolutionary Biology. Allen Press Inc & The Association of Systematics Collections. Lawrence, Kansas.

Winn, H.E. & B.L. Olla 1978 Behaviour of Marine Animals. Current Perspectives in Research, vol. 3, Cetaceans. Plenum Press, New York.

Würtz, M. & N. Repetto 1998 Wale & Delphine. Biografie der Meeressäuger. Jahr-Verlag, Hamburg.

WEBSITES

ACCOBAMS - Agreement on the Conservation of Cetaceans of the Black Sea, Mediterranean Sea and Contiguous Atlantic Area - www.dainet.de/cms/abkommen.htm

American Cetacean Society - www.acsonline.org/links.htm

ASCOBANS - Agreement on the Conservation of Small Cetaceans of the Baltic and North Seas - www.ascobans.org, www.ascobans.mc

Atlantic Whale Foundation - www.whalefoundation.f2s.com

BBC - www.bbc.co.uk

Biosis - Zoological Record - Biological Abstract - www.biosis.org.uk

Cascadia Research for the Protection of Marine Mammals - www.cascadiaresearch.org

Center for Marine Mammals Research/Leviathan - www.leviathan.cl

Cetacea - www.cetacea.org, www.cetacea.de

CITES - Convention on International Trade in Endangered Species - www.cites.org

Delphin-Institut - www.delphin-institut.de

BIBLIOGRAPHY

Espacotalassa - www.espacotalassa.com

Greenpeace - www.greenpeace.org, www.greenpeace.de

GSM - www.gsm-ev.de

IFAW - International Fund for Animal Welfare - www.ifaw.org

IUCN - International Union for the Conservation of Nature - www.iucn.org

IWC - International Whaling Commission - www.ourworl.compuserve.com/homepages/iwcoffice/iwc.htm

Marine Mammal Research and Conservation - www.sdgateway.net/mailinglist/list37.htm, www.marine-mammals.de, www.Ozeane.de

Marine Mammalogy Reference Website - www.wiu.edu/users/mibiol/facstaff/thomas/marmamm.htm

Museu Nacional de Historia Natural - www.mnhn.cl

NOAA - National Oceanic and Atmospheric Administration - www.noaa.org

Smithsonian Institute/MSW - www.nmnh.si.edu/msw

Society for Marine Mammalogy - www.pegasus.cc.ucf.edu/~smm/mms.htm

University of Michigan - Museum of Zoology - www.animaldiversity

WDCS - www.WDCS.org

Whales in Danger Information Service - www.whales.magna.com.au

Yaqupacha - www.yaqupacha.de

Magazines and Journals

Marine Mammal Science, Cetology Behaviour, Journal of Zoology, Journal of Mammalogy, Canadian Journal of Zoology, Report of the International Whaling Commission, Scientific American, American Scientist, Nature, Zoologica, Greenpeace Magazine, WWF Magazine, GSM (Gesellschaft zum Schutz der Meeressäugetiere, Society for the Protection of Marine Mammals), National Geographic, Geo.

MAN AND WHALE

LIONEL POZZOLI

DOUG PERRINE

HOWARD HALL

LIONEL POZZOLI

ROD HAESTIER

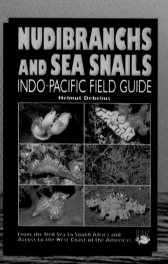
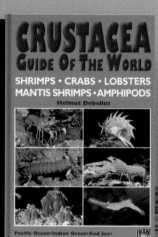
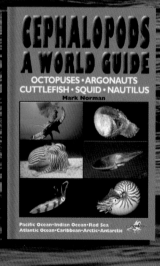